International Antenna Collection 2

Edited by

George Brown, PhD, CEng, FIEE, M5ACN

Radio Society of Great Britain   American Radio Relay League

Published jointly by the Radio Society of Great Britain, Lambda House, Cranborne Road, Potters Bar, Herts. EN6 3JE, UK and American Radio Relay League Inc, 225 Main Street, Newington, CT, 06111-1494 USA.

First Published 2004

ISBN 1-905086-01-6

Cover design: Jodie Escott, M3TPQ.
Subediting and typography: Chris Danby, G0DWV.
Production: Mark Allgar, M1MPA

Printed in Great Britain by Nuffield Press Ltd. of Abingdon, Oxfordshire.

Contents

Preface

After the success of the *International Antenna Collection* the publishers made an immediate call for a follow-up, in the same way that *Son of Paleface* followed *Paleface*. Given that there was a large amount of material that I was forced to omit for space reasons from the first book the opportunity was welcomed. I am only sorry not to be able to call this book *Son of International Antenna Collection*, but realise that *International Antenna Collection 2* is probably a fairer reflection of this entirely new collection of aerial articles.

It is intended to be used as a reference book whenever a new aerial design is required, and follows closely the format of the original book, with articles from authors of many countries using, where possible, the same diagrams as in the parent publications.

The choice of the articles is mine alone; it is highly subjective, but intended to cover as wide a range of frequencies as practicable. You will find aerials for most of the amateur bands between 136kHz and 2.4GHz, together with three general articles – one on earths, one on aerial tuner modifications and one on 'stealth' aerials.

I invited an article on the use of aerial tuners (ATUs), having noticed many published articles apparently contradicting each other when discussing how signals get from the transmitter to the aerial via the ATU and feeder. My choice of author was a guru on the subject, Kurt N Sterba, who lurks in *nom-de-plume* anonymity behind the hallowed portals of the American amateur radio magazine, *WorldRadio*. He champions the cause of M Walter Maxwell, W2DU, whose work on aerials and matching is without equal, and is published for all to read in *Reflections II*, published by, and available from, WorldRadio.

The 'international' theme has been achieved by close cooperation with the editors and staff of several amateur radio magazines, whom I would like to thank individually, but in no significant order:

Gail Schieber, K2RED, Dick Ross, K2MGA, and Elizabeth Ryan of *CQ*;
Colwyn Low, VK5UE, of *Amateur Radio* (WIA);
Steve Ford, WB8IMY, of *QST* (ARRL);
Jürgen Sapara, DH9JS, of *CQ DL* (DARC);
John Walker, ZL3IB, of *Break-In* (NZART);
Nancy Kott, WZ8C, of *WorldRadio*;
Karen Griffiths, for the translation of the articles from *CQ DL*;
not to mention, of course, the many radio amateurs whose articles are used in this book. My thanks to you all.

As in the previous book, no index is provided, other than a contents list. However, having discovered by painful experience how frustrating it can be trying to find an aerial design for a particular band, mobile or fixed, I have repeated the table of articles, about which many readers have expressed approval. This lists all the articles by title, with their source magazines and page numbers in the book, together with a list of the bands covered by the aerials in the articles. This simplifies the search procedure enormously.

As anyone who has constructed an aerial from someone else's design will tell you, you can never predict exactly how that aerial will perform. Your particular environment may be the deciding factor. Nevertheless, you won't know until you try, and that's

what makes experimenting with aerials so challenging. It is like amateur radio itself –
you never know whom you will work next and where he or she will be located until you
make, or answer, a call.

If you have comments about the designs in this book, please contact the authors
directly. All you have to do is go to one of the many call-books on CD or the Internet
for a postal or e-mail address. Interested as I am to hear from you, I do have a full-
time job, and forwarding information to authors is a time-intensive business.

Finally, I hope you enjoy using this book. If you do, it is a tribute to the individual
authors who have given their time and effort to communicate their ideas and designs
to their national amateur radio magazines. It will also have made my spare-time
efforts in bringing the articles together even more enjoyable.

George Brown
Potters Bar, England
September 2004

160m VERTICAL

by Dave Jacobs, KK7DP

Are you an operator who is interested in trying 160m operation with a vertical aerial, but is precluded from erecting a 60ft vertical in your backyard? How does the possibility of having a 31ft 9in-high aerial that fits into a corner of most backyards and covers at least a 130kHz bandwidth at the 2:1 VSWR points sound to you? That is exactly what I use at my QTH, and this article will describe how you can replicate this aerial.

The basic configuration is an inverted cone (photos A and B), hence the name I gave the aerial: the 'Conix Class 160', or CC-160. With four radials installed and 425W, I worked 225 stations in 15 hours in the

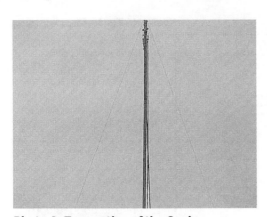

Photo A: Top section of the Conix Class 160 vertical.

2003 *CQ* World-Wide 160m Contest. This may not sound like a very successful contest performance until you consider that my QTH is Montana, the original black hole of propagation. The path from my station to Europe or Japan is completely blocked by the polar auroral zone, and I am so far north that the ionisation levels that support propagation have decayed to very low levels. Nevertheless, I received several 59+30dB signal reports, copied CT2 stations at S7, and worked Caribbean stations at the S9+20dB level.

All that having been said, the aerial is still a physically-shortened radiator with gain

figures to match. Do not expect it to be a giant-killer; it is a compromise that will fit into a limited space, but still function very satisfactorily. It is very quiet in the receiving mode, because it is a closed loop, similar in design to the cubical quad and

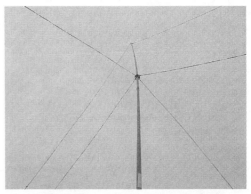

Photo B: Another view of the top section, looking up. Note the diagonal wires coming off the upper mast section.

is operated at DC ground potential (which additionally gives some degree of lightning protection). This design effectively shorts out static voltages and couples them to ground before they can cause a noise-generating arc. This should be of great benefit to amateurs living in the south who experience a great deal of static-induced QRN.

Since this vertical aerial is non-symmetrical, a good ground is required. My current configuration utilises four radials, each one 130ft long and surface-mounted on the ground. The aerial will actually work without any radials, because the ground braid of the coax acts as a first radial. However, a minimum of two is highly recommended. What is important is to decrease the effective ground loss by installing a sufficient number of radials to couple the aerial to ground electrically. With four radials installed, the ground loss reduction is 1.2dB, or an increase in the effective radiated power of 1.2dB. Every time the number of radials is doubled, the effective radiated power increases by an additional 0.6dB, with 4.2dB being the maximum gain for 120 radials. That is why adding a few radials to an existing installation provides only a little improvement unless the installation has no (or few) radials to start with. While it may

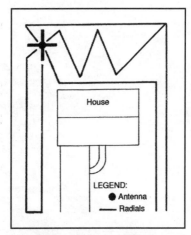

Fig 1: Possible installation of aerial with four radials on a small lot. Note that the radials do not have to be straight to be effective.

not be feasible to expect an average backyard to support 20 radials, almost any backyard can support at least two 130ft radials if they are installed in a bent pattern. Additional radials of that length, or even shorter ones, can be installed into whatever space is available. **Fig 1** is a possible layout of four radials in an average yard. A full acre is required to install 120 radials, and yet the effective radiated power will only be 4dB higher than that of a station with only two radials.

The aerial is resonant and will cover the entire 200kHz of the 160m band if it is erected in the open, and if you spend sufficient time fine-tuning the aerial. Even without fine-tuning, the aerial will cover 130kHz of the band within the 2:1 VSWR points. The purpose of the series capacitor (see detail in **Fig 2**) is to tune out the +j inductive reactance that the aerial

possesses, making it a pure resistive load. Aerial resonance is a function of aerial height and skirt length, and fine-tuning is accomplished by varying the length of the skirts. I use $1/16$in steel aircraft cable for my skirts, looped through dog-bone-style insulators and secured at the 6ft level. This technique makes the adjustment of the skirt length very simple. The impedance will usually fall between 45+j400 and 75+j475.

The design uses a 500pF variable capacitor with 0.125in plate spacing for full 1kW operation; however, any variable that covers this range will work if the spacing between the plates is adequate to handle the proposed power output. Tuning the capacitor changes the +j inductive reactance component, and cancellation of reactance usually occurs at about 1.875MHz with a VSWR of 1.2:1.

As a plus, even though the aerial has been optimised for 160m operation, it also covers the 40m band and will out-perform a full-size quarter-wavelength 40m vertical.

CONSTRUCTION

The mast section of the aerial is constructed from $1^1/_8$in aluminium tubing with a 0.058in wall thickness. The tubing is not tapered, and sections are fastened together by a 12in section of the next smaller diameter tubing. Silicon conductive grease is applied to this 12in connecting section in order to ensure good electrical conductivity between sections of the mast. The total mast length is 33ft 9in, including 18in buried below ground level. No insulator is required, because the aerial is operating at DC ground potential.

To support the aerial, bury an 18in length of $1^1/_4$in galvanised water pipe and drop the mast down into this pipe. If the characteristics of your ground are such that the mast may continue to

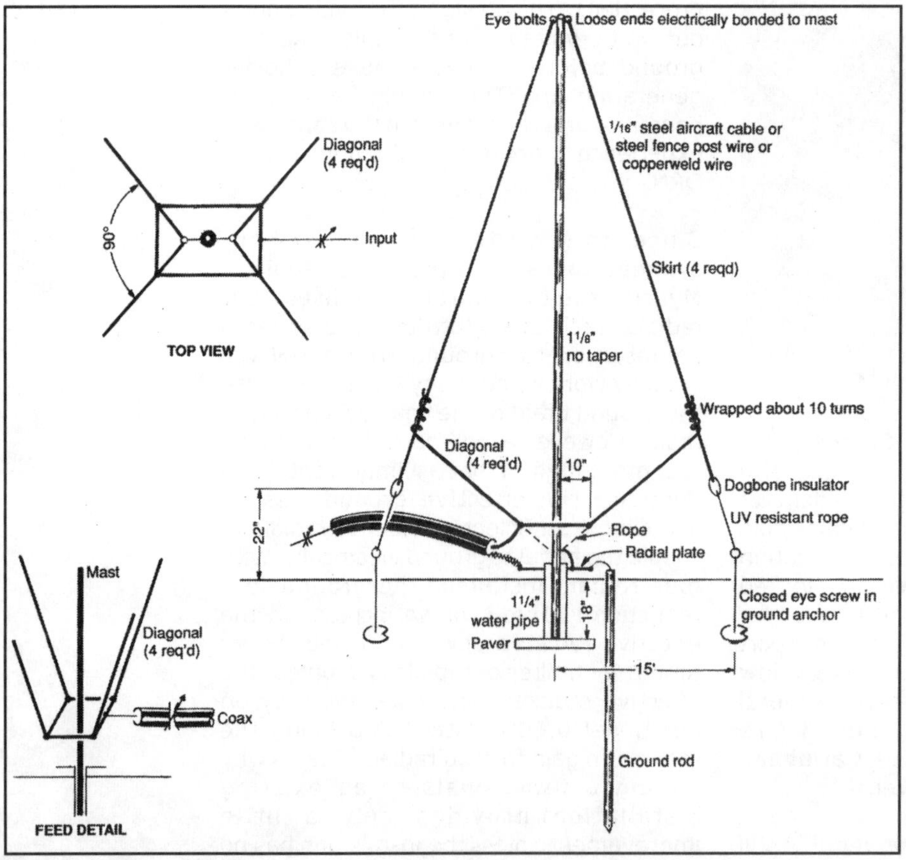

Fig 2: Construction details of the Conix Class 160 aerial.

sink, insert a concrete paver at the bottom of the hole to prevent this from happening. Lay a 12in radial ground plate over the 1¹/₄in pipe (see Fig 2) and insert the mast through the centre hole. All of the radials and the ground wire from the coax are attached to this plate by stainless-steel screws.

Two inches below the top of the mast, drill two holes to hold two closed eyebolts as shown in Fig 2. Attach four skirts as shown and electrically bond them to the mast. As indicated earlier, I use aircraft cable for my skirts, but copperweld or equivalent material is suitable. At my location, I experience intense winds, so not only is aircraft cable required for support, but I also add nylon rope at the 16ft level for additional strength. For ground anchors, I use screw-in type bolts available at most hardware stores.

Next, install the four aerial diagonals using No 12 copperweld wire as shown in Fig 2. The aerial diagonals are connected to the skirts by tightly wrapping 10 turns of one end of the diagonal on each skirt and attaching the other end 7in from the mast with nylon rope. The mast ends of the four diagonals are connected together and then connected to the variable capacitor. I mount the variable capacitor in a metal box (photo C) to seal it from the elements and attach it directly to the mast just above the ground plate, insulating it from the mast with ceramic standoffs. The coax

Photo C: Base of the aerial. The box holds the tuning capacitor and the plate to which it is mounted attaches the capacitor unit to the aerial.

cable feed-line is connected directly to the aerial (via the capacitor) as shown in Fig 2. Solder the inner wire conductor to the variable capacitor and firmly attach the

ground braid to the ground plate.

TUNING THE AERIAL

To tune the aerial, simply adjust the variable capacitor for the minimum VSWR that will occur at only one discrete frequency. If the lowest VSWR point is too high or too low in the band, adjust the skirt length accordingly. It may require two individuals to simplify this tuning process, but it is not impossible for one person to accomplish it. Plots of elevation and azimuth radiation for a four-radial aerial are shown in **Figs 3** and **4**. This plot was made using *MiniNEC* and the characteristics are those over real ground.

A word of caution: Do not erect this aerial under or in the vicinity of overhead electrical wires or over an underground electrical distribution system. The potential for serious injury is much too great.

I would appreciate hearing of your experiences with this aerial and the results that you achieve, especially for those stations with better locations than mine in Montana. Your comments and suggestions will provide me with additional information to evaluate this aerial and to perhaps improve upon its design. I hope to hear your signal in one of the future 160m contests. Good luck!

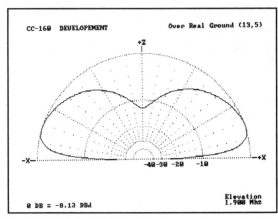

Fig 3: *MiniNEC* **plot of elevation pattern for the CC-160 aerial.**

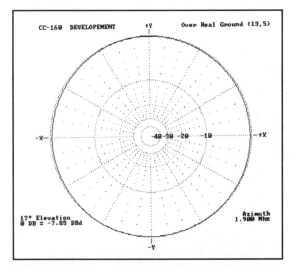

Fig 4: *MiniNEC* **plot of azimuth pattern for the CC-160. Note that both patterns are consistent with an omnidirectional vertical aerial.**

TWO THREE-ELEMENT YAGIS FOR 6m

by L B Cebik, W4RNL

Yagi aerials provide good forward gain in a favoured direction and excellent front-to-back ratio (F / B) for unwanted-signal rejection. A three-element Yagi for 6m is a simple constructional project, and can make use of readily-available materials. However, newer aerial builders are often faced with the question, "Which design should I use?".

To help you make the decision, let's look at two quite different designs. Each aerial is a bit over 6ft long. One presses for maximum gain and a good F / B, but sacrifices bandwidth. The other achieves total coverage of 6m, but surrenders some gain in the process. By comparing the aerials' capabilities with your operating requirements, you can select the one that best suits your needs.

Despite the similar boom lengths, the two designs have quite different profiles, as shown in **Fig 1**. The wideband model places more distance between the reflector and the driven element and decreases the driven-element-to-director spacing. In contrast, the high-gain model sets the director far ahead of the driven element and decreases the spacing between the driven element and the reflector. The reflector-to-driven-element spacing not only has an impact on gain, but affects the array feed-point impedance as well. In general, reducing the reflector-to-driven-element spacing lowers the feed-point impedance.

GAIN

Let's first look at the high-gain model, to see what we can achieve and what it will cost. A three-element Yagi is capable of exhibiting a free-space gain of 8dBi with a F / B greater than 20dB. However, these figures can be sustained for a bandwidth of only little over ±1.5% of the

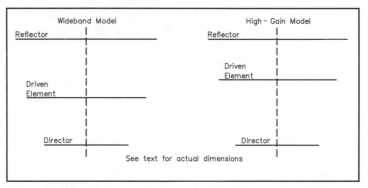

Fig1. General outline of the wideband and high-gain three-element 6m Yagis.

design frequency. Across this span, the aerial's gain tends to increase, while the F / B peaks at over 25dB near the design frequency. Our sample high-gain Yagi is adapted from an optimised 20m design by Brian Beezley, K6STI. His original design covers all of 20m, but that band is narrow compared with 6m. When we scale the aerial for 51MHz, its bandwidth is only about 1.5MHz while retaining the desired operating characteristics. **Table 1** shows the aerial dimensions for a design using ½in-diameter tubing. Single-diameter elements are quite practical in VHF Yagis

Element	Length (in)	Spacing from Reflector (in)
Reflector	114.26	-
Driven Element	108.96	37.8
Director	102.43	77.94

Table 1: Element lengths and spacing for the high-gain 6m design with ¹/₂in-diameter elements.

Frequency (MHz)	Gain (dBi)	F / B (dB)	Feed-point Impedance (R ± jXΩ)	25Ω SWR
50	7.92	16.55	26.9 - j20.2	2.14
50.5	8.07	22.59	26.4 - j11.6	1.57
51	8.24	25.86	24.9 - j2.4	1.10
51.5	8.43	19.33	22.8 + j7.8	1.40
52	8.64	14.66	20.3 + j19.2	2.34

Table 2: Modelled performance of the high-gain 6m design from 50 to 52MHz.

but, before we're finished, we'll see what to do should we decide - or need - to use two tubing sizes for each element.

Table 2 shows the aerial's anticipated performance characteristics, as modelled using *NEC 4*. The driven-element length is set near resonance on 51MHz, and the feed-point impedance is about 25Ω. That value isn't a direct match for the 50Ω coaxial cable normally used in amateur installations. If we shorten the driven element, we can install a beta-match. If we lengthen the driven element, we might use a gamma-match or a T-match. If we leave the driven element length as is, we could employ a $\lambda/4$, 37Ω matching section made by connecting two lengths of RG-59 (or RG-11 for high-power operation) in parallel. All of these matching systems are described in the *ARRL Antenna Book*.

The table of projected gain and F / B values shows the rise in gain across the passband, as well as the peak F / B near the design frequency. Notice that the F / B drops rapidly as we approach frequencies only 1MHz from the design centre. For point-to-point communications at the low end of 6m, however, the narrow passband, combined with the higher gain, may be just what we need.

The target centre frequency can be adjusted up or down, within the 6m band, by adjusting all three element lengths by the percentage of frequency change. To change the design frequency to 50.5MHz to cover the 50 to 51MHz range, increase all lengths by about 1%. If we stay at the

low end of the band, we need not change the element spacing or diameter.

Builders who are more interested in raw gain than F / B can scale the performance at 52MHz (or a bit above) down to the desired frequency. Simply scale the aerial dimensions, as given for the 51MHz design frequency, to about 50MHz or just a bit lower. You can adjust the driven-element length to resonance or use your favourite matching system. Changing the driven-element length to vary the feed-point impedance by as much as 25 to 30Ω has very little effect on the other performance figures.

BANDWIDTH

Suppose we want to cover the entire 6m band with a well-matched Yagi having relatively constant performance all the way. Although this 4MHz span represents a ±4% bandwidth relative to a design frequency, we can re-design the Yagi to achieve this goal. However, we'll pay for the bandwidth with reduced gain and a lower peak F / B. The gain drops about 1dB and the F / B is perhaps 5dB off the peak.

From the same ½in-diameter aluminium tubing, we can build a three-element Yagi with a free-space gain of about 7dBi and a F / B of up to 21dB. This aerial exhibits a feed-point impedance that permits direct connection to a 50Ω coaxial cable (with a suitable choke to attenuate common-mode currents). The design dimensions shown in **Table 3** are adapted from a design for another band originally developed by Bill Orr, W6SAI [1].

The modelled performance parameters appear in **Table 4**. Notice that the gain curve is not a single rising line, but has a slight dip toward the low end of the band. The F / B peak has been set at the mid-band frequency, because it tends to taper off fairly equally above and below the design frequency. Most notable are the feed-point impedance and VSWR values. If we insulate the driven element from the boom, we can avoid the use of a matching network altogether.

The wideband model is suited to operators who want to cover the

Element	Length (in)	Spacing from reflector (in)
Reflector	116.80	-
Driven Element	108.10	40.7
Director	96.10	73.5

Table 3: Element lengths and spacing for the wideband 6m design with ¹/₂in-diameter elements.

Frequency (MHz)	Gain (dBi)	F / B (dB)	Feed-point Impedance (R ± jXΩ)	50Ω VSWR
50	7.00	14.90	48.4 - j21.2	1.54
51	6.92	18.08	51.9 - j9.9	1.22
52	6.96	20.31	51.9 + j1.7	1.05
53	7.13	21.02	48.8 + j15.0	1.35
54	7.44	18.40	43.0 + j31.1	1.96

Table 4: Modelled performance figures for the wideband (50 to 54MHz) 6m design.

entire 6m band. However, effective use may require a mechanical scheme that lets you flip the beam from horizontal to vertical. In the vertical position, as shown in **Fig 2**, at a height of 30ft above average ground, the pattern is wider and less strong than when the aerial is used horizontally. Still, these beams are both simple and inexpensive. Hence, you might want to build a high-gain model for the low end of 6m and a wideband model to cover the upper 3MHz of the band.

Fig 3 overlays free-space azimuth patterns of both beams at their design frequencies. The patterns will give you a good idea of their relative performance potentials.

STEPPED-DIAMETER TUBING

The beam dimensions for both models used uniform $^1/_2$in-diameter elements. A common building practice is to use at least two tubing sizes in 6m beams. Most often, we start with $^1/_2$in tubing at the centre and use $^3/_8$in tubing for the element ends. Let's suppose we make the centre portions of each element from 6ft lengths of $^1/_2$in tubing - 3ft of tubing on each side of the boom. What happens to the overall element lengths?

Table 5 compares the element lengths from the boom outward for each beam (commonly called 'element half-lengths'). One model uses $^1/_2$in-diameter tubing throughout, and the other uses $^3/_8$in-diameter tubing for the ends. The stepped-diameter lengths are chosen so that the aerial performance is essentially the same as with uniform-diameter elements. Note that the element lengths become significantly longer when we step the element diameter downward on the way

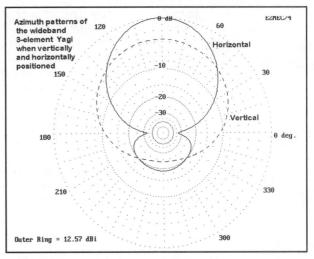

Fig2. Modelled azimuth patterns for the wideband three element 6m Yagi in horizontal and vertical orientations at 30ft above average earth.

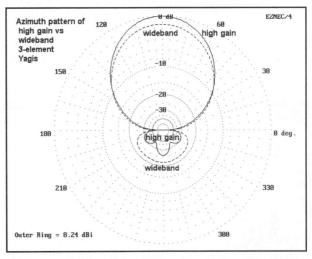

Fig3. Overlaid models of free-space azimuth patterns for the high-gain and wideband 6m designs at their design frequencies.

High-Gain Design		
Element	**Uniform diameter length**	**Stepped-diameter length**
Reflector	114.36	116.4
Driven element	108.96	111.0
Director	102.43	104.0
Wideband Design		
Element	**Uniform diameter length**	**Stepped-diameter length**
Reflector	116.80	118.6
Driven element	108.10	110.0
Director	96.10	97.6

Note: All dimensions are in inches. For the stepped-diameter elements, the inner 36in length uses $^1/_2$in-diameter tubing, with $^3/_8$in-diameter tubing used for the remainder of the element.

Table 5: Half-element lengths for uniform half-inch and stepped $^1/_2$in to $^3/_8$in-diameter elements

to the element end. The amount of change differs for each element.

You can calculate the end lengths by subtracting 36in from the overall element length. However, be sure to add about 3in per end section to allow for telescoping the tubing.

I'll leave the remaining construction details up to you, since there are many acceptable ways to construct either of these Yagis.

Again, the *ARRL Antenna Book* and articles in *QST* and recent editions of the *ARRL Antenna Compendium* are full of good ideas. Simply select those that best fit your available materials and individual skills.

Both of these Yagis - adapted from the work of veteran aerial designers - are good designs. Which you choose will depend on what you want to do on 6m during the present sunspot cycle and beyond.

NOTE

[1] Bill Orr, W6SAI, 'Ham Radio Techniques, May Perambulation', *Ham Radio Magazine*, May 1990 pp56 - 61.

TWO-METRE BEAMS MADE EASY

by Roger Davis, ZS1J

PROBLEMS WITH BUILDING YAGIS

One of the major problems with building a Yagi is not the mechanical construction, which is relatively simple, but how to match the 50Ω coaxial cable to the driven element. This difficulty has been the major stumbling block for many amateur antenna builders.

LOOKING AT OPTIONS

Over the years, I have tried various methods, including the Gamma match, but most designs have posed problems both with waterproofing and the frustration of setting up. So, necessity being the mother of invention, I eventually decided to find an easy method of feeding the driven element directly with coaxial cable.

THE FOLDED DIPOLE REVISITED

Looking at all of the available options in antenna construction, the model that required the least 'fiddling' was the folded dipole (**Fig 1**), which has a feed impedance of 300Ω balanced. I thought about the possibilities of making a 6:1 balanced-to-unbalanced transformer (balun), but rejected that option, as I did not have a toroid that could take the high RF current. I then thought that if I fed just one half of the folded dipole against the electrical centre, which is also the point of connection to the boom, I will have an impedance of 150Ω unbalanced. Now, feeling that I was on the right track, I removed the unwanted section of the other half of the dipole, which gave a 'J'-

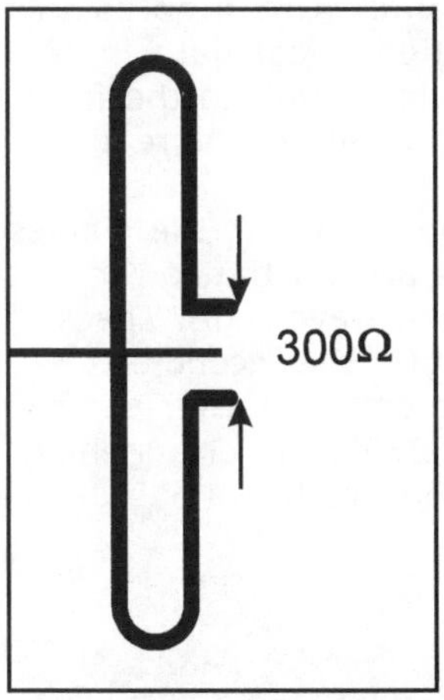

Fig 1: The basic folded dipole.

appearance to the element (**Fig 2**).

My next step was to find a way to drop the 150Ω impedance down to 100Ω. The reason for this target impedance is that, should I be able to achieve it, I could then use a λ/4, or 3λ/4 length of 75Ω coaxial cable, less velocity factor, as an impedance transformer, which will change the 100Ω to 50Ω. At 50Ω, the antenna can now be fed with normal coaxial cable (**Fig 3**).

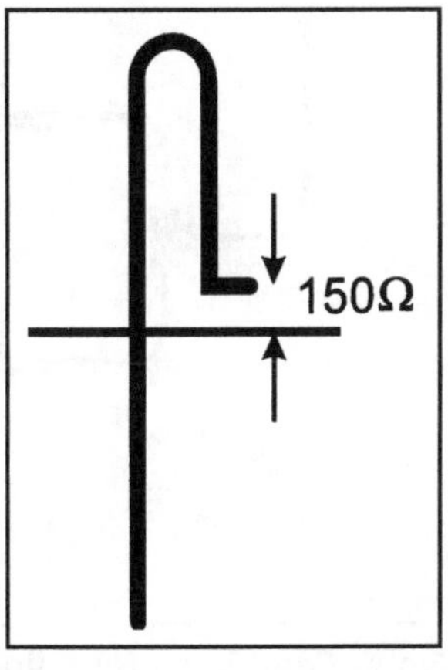

Once I had made this transformer, I fitted it to the driven element, which was then mounted on to the Yagi boom in its correct position with regard to the director elements. To achieve the required drop in the driven element impedance, I made the reflector element movable and by sliding the reflector closer to the driven element than normal, the VSWR immediately dropped to 1.1:1 at the correct position and rose again as the reflector became too close. With the reflector now fitted permanently in this position, the antenna was air-tested and was found to work well, with an exceedingly good bandwidth.

In 1988, I approached Antronic, a company that manufactures commercial antennas, and requested them to manufacture a range of Yagis for the VHF amateur bands utilising this feed method. Over the ensuing

Fig 2: The modified version.

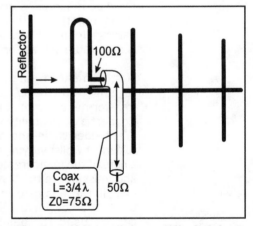

Fig 3: Feeding the modified driven element.

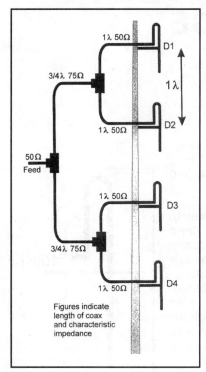

Fig 4: Combining four dipoles.

years, Lima Electronics sold many hundreds of these, which were used with great success and, in many cases, by the winners of VHF contests.

I have heard some criticism about the offset feeding of dipoles 'skewing' the radiation pat- tern but, in practice, this has never been found to occur and, if one considers that equal currents must occur in each half of the dipole for it to work, I dismiss this claim until scientifically proved otherwise.

FOR BASE AND REPEATER USE

Way back in 1978, I manufactured dipole antennas for commercial use which were based on this coaxial feed method and, with a little ingenuity, four of them could be mounted, stacked one above the other, together with a suitable phasing harness, for use where a high gain antenna is required, such as for a 2m repeater.

Firstly, make a single driven element, together with the λ/4 75Ω coaxial cable transformer and mount it on a short boom. Connect a good quality VSWR meter in the 50Ω feeder cable and offer the dipole up to a mast whilst varying the distance. Make a note of the measurement between dipole and mast where the VSWR drops to 1.1:1 and fit the boom-to-mast clamp at this point. You now have a single dipole which can be used for base station use. If, however, you wish to make a high-gain, four-stack vertical array, remove the 75Ω

matching section and coaxial cable and manufacture an additional three dipoles exactly as the first, but fit all four dipoles with one wavelength of 50Ω coaxial cable, less the velocity factor, and PL-259 coaxial connectors on the free ends.

Mount the dipoles on the mast, one above the other, at one wavelength, centre to centre as shown in **Fig 4**. The one wavelength of 50Ω coax cable will mirror the 100Ω impedance at the free end, allowing dipoles one and two to be connected in parallel and dipoles three and four to be connected in parallel using a three-way, T-piece connector on each pair. Each paralleled pair will now give an impedance of 50Ω and this impedance must now be transformed back up to 100Ω to allow both pairs to be connected in parallel for the 50Ω feed line. This is accomplished with a 3λ/4 transformer of 75Ω coaxial cable with a PL-259 on each end. One end of each of these is screwed into the T-piece of each pair using a PL-258 barrel connector and these two 75Ω cables are joined using a third T-piece bringing the impedance back down to 50Ω. The remaining socket on the third T-piece is for connection to the 50Ω feed-line using a PL-259 connector and a PL-258 barrel. See Fig 4.

The radiation pattern of this arrangement would be 'cardioid', favouring the side of the tower on which the dipoles are mounted. The theoretical gain in this configuration would be 9dB to the front, 6dB to the sides and 3dB to the rear.

For omnidirectional radiation, the dipoles should be placed around the tower, but keeping to the one wavelength spacing, the top element at 0°, the second element at 90°, the third element at 180° and the lowest element at 270°. This arrangement should give an omnidirectional 6dB gain.

LOW-PROFILE HELICES for 2.4GHz

by Paolo Antoniazzi, IW2ACD, and Marco Arecco, IK2WAQ

The theory and practice of helical antennas have been developed largely by J D Kraus and his associates at Ohio State University [1].

For circular polarisation applications, the axial-mode helix antenna is an interesting candidate, because its good polarisation performance is an inherent attribute of the antenna shape without the need for a special feeding arrangement. Polarisation properties of the helix have been the subject of several publications since the early work of Kraus [2, 3].

A typical helical antenna operating in the axial mode has a circumference $C = \pi D$ of approximately one wavelength and a pitch spacing, S, of approximately one quarter-wavelength.

Traditionally, the pitch angle, an important parameter of the helix, may range from about 12 to 16°; approximately 12° (pitch = 30mm) is typical in most 2.4GHz satellite receiving helices.

The pitch, α, is the angle that a line tangent to the helix wire makes with the plane perpendicular to the axis of the helix, and it can be found from the relation $\tan(\alpha) = S / \pi D$, where S is the pitch spacing and D the diameter of the helix.

This article refers to the simulation and measurements of some forward-fire-mode helices with very low-profiles. In the past, low-pitch helices have been recognised as ineffective radiating elements for a circularly-polarised wave. Field measurements and numerical results using *NEC-Win Pro* and *NEC-Win Synth* [4] however, lead to some low-pitch helices with gains comparable to that of a conventionally long helix.

WAVE POLARISATION
A circularly-polarised wave radiates energy in both the horizontal and vertical planes as well as in every plane in between. The difference, if any, between the maximum and the minimum signal peaks as the antenna rotates through all angles, is called the axial ratio, or ellipticity, and is usually specified in decibels (dB). Normally, if the axial ratio is less than 2dB, the antenna is said to be circularly-polarised. If the axial ratio is greater than 2dB, the polarisation is referred to as elliptical.

The polarisation, orientation, and sense of each antenna in a system should be identical in order to optimise the signal strength between stations. For example, linearly-polarised antennas that are identically-orientated (eg vertical or horizontal) work best together, as do circularly-polarised antennas that are using the same sense (RHC, LHC). Even so, circularly-polarised antennas are compatible with linearly-polarised antennas, and *vice versa*, because a linearly-polarised antenna can receive components of the circularly-polarised signals in its linear plane.

When linearly-polarised antennas are misaligned by 45°, the signal strength will degrade by 3dB, resulting in up to 50% signal loss. When misaligned by 90°, the signal strength degrades 20dB or more. Likewise, in a circularly-polarised system, both antennas must have the same sense, or a loss of 20dB or more will be incurred. Combining a linearly-polarised transmitting antenna with circularly-polarised receiving antenna, will incur a loss of 3dB in signal strength between the two formats.

STANDARD HELICES
The famous work of J D Kraus on helices started in 1946, but only in the 90s was the simulation study carried out by D T Emerson [5], a very important starting point for those interested in the simulation and manufacture of axial helical antennas. Before starting the simulation phase, using *Nec-Win Pro* and *NEC-Win Synth*, we tried

to define the main parameters and the general performances of our antennas (power gain, radiation angle, input SWR and axial ratio).

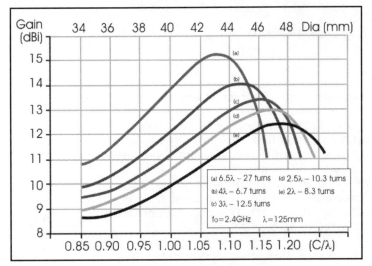

Fig 1: *NEC-2* **simulated gain versus helix diameter and C/λ at 2.4GHz.**

The power gain of the helices can be easily estimated using the graph of **Fig 1** where the performances, at 2.4GHz, of different lengths of antenna are compared. The range from 2λ to 6.5λ is covered, corresponding to 8.3 to 27 turns. The constant parameter of the helices is the pitch between two contiguous turns that is S = 0.24λ (or α = ~12°, corresponding to 30mm at 2.4GHz). In this graph, the power gain
is plotted versus C/λ. This means that, for each antenna length, there is an optimum turn diameter that maximizes the gain.

The beamwidth (radiation angle) and the power gain (in dB) are closely connected to each other by the following relationship:

$$G = 10\log_{10}\frac{360^2\eta}{\pi\theta^2} \cong 10\log_{10}\frac{41253\eta}{\theta^2},$$

where θ = half power beamwidth in degrees and η = efficiency (<1).

If we do not consider the efficiency, the equation represents the antenna directivity, which is easier to measure than the power gain at 2.4GHz, because it can be calculated through the simple measure of an angle.
The power gain and the directivity are also affected by the size and shape of the ground plane; this can be square or

circular, but it needs a side or a diameter equal to λ (125mm @ 2.4GHz) to obtain good performance.

With a smaller dimension screen, we take the risk of the inversion between the main lobe and the back one of the antenna!

The VSWR is guaranteed by the matching between the typical 120-130Ω. input impedance of the helix and the 50Ω impedance of the coaxial cable feeder. This is obtained using a λ/4 transformer made using an industrial Teflon support with h = 2.5mm and line width W = 3mm, (Z approximately 81Ω). The transformer layout is shown in **Fig 2** and was designed using the Agilent software *AppCAD* [12]. The axial ratio values are included within 1 - ∞, and are defined by

$$AR = \frac{|E_\phi|}{|E_\theta|},$$

where E_ϕ and E_θ are the electric fields in time-phase quadrature, perpendicular to the axial direction of the helix.

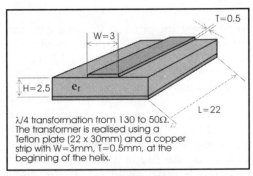

λ/4 transformation from 130 to 50Ω. The transformer is realised using a Teflon plate (22 x 30mm) and a copper strip with W=3mm, T=0.5mm, at the beginning of the helix.

Fig 2: Layout of the λ/4 Teflon transformer calculated using HP *AppCad*.

The polarisation is as much circular as the AR ratio is near unity (0dB). The matching of this requirement can be confirmed by analysing the radiation patterns generated by the *NEC-Win Pro* simulation program. The following criteria are suggested
for the design.

- Use a copper wire, gold- or silver-plated, having a suitable diameter: 0.024λ (3mm @ 2.4GHz).
- Wind the helix in a cylindrical shape.
- Divide each turn in 10 segments in order to satisfy the *NEC-Win Pro* rule that fixes the minimum ratio between the length of the segment and the wire radius for

better simulation accuracy. The use of 20 segments per wavelength is suggested only for critical regions (complex shapes).

- Use a 6mm stub between the ground plane and the helix, during the simulation phase, to minimise the current induced in the screen by the proximity of the first turn of the helix winding.

Using the above criteria, we simulated and built two different antennas (see the photograph), one to receive the *AO-40* satellite [6], having 16.7 turns (simulation results: power gain 14.5dB, radiation angle 26°) and another with 5 turns (power gain 12dB, radiation angle 45°) to be used both as a reference antenna and as transmitting antenna for the directivity measurements described later. The simulation files are available to experimenters on request.

LOW-PROFILE HELICES
The behaviour of the current versus length of a typical helix shows three different regions.

Field test: 5- and 16.7-turn helices.

- Between the two helix ends where there is a relatively uniform current and small SWR (transmission line).

There are two ways to obtain a good circular polarisation helix: firstly, tapering the helical turns near the open end, to reduce the reflected current from the arm end; secondly, using only the first helical

Low-profile helix with 1.7 conical turns.

turns where the decaying current travels from the feed-point to the first minimum point (see **Fig 3** for a 5-turn helix).

Starting from these considerations, our final low-profile helix uses a pitch S = 0.16λ (20mm @ 2.4GHz) and is both conically wound with a cone of 62/41mm

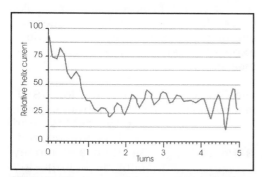

Fig 3: Helix current distribution at a frequency near the centre of the axial-mode region.

- Near the feed point where the current decay is exponential.
- Near the open end with a visible standing wave.

Type	Measured radiation angle (°)	Equivalent directivity (dB)	Simulated radiation (°)	Simulated directivity (dB)	Notes
16.7 turns	28	13.5	26	14.5	AO-40 type
5.0 turns	45	11.0	42	12.0	Reference
1.7 turns	58	10.0	60	9.6	Low-profile

Table 1: Comparison between measurements and simulation for standard and low-profile helices.

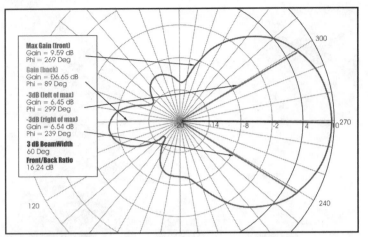

Fig 4: *NEC-Win Pro* **simulated radiation diagram of the 1.7-turn conical 2.4GHz helix. (Pitch = 20mm, Cone dia = 62/41mm).**

Inside Fig 4:

Max Gain (front)
Gain = 9.59 dB
Phi = 269 Deg

Gain (back)
Gain = Ð6.65 dB
Phi = 89 Deg

-3dB (left of max)
Gain = 6.45 dB
Phi = 299 Deg

-3dB (right of max)
Gain = 6.54 dB
Phi = 239 Deg

3 dB BeamWidth
60 Deg

Front/Back Ratio
16.24 dB

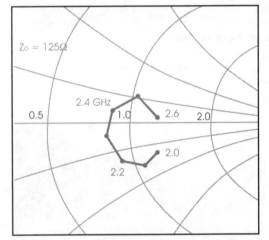

Fig 5: Input impedance simulation (Smith chart) of the low-profile helix.

$Z_0 = 125\Omega$

Table 1 for comparison between low-profile and standard helices.

The equivalent directivity obtained from radiation angle measurements is about 10dB for the low-profile helix (only 40mm thick) and 11dB for the 150mm-long 5-turn helix. The measured radiation angles (-3dB) are respectively 58° and 45°. Thanks to the very small mechanical dimensions, this antenna is particularly useful also for Wi-Fi (wireless LAN) applications.

The results obtained with *NEC-Win Pro* are very interesting. The radiation diagram and the input impedance (Smith chart) of the low-profile 2.4GHz helix are shown in **Fig 4** and **Fig 5**.

diameter and very short (only 1.7 turns – see the photograph).

The simulated and measured results are very interesting and the directivity is not significantly different from that of a conventional multi-turn helix. See

From the response plots of **Fig 6** we can also see the improved bandwidth resulting from conical helices. Also shown in **Table 2** is a comparison of the simulated values of gain, radiation angle and front-to-back ratio of four different 1.7-turn helices (conical, linear, different diameter, square or circular reflector).

MEASUREMENT ERRORS

It's not very difficult to design and make helices for different working frequencies and gains. More difficult, for the serious experimenter, is making precise measurements.

The first critical point is the low-VSWR measurement, because extremely high quality cables and adapters are needed. The time and money spent on high-quality cables can be wasted if there are large impedance mismatches within the connectors, at the connector-cable interface and with the adapters (only N or SMA for the 2.4GHz tests). David Slack of Times Microwave Systems [7] writes: "…a microwave cable assembly is not 'just a wire'. It is a passive, TEM-mode, microwave component and an integral part of a system…"

Helix type		Frequency (GHz)				Reflector
		2.0	2.2	2.4	2.6	
		Gain (dB)				
A	Dia 67/45mm conic	9.17	9.49	9.64	8.80	125 x 125mm
B	Dia 62/41mm conic	8.93	9.35	9.73	9.84	125 x 125mm
C	Dia 62/41mm conic	8.84	9.31	9.59	9.44	**Dia = 124mm**
D	Dia = 56mm **linear**	9.03	9.38	9.68	8.52	125 x 125mm
		Radiation angle (°)				
A	Dia 67/45mm conic	63	59	58	56	125 x 125mm
B	Dia 62/41mm conic	64	61	57	57	125 x 125mm
C	Dia 62/41mm conic	67	63	60	58	**Dia = 124mm**
D	Dia = 56mm **linear**	62	58	56	65	125 x 125mm
		Front-to-back (dB)				
A	Dia 67/45mm conic	18.0	18.0	20.0	17.0	125 x 125mm
B	Dia 62/41mm conic	17.3	17.6	18.0	19.0	125 x 125mm
C	Dia 62/41mm conic	14.0	15.0	16.0	18.0	**Dia = 124mm**
D	Dia = 56mm **linear**	17.0	17.0	17.0	24.0	125 x 125mm

Table 2: Simulation of gain, radiation angle and front-to-back ratios for different 1.7-turn helices.

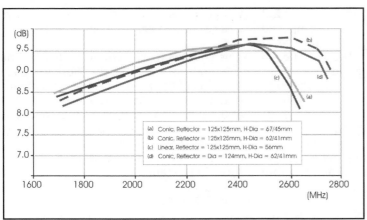

Fig 6: Frequency responses of four different 1.7-turn helices

particular, the transition between the inner conductor and the N-type panel connector lead may have different dimensions.

The use of a slotted line is becoming a lost art, but learning it is not too difficult. The first suggested measurement with a slotted line is the VSWR of a system with a very good commercial termination. Our first results with an old HP termination model 909A (N-male connector) are not the best. Better results are obtained using the Minicircuits termination type Anne-50 with an SMA-male connector (VSWR = 1.03 at 3GHz) and a good Amphenol adapter N-male/SMA-female. The measured values on our self-made slotted line (shown in the photograph) are shown in **Fig 7**. For almost all the tests, we used a generator (2.2 to 2.7GHz) composed of a VCO type JTOS-3000 followed by the 3x3mm wide-band amplifier type MNA-6 (complete package).

Assuming a high-quality cable is used, the predominant contributor to the VSWR of a cable assembly (on a 10-50cm short assembly) is the connector. Improperly-compensated geometry changes in the connector interface will exhibit very poor VSWR characteristics.

A complete 1-3GHz home-made slotted line.

RF signal levels during the measurements

The output level from the oscillator is very high (+10dBm), but some attenuation was included for stability (the wide-band amplifiers will oscillate with loads of not exactly 50Ω). Using the Boonton RF Millivoltmeter (model 92B) as a detector, there is a sensitivity loss of about 10dB at 2.4GHz (referred to the maximum suggested operating frequency of about 1.2GHz) and, consequently, the level sampled by the probe of the slotted line is very low (typically 0.3 to 3mV).

Previously, trial and error was a key part of high-performance design, but today the computer simulation of discontinuities in connectors is an art and the practical results are visible when the VSWR performance of a very good cable assembly is analysed. Another cause that can affect the characteristic impedance is the VSWR induced by the incorrect characteristic impedance of parts of the line [8, 9], in

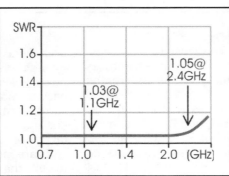

Fig 7: Slotted line measured values of VSWR up to 2800MHz.

In future measurements, we will use a 2.2 to 2.6GHz heterodyne system composed of a harmonic mixer and a 1.0GHz fixed-frequency local oscillator. The IF will be in the range 100-500MHz, limited by a 550MHz low-pass filter. This solution is free from oscillation risks and the gain is obtained with a simple wide-band 100-500MHz amplifier followed by the RF millivoltmeter. In effect it's very important to minimise the coupling between the probe and the line to obtain reliable results.

The RF power supplied to the 5-turn transmitting helix is also about 10mW (+10dBm) followed by a 6dB N-attenuator.

To reduce the measurement errors, the distance between the transmitting and receiving antennas has to be considered. To determine this distance, you need to be able to measure the signal level with a filtered RF voltmeter having a 20 - 30dB dynamic range. Also, the wave reaching the receiving antenna should be as planar as possible.

The first condition can be easily established starting with the received power and calculating the attenuation experienced by the wave in free space:

$$A = 32.4 + 20\log(f) + 20\log(d) - G_t - G_r .$$

Here, A is the attenuation in decibels, f is the frequency in megahertz , d is the distance in kilometres, G_t is the gain of the transmitting antenna in dBi, and G_r is the gain of receiving antenna, also in dBi, obtained by simulation.

There is also a simple, easy-to-remember method of calculating the free-space attenuation, by considering the distance between the two antennas in terms of wavelengths. When $d = \lambda$, A is always 22dB between isotropic antennas.

This equates to 12.5cm at 2400MHz. The attenuation increases by 6dB for each doubling of the path distance. This means that the free-space attenuation is 22dB at 0.125m, 28dB at 0.25m, 34dB at 0.5m, etc. To make the wave reaching the receiving antenna as planar as possible, the capture area in square metres of the receiving antenna is:

$$A_c = G_r . \lambda^2 / 4\pi .$$

This expression is valid for an antenna with no thermal losses and was certainly useful for our experiments. With a circular capture area, the minimum distance in metres between the antennas is:

$$d > n.G_r.\lambda / \pi^2 .$$

A maximum acceptable phase error will also be considered.

For a phase error of 22.5°, which is usually enough, $n = 2$. If a phase error of only 5° is required, $n = 9$. In the case where one dimension prevails, the maximum length, instead of the capture diameter, is used. In this case, the minimum distance in metres becomes [10, 11]:

$$d > n.L / \pi^2 ,$$

where L is the maximum length in metres (50cm for the 16.7-turn helix).

A site in the garden was found to be particularly useful for all our helix measurements ($d = 4m = 32\lambda$ at 2400MHz).

NEC-WIN SYNTH

NEC-Win Synth is designed to allow users to build complex antenna structures quickly. The structures can be created in several ways; the 47 predefined models, together with the ability to import NEC, ASCII, and DXF files, allow for very creative ways to generate 3D structures. Geometric data are displayed in a spreadsheet with access to 134 predefined functions and constants and 52 user-defined variables. Dialogue boxes linked to the spreadsheet make it easy to rotate, move or scale individual wires or complete models. As you build and modify your model, the structure is displayed and dynamically updated as edits are made. We used *NEC-Win Synth* to build the circular reflector for the helix.

REFERENCES

[1] John D Kraus, 'The Helical Antenna', pp265-339, *Antennas*, McGraw-Hill, 2nd Edition,1988.

[2] H E King and J L Wong, 'Characteristics of 1- to 8-Wavelength Uniform Helical Antennas', IEEE *Trans Antennas Propagation*, pp291-96, 1980.

[3] H Nakano, Y Samada and J Yamauchi, 'Axial-Mode Helical Antennas', IEEE *Trans Antennas Propagation*, pp1143-48, 1986.

[4] www.nittany-scientific.com

[5] D T Emerson, 'The Gain of the Axial-Mode Helix Antenna: a Numerical Modelling Study', March 1995, National Radio Observatory, Tucson, AZ, USA.

[6] 'Microwave Radio via AMSAT Oscar AO-40', *RadCom* Aug 2001 and Nov/Dec 2001.

[7] David Slack, 'Microwave and RF Cable Assemblies: the Neglected System Component', *Applied Microwave & Wireless*, Nov/Dec 1997, pp36-45.

[8] *Reference Data for Radio Engineers*, H W Sams & Co, 5th Edition, 1989, pp29- 19 to 29-23.

[9] *Microwave Handbook*, Vol 1, RSGB, 1989, pp5-22.

[10] Paolo Antoniazzi, Marco Arecco, 'Measuring Yagis', *Electronics World*, Dec 1998, pp1002-06.

[11] Donald R J White, *Electromagnetic Interference and Compatibility*, Vol 2, Don White Consultants Inc, 1980.

[12] *AppCAD*, free download from www.agilent.com

ACTIVE AERIAL FOR 160 to 4m

by Ian Braithwaite, G4COL

This active aerial has been doing its job in my loft for well over 10 years. I've seen a number of designs over the years, and this is the simplest, deriving from experiment. When I recently saw a highly sophisticated-looking commercial unit, I felt it was time to 'go public'.

Active aerials rely on a combination of an aerial element (such as a dipole, monopole, or loop) and an amplifier, which is the 'active' part. The aerial element is non-resonant, and tends to be physically small. Such aerials have broad operating bandwidths, so don't need to be tuned. In comparison, a resonant aerial would need tuner adjustments to cover the whole HF and lower VHF spectrum. So, the attraction of active aerials is convenience.

It is only fair to point out that some people dislike them, and there are pitfalls, which I shall point out. If you want a really excellent receiving aerial for all the HF amateur and broadcast bands, and have masses of space, why not put up a Beverage or rhombic aerial? If, as in my case, that's out of the question, then consider an active aerial and, better still, try building your own! This one can be put together in a few hours and covers 160m to 4m.

DESIGN CONSIDERATIONS

The choice of a small aerial element (less than $^\lambda/_{10}$ or so) is between the dipole and monopole - which respond to the electric field component of the radio wave - and the loop, which responds to the magnetic field component. A broadband active loop aerial is still on my list of things to try.

My first homebrew active aerial was a dipole, and was quite successful. The main thing it taught me was that it's not a good idea to have too much gain. It is natural to conclude that, as a short aerial picks up a smaller signal than a resonant dipole, the gain must be made up in the amplifier. Being a broadband device, the amplifier is subjected to the entire HF radio spectrum including powerful broadcast transmitters. What tends to happen in practice is that it distorts, generating intermodulation products. These appear to the receiver as additional signals and, though giving the impression of a 'lively' receiving system, are entirely unwanted. An attenuator between the active aerial and receiver is of no use at all, if the distortion has already happened in the active aerial.

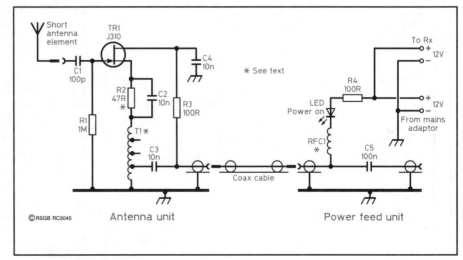

Fig 1: Circuit diagram of the aerial and power feed units.

It occurred to me to try a single wire monopole, which made for a simpler amplifier. This worked and has been in use ever since.

CIRCUIT DESCRIPTION

The amplifier, shown in **Fig 1**, is a source-follower circuit designed around Tr1, a J310 FET (field-effect transistor). This has to present a high impedance to the small monopole, otherwise signal voltage is lost, and then deliver the signal to the receiver input, commonly a 50Ω impedance.

The FET has an output impedance in the region of 50 to 100Ω, which means that, if the FET source fed the receiver 50Ω input, more than half the signal voltage would appear across the FET, and less than half would be delivered to the receiver. That's where the transformer T1, in the source circuit, comes in. I used a quadrifilar winding to give a 4:1 voltage step down ratio. This gives the source follower an overall gain of almost $^1/_5$ in voltage (-14dB when the ratio of gate voltage to output voltage is expressed in decibels).

The benefit of doing this is that the FET has much less work to do. The action of the transformer makes the impedance presented to the FET source bigger by a factor of $4^2 = 16$ times, which is 800Ω. The result is improved linearity. Locations differ, but I have never known the active aerial produce unwanted signals. You may be concerned that this low gain would produce a rather 'deaf' receiving system but, from experience, comparing it to a transmitting dipole and tuner, you won't miss much, if anything. The internally-generated noise is very low, and the background noise in most of the HF spectrum is high.

Power to the active aerial is fed via the coaxial cable, and the supply is injected via choke RFC1, housed in the power-feed unit near the receiver. R4 is included to limit the current in the event of an accidental short-circuit. An LED in series with the supply indicates that current is being drawn, and protects against inadvertent supply polarity reversal. Shown on the circuit diagram is a power feed for a receiver. This is for the case where the receiver and aerial can share the same power supply. You may choose to omit it.

The frequency response is shown in **Fig 2**, and is nominally flat within 1dB to 60MHz and within 2dB to 100MHz.

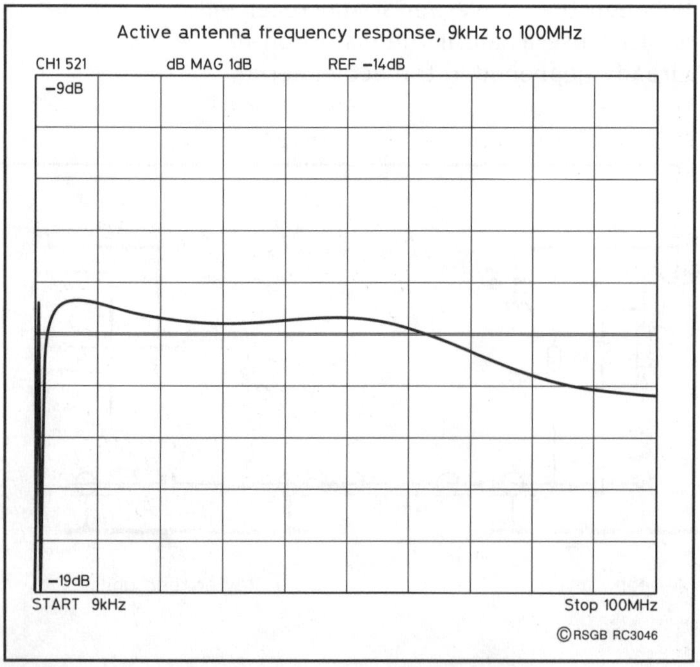

CONSTRUCTION

Transformer T1 requires some care in construction, and is described in some detail, starting with the quadrifilar wire itself. This would probably be a labour-intensive and expensive item to produce commercially, and is where the amateur's craft skills come into their own.

Take four strands of 0.2mm diameter (35/36SWG) enamelled copper wire, length approximately 300mm for each strand. Placing the wires side-by-side, clamp one end and, pulling the wires taut, fix the free end in the chuck of a hand drill. Turn the drill to twist the strands together. There is no need to twist too tightly, a few twists per centimetre being adequate.

The core should be a high-permeability (>100) ferrite toroid, 10 to 15mm in

Active antenna frequency response, 9kHz to 100MHz

CH1 521　　　　dB MAG 1dB　　　　REF −14dB

Fig 2: Frequency response of the active aerial.

diameter. The purpose of the core is to produce a sufficiently high inductance to avoid gain roll-off at low frequencies, and given a high enough permeability, a wide variety of types, still to be found at rallies, should be suitable. If you are buying new, **Table 1** shows the types that should be suitable. Supplier contact details are given at the end of the article. Between them, they should be able to source all items needed for construction.

Wind seven or eight turns of the quadrifilar wire on the core. (Each time the wire passes through the core counts as one turn.) The photograph shows how this has been done on a T37-61 core. To secure the winding, the core has been dipped in polyurethane varnish and left to dry.

The individual wires need to be separated and the windings identified. Each wire end should be stripped of its insulation. An easy way to do this is to hold the wire end in a blob of solder on the end of a soldering iron for a few seconds. Make sure you do this in a well-ventilated area and avoid inhaling the fumes or getting them in your eyes.

The ends of each winding can then be identified with a multimeter or continuity tester. I found it useful to mark the windings with short strips of insulation stripped from ribbon cable, and slid over the wires as shown in the same photograph. If you do this with three windings, the fourth can be left plain.

Naming the windings arbitrarily 1 to 4, take the *end* of winding 1, and twist together with the *start* of winding 2. The *end* of 2 is then twisted with the *start* of 3, and so on. Twist fairly close to the toroid, and make electrical connection using the soldering iron, as described above, observing the precautions. The transformer is now complete. Check for electrical continuity through the whole

Maker	Maker's part no	Supplier
Amidon	FT37-61	JAB, Sycom
Amidon	FT50-61	JAB, Sycom
Philips (3C85 material)	433003037790	Farnell (stock code 178-504)

Table 1: Suitable toroidal cores and their suppliers.

transformer by measuring across the un-paired wires.

Once the transformer is done, the rest of the construction is straightforward. Start with R2 as 47Ω or 68Ω. It may need to be changed on test. The photograph shows my loft unit built into a diecast box, with a couple of solder tags for earthing to the box. Alternatively, the circuit can be built above a small piece of plain copper-clad board, which can then be fitted inside a weatherproof

The active aerial circuitry built into a diecast box.

enclosure if outdoor mounting is required. The enclosure itself can be plastic - it is an aerial after all!

Make sure you select the correct tap on transformer T1 for the output, and take care to prevent the unused taps from shorting to any other part of the circuit.

THE POWER FEED

As the photograph illustrates, I built my power feed unit in a small plastic box. The choke is a single winding of around 20 turns on another high-permeability toroid, which can be the same type as that used for the transformer. A metal enclosure would make sense for the power feed unit, since it will

The power feed unit.

be near the receiver and possibly also domestic interference sources. If using a plastic housing, link the coaxial sockets

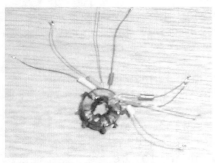

Detail of the toroidal transformer, T1. Notice the placement of the individual turns, and their identification with coloured sleeving from ribbon (rainbow) cable.

with coaxial cable - I used some RG-178. Keep the braid 'tails' short to avoid unwanted pickup.

TESTING AND COMMISSIONING

Check carefully for wiring errors. For bench testing, the power feed and aerial units can be linked with a short coaxial cable. Having ensured that its voltage and polarity are correct, connect the power supply and check that the LED is lit. Measure the voltage across R2 and divide this by its resistance to find the current, or measure the supply current directly. This should be in the region of 10 to 20mA. I selected R2 for a current of around 15mA.

If the power feed output is now connected to a receiver, a small amount of additional hiss should be heard.

Nothing should be heard until a short wire (1m or less) is placed on the aerial input. Signals should be heard on the HF bands, given suitable propagation conditions, or perhaps television or PC monitor timebase harmonics.

The aerial unit should be installed as high and as far away from local sources of interference as practicable. Mine is at the apex of the loft, with an aerial wire of around 1m length, suspended from a hook in the highest beam. Avoid the temptation to increase the wire length excessively in order to increase the signal. This brings the risk of distortion, and departure from a flat gain with frequency.

POSITIVE - EARTH VERSION

With a negative supply and positive earth, a couple of components can be omitted. This is shown in **Fig 3**. However, note that, while this is fine on its own, *it must not be connected to a receiver with a negative earth, because this shorts out the supply*.

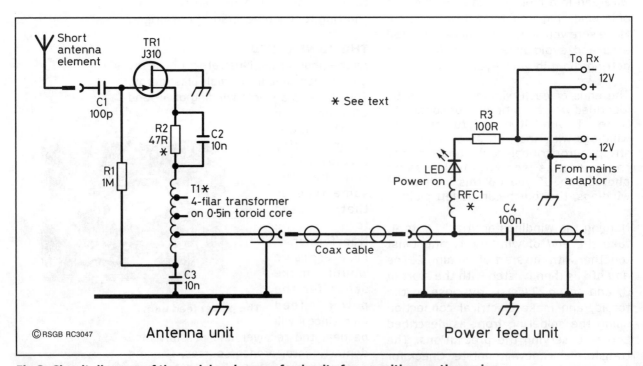

Fig 3: Circuit diagram of the aerial and power feed units for a positive-earth version.

COMPONENTS LIST

Positive supply (negative earth) version

Resistors (0.25W metal film)

R1	1MΩ
R2	see text
R3, 4	100Ω

Capacitors

C1	100pF ceramic plate
C2, 3, 4	10nF ceramic disc
C5	100nF ceramic disc

Inductors

T1	see text
RFC1	20 turns on high-permeability toroid

Semiconductors

Tr1	J310
LED	Red or chosen colour

Negative supply (positive earth) version

Resistors (0.25W metal film)

R1	1MΩ
R2	see text
R3	100Ω

Capacitors

C1	100pF ceramic plate
C2, 3	10nF ceramic disc
C4	100nF ceramic disc

Inductors

T1	see text
RFC1	20 turns on high-permeability toroid

Semiconductors

Tr1	J310
LED	Red or chosen colour

Miscellaneous

Enclosures
BNC or favoured sockets
4mm terminal post
Power connectors
Solder tags
Nuts & bolts

Supplier details:

Farnell: Canal Road, Leeds LS12 2TU.
Tel: 0113 263 6311.

JAB: PO Box 5774, Birmingham B44 8PJ.
Tel: 0121 682 7045.
Fax: 0121 681 1329.

Sycom: PO Box 148, Leatherhead,
Surrey KT22 9YW.
Tel: 01372 372 587.
Fax: 01372 361 421.
www.sycomcomp.co.uk

PORTABLE AERIAL FOR THE FT-817 (and a battery to go with it)

by William A (Tony) Blalock, WN4BML

When I first thought of purchasing a Yaesu FT-817, I thought of it both for portable use and shelter operation during emergencies. My first concern was portable power.

I have a 6.5Ah battery pack that weighs about 4lb that can be used, but I wanted a smaller, yet reasonably-powerful pack. I settled on the use of 12 AA nickel metal hydride (NiMH) batteries made up in a pack using a four-battery pack and an eight-battery pack. This gave me about 14.7VDC from a fresh pack with a capacity of 1700mAh.

I built two of them using the Radio Shack #270-391 four-AA pack and an RS #270-407 eight-AA pack wired together in series and connected to a cable with the 4.0 x 1.7 mm coaxial DC plug on its end. Great care must be taken to wire the plug correctly to prevent damage to the FT-817. I made sure to double and triple check the wiring.

Each pack's construction costs about $5 plus the batteries, which were $3.25 per cell, so the total cost for each pack was about $44. I use a multiple-cell battery charger to charge the batteries.

A PORTABLE AERIAL

My thoughts then went to how to build my own portable aerial, something that could be very compact, yet functional. Maldol had not yet released its design, but I was thinking of a base-loaded whip aerial, along the lines of a Hustler model.

I came across GM0RWU's website, which features a programme for building an aerial using loading coils [1]. The programme produces the value of inductance needed at the base for a given length of radiator. I then had the programme calculate the values needed for each band and/or frequency range. All I needed were the dimensions. This same site directed me to one which would produce that data [2]. The data generated are included in this article, as are the

Dimensions and Coil Data

Band (m)	Freq (MHz)	L (µH)	³/₄in pipe Turns	Length (in)	1in pipe Turns	Length (in)
10	28.4	1.11568	7	0.3	6	0.4
12	24.9	1.8917	9	0.3	9	0.4
15	21.1	1.687	9	0.3	8	0.4
15	21	3.1994	12	0.3	—	—
17	18.1	4.75	15	0.33	13	0.4
20	14.2	5.94	17	0.38	14	0.4
20	14	8.835	23	0.51	17	0.4
31	10.1	18.03	39	0.86	28	0.61
40	7.2	28.423	57	1.24	38	0.84
40	7.0	39.276	74	1.63	49	1.08
60	5.5	64.435	114	2.52	73	1.60
75	3.945	98.985	169	3.72	104	2.29
75	3.945	126.48	213	4.68	129	2.84
80	3.5	161	265	5.83	160	3.52

Table 1: **Coil data, including inductance, number of turns, and coil length at a variety of amateur frequencies. Separate listings are provided for ³/₄inch and 1in coil formers. Calculations performed on GM0RWU website.**

websites. Refer to **Table 1** for the dimensions and number of turns for each coil, based on band and coil diameter. (The table provides data for $^3/_4$in and 1in diameter PVC pipe as the coil former.)

I settled on $^3/_4$in PVC pipe for my coil formers and PVC caps for the ends (see **Photo A**). I chose the flat PVC caps for ease of construction, specifically drilling holes for installing the BNC chassis-mount jacks—one at each end.

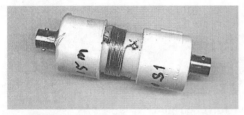

Photo A: This 15m coil is typical of the band coils wound by the author for his multiband portable HF aerial. With the appropriate coil, this aerial will cover 80 – 10m.

CONSTRUCTION

I installed the jacks on the caps and epoxied the nuts to the inside of the caps, and let the epoxy dry. Next I soldered a piece of copper wire from a piece of RG-6 to the centre conductor of each BNC connector. This would be used to attach the coils once they were wound.

I then cut each piece of PVC stock to length by adding together the dimension of the coil length and the depth of each cap and cutting them to length with a hacksaw. I determined where the coil would be located on the former and drilled two very small holes where the wires from the BNC connectors would come out. Next, I pulled the wires through and installed the caps with connectors on each end of the PVC stock.

Using magnet wire, I then wound the coil on each form according to the size specified in Table 1. I soldered only one end of the coil to the protruding wire, being sure to scrape the enamel

insulation from the magnet wire first. At the other end of the coil, I just scraped off the enamel and wrapped the magnet wire around the protruding wire. I did this for each coil for each band. Next, I trimmed the protruding wire so only about 1in stuck out from the wrapped end. I trimmed back the wires at the soldered end to the soldered connection. Tuning would come later! I used #22 wire to wind all the coils for 40 to 10m, with #24 wire used to wind the 80m coil (**Photo B**).

WHIP CONSTRUCTION

The whip aerial was next. I made it from a 72in telescoping aerial mounted to a PL-259 connector using a combination of $^1/_8$in brass threaded stock and $^3/_8$in brass flat stock obtained from a local hardware store (**Photos C** and **D**). I drilled the flat stock so I could mount the whip to it using brass screws. Next, I bent the stock just above the mounting point to which the threaded stock would be attached. Using a long piece of $^1/_8$in threaded stock, I attached the threaded stock to the flat stock, and then ran it into the PL-259 and soldered the threaded stock to the centre conductor using a $^3/_8$in nylon spacer both to insulate and keep the stock centred. I then tightened the nuts to the flat stock and soldered them.

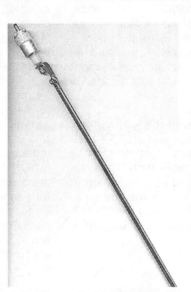

Photo C: A 6ft whip made from a telescoping aerial goes on top of the coil. You may adjust the size of this whip as needed for a good match on your selected band.

FINAL ASSEMBLY AND TUNING

The next step was the final assembly and tuning of each coil. I first experimented with the 20 and 15m coils to get the hang of it. In many cases, I found that I had too many turns on the coil – but too many is better than too few! I then built all my other coils, covering all bands with the exception of the 31m shortwave broadcast band.

In all cases, I got the aerial to resonate below the band. To determine initial

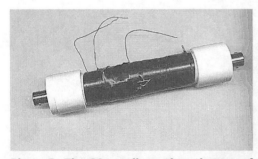

Photo B: The 80m coil requires the use of thinner wire—in this case #24 instead of #22 – in order to get enough wire on a reasonable-size coil former.

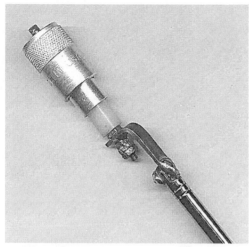

Photo E: The selected band coil goes between a series of adapters and connectors that tie the aerial and radio together. With 1in PVC tubing, you might be able to use SO-239 connectors on the coils and eliminate the need for one set of adapters.

Photo D: Detail of the connection of the whip portion of the aerial to the PL-259 connector (see text).

resonance, I used the MFJ Antenna Analyser. It was a big help. I unwrapped a few turns of magnet wire, scraped the insulation off, wrapped the magnet wire around the protruding wire, and checked for resonance. In a couple of cases, I had to add windings, so I just soldered additional wire to what was on the coil and added a few turns. Final dimensions are given in Table 1.

To tack down the windings after final alignment, I used epoxy and wrapped the coils with tape after soldering and trimming the excess protruding wire. I even made a coil for 80m using taps for about 3.940, 3.800, and 3.500MHz.

Note: I used a needle file to file the male locking rings of the BNC connectors. This made it easier and faster to lock the coils to the adapters.

OPERATION AND TEST

I have used these coils successfully on 40, 20, and 15m. To resonate the aerial, I either shorten or lengthen the whip until it is resonant. I use a counterpoise of about 20ft of wire attached to the radio with alligator clips. I have checked into nets here in Florida both on amateur bands and MARS frequencies with good results. Many times I have also used a Dentron Jr tuner to make tuning faster and easier, but both approaches work well.

In **Photo E** you can see the combination of PL-259 adapters and BNC adapters that I use to attach the aerial to the radio and/or tuner. Of course, all of these adapters introduce some loss into the system, but if your goal is to get on the air and get a signal out with a minimum of expense, this approach should be considered.

NOTES

[1] GM0RWU Loading Coil Design Programme
http://ecosse.org/jack/radiocoil.html
[2] GM0RWU Loading Coil Calculations
http://ecosse.org/jack/radio/software/loading.html

BASIC MATERIALS

Description	Source	Part #	Quantity
BNC chassis jack	RadioShack	278-105	2 per coil
PL-259	RadioShack	278-188	1
Magnet wire pack	RadioShack	278-1345	Spool pack #22, #24, #30
72in telescoping whip	RadioShack	270-1408	1
$^3/_4$in PVC flat caps	hardware store		2 per coil
$^3/_4$in PVC S#40	hardware store		10ft length
$^3/_8$in flat brass stock	hardware store		1
$^1/_8$in threaded stock	hardware store		1
Brass nuts & washer	hardware store		as needed
5-minute epoxy	hardware store		as needed

Table 2: Materials needed for the portable QRP aerial. Virtually everything is available from Radio Shack and your local hardware store.

CHEAP 2m AERIALS

by Arnie Coro, CO2KK

Two metres is the most popular amateur band worldwide, and everything indicates it will continue to be a favourite for newcomers to the hobby. In some parts of the world, the band spans a full 4MHz, while in others it is just 2MHz wide. Building your own 2m aerials is a lot of fun, will cost almost nothing, and will give you a lot of hands-on experience in aerial work. It will also be a challenge for you.

Each of the projects that follows will give you an aerial better than a 'rubber duck', but will require some skill and patience. On the other hand, building your own rubber duck is no simple task, either.

Nearly every amateur in the world today owns at least one 2m FM radio. Many of us own two or more. Some hams give their 2m handheld (HT) a lot of use, while others enjoy working mobile FM. Still others own multi-mode rigs, so they need to install a horizontally-polarised aerial for the weak-signal modes, as well as a vertical aerial for FM.

It is well-known that the helically-wound short vertical aerial, or 'rubber duck', supplied with the typical 2m handheld is a pretty poor radiator. Losses may range from -6dB to as much as -10dB when compared with a reference-standard half-wave vertical dipole. Why do we keep using it? The obvious answer is that the popular rubber-duck fits nicely and provides communications when you are either talking to a nearby station or using a hilltop repeater. At home, you may be tempted to hook up your HT to a big outdoor aerial (**Photo A**),

but that may have drawbacks as well as benefits. The typical HT cannot handle the high field intensity of nearby out-of-band stations, something that leads to very bad cross-modulation problems. A rubber duck isn't sensitive enough to pick up these stations, but a big outdoor aerial is. HTs require either smaller aerials or tight bandpass filters between the external aerial and the radio.

BETTER HT AERIALS

Of course, you can carry a better aerial for your handie-talkie, such as my favourite 0.32λ vertical, which provides a substantial increase in signal strength while at the same time matching the 50Ω output impedance of the transceiver. Aerial experts will tell you that the 0.32λ vertical has a resistive component that is near 50Ω, while also having a reactance that is easily

Photo A: Full-size, 2m, omnidirectional, vertically-polarised aerial at CO2KK's QTH using three $5\lambda/8$ elements. With its estimated 6dB gain over a dipole, it's my standard of comparison for 2m FM work.

compensated by introducing a series matching capacitor between the aerial and the rig's aerial connector.

The 0.32λ aerial measures about 56cm (22in) in length when cut for the 145 to 146MHz segment and a little less when you resonate it for operation between 146 and 148MHz.

Homebrewing your 0.32λ vertical for a handie-talkie is a nice weekend project, but remember that you must tune out the aerial's reactance by using a small trimmer capacitor, located at the base of the aerial and connected in series with the radiator.

Because handheld FM transceivers happen to use the case of the radio as part of the aerial system (yes, believe me, the metal case of your radio is the actual 'ground system' to complete the vertical aerial's image), you must adjust the 0.32λ vertical with the help of a field-strength meter and a lot of patience.

A weak station will provide the first approximation, because you can tune the series trimmer capacitor with a non-inductive tool, looking for maximum signal strength. The second step will be to use the field-strength meter out in the open and carefully adjust the series trimmer for maximum radiated signal.

One of the difficulties involved in this otherwise very effective and low-cost replacement for the rubber-duck helical whip is that you must make it in such a way as to provide good mechanical strength, while at the same time not causing too much stress on the HT's often-fragile aerial connector.

HALF-WAVE VERTICALS ARE STILL BETTER

By combining a small loading and matching coil, plus a simple impedance transformation network, commercial manufacturers offer telescopic half-wave verticals specially designed for handie-talkie use. The typical λ/2 aerial for 2m FM use will be about 95cm (37$^1/_2$in) long when extended, something that certainly will require a lot of care when handling a radio equipped with such an aerial. In practice, the telescopic whip and matching network can be designed so that, when the whip is *not* extended, it can provide the user with the performance of the standard rubber-duck aerial. When the

whip is extended to its full length, the increase in efficiency of the radiating system is outstanding.

The fact is, a half-wave aerial, when fed at the bottom, presents a very high impedance, so it requires much less of a 'ground system' than a λ/2 vertical or any other similar aerial, such as the rubber duck. Homebrewing a 2m λ/2 vertical for use on a handheld radio does require using a telescopic whip and some kind of weatherproof box in which the tuned matching network can be housed.

Again, the use of a telescopic whip is a must, and finding the appropriate circuit parameters to make the λ/2 vertical work properly when fully extended as a true λ/2 aerial, and as near as possible to a λ/4 vertical when the whip is collapsed to its minimum length, can be tricky, to say the least.

My advice for newcomers and old-timers alike is that the λ/2 is an excellent aerial for portable work if it is properly built from both an electrical and mechanical standpoint. This leaves little room for homebrewing, except for those *CQ* 'Antennas' column readers who have a lot of practical experience in building their own VHF and UHF aerials. Commercial versions are inexpensive, and if you're mainly looking for improved communication, consider buying one. If you're looking for a challenge, build one instead.

MAGNETIC LOOPS ON 2m

Yes... they are both pretty small and work very well when properly designed and tuned to the operating frequency. Magnetic loops for VHF work have the same narrow bandwidth feature as those made for the HF bands, so you may find yourself having to retune the magnetic loop when changing frequency. Not doing so may harm your radio's output stage, something that many of us have learned the hard way (your columnist is among those who have blown a nice HT output module while testing a magnetic loop).

What may move the average ham to build and use a magnetic loop with a 2m radio? The answer is not that difficult to find. The magnetic loop is a very small aerial, and it has two very marked nulls, something that will help fox-hunters a lot!

Following standard magnetic-loop practice, the aerial must be used with a variable tuning-capacitor, and you may use one of the two typical matching systems – the gamma match or the coupling-loop method. Both work well but, for the 2m band magnetic loop, I prefer to use the gamma-match system because, once set, the VSWR at the operating frequency will stay low. (I don't have space here to get

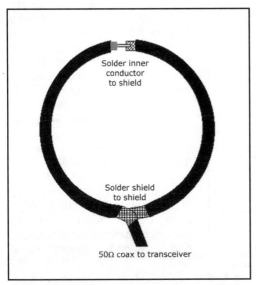

Fig 1: If you build a magnetic loop and want to feed it using the coupling-loop method (although I recommend a gamma match, because these loops are so small), this is how it should be made.

into the specifics of building a gamma match, but standard aerial references such as the *ARRL Antenna Book* and Joe Carr's *Practical Antenna Handbook* cover the topic well. In contrast, the coupling loop (**Fig 1**) is more prone to moving out of the place where it gives the best match, something that may prove dangerous to your rig, as the VSWR may go up abruptly when the coupling loop moves.

Don't be surprised by the small size of even the largest 2m magnetic loop (**Fig 2**). According to aerial theory, a magnetic loop cannot be more than approximately $\lambda/10$ long. Thus, for the 2m band, with a wavelength between 2.08m and 2.02m from 144 to 148 MHz, the maximum length of the magnetic loop should be around 20.5cm (8in) for the centre of the band. That gives a diameter of $20.5/\pi$, so the diameter of the magnetic loop is just 6.42cm (about 2.5in).

I have made several of these aerials using either 3mm ($^1/_8$in) diameter wire or a 10mm ($^3/_8$in) wide copper strip. Both materials provide excellent results and, as a matter of fact, local hams here have built the 2m magnetic loop to replace lost rubber-duck verticals. The magnetic loops are pretty efficient, and they do have two rather sharp nulls that can be used very effectively during a foxhunt, or to find a source of interference.

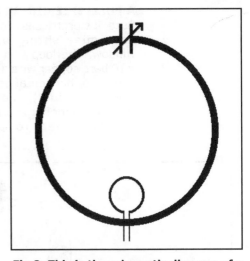

Fig 2: This is the schematic diagram of a typical magnetic-loop aerial using the coupling-loop method. Again, this is not especially practical for 2m aerials due to the extremely small size of the coupling loop required.

COPPER-TAPE AERIAL FOR WINDOW USE

Copper-foil tape used by glass artists usually comes with an adhesive backing, so it makes an ideal material with which to build a group of low-cost aerials that are taped to glass windows. The easiest of them all is the $\lambda/2$ vertical dipole which, when properly fed, gives excellent results. Two 1cm wide ($^3/_4$in) copper-foil tape strips make excellent broadband 2m aerials!

Of course, you must win the approval of the lady of the house to install a copper-foil window aerial but, once installed, it will last for a long time, and you can always use it (even right in the middle of a storm), because the aerial is indoors.

I use RG-174 coaxial cable to feed my copper-foil dipole that is located exactly behind my workbench. Tuning the dipole for minimum VSWR is not difficult at all using a standard VHF VSWR meter. Do remember to run the coaxial feeder at exactly 90° from the dipole centre, and run it for no less than 60cm (about 2ft) before making any turns. You may also try feeding a $\lambda/2$ vertical made of copper foil at the bottom, but that will require a matching network that somehow must be hidden from sight.

A FULL-SIZE CIRCULAR LOOP

Sure, it's pretty easy to build this aerial. I have mine sitting behind a wooden window. The loop is made using #12 or #10 bare copper wire and is fed either for vertical or horizontal polarisation. I made two loops (**Fig 3**), one of which is fed at the bottom for horizontal polarization and the other fed to provide vertical

coil former. Before using the coaxial choke balun, the nulls were not as sharp!

LAST BUT NOT LEAST...

... A rectangular loop that matches 50Ω. With appropriate tweaking , a full-size rectangular loop can be made to provide an almost-perfect match to a 50Ω coaxial line. However, please don't forget to include the vitally-important decoupling coaxial choke balun right at the feed-point. My rectangular loop, seen in **Photo B** just before soldering the feed-line, was tested at the same window position as the circular loop, and there was no measurable change in performance. This loop was made using #8 copper wire that came from a burned-out power transformer, making it an aerial from recycled materials.

As you can see, there are plenty of alternatives to your rubber-duck aerial. All it takes is patience, careful construction, and little or no money! Have fun!

Fig 3: A 2m magnetic loop made using wide copper laminate in order to increase the bandwidth. Notice the use of a ground plane below the aerial, the trimmer capacitor required to tune the aerial to resonance, and the gamma-match feed system used. In order to fulfil the magnetic-loop design criteria, the aerial may not exceed λ/10.

polarization. Changing from one loop to the other takes less than a minute!

The full-size loop is 208cm (82in) long, and it does require a λ/4 coaxial matching section made from 75Ω cable in order to match the loop's approximately 110Ω impedance to the 50Ω typically used by 2m radios. One advantage of this low-cost, homebrew, full-size 2m band loop is that it is quite effective for direction finding if you carefully wind the quarter-wave matching section as a coil using a 25mm (1in) diameter PVC pipe section as a

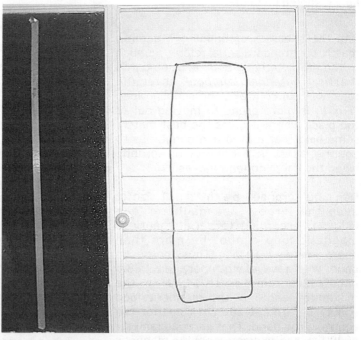

Photo B: Two of my indoor 2m band aerials – the copper-foil-tape λ/2 end-fed, and the elongated rectangular loop. There is no feed-line connected to the loop.

BALLOON-SUPPORTED VERTICALS

by Peter M Livingston, W3CRI, Dave Kunkee, K0DI, and Elizabeth Kunkee, KS4IS

On the air with the balloon-supported vertical aerial at sunset during the 2001 *CQ* World-Wide 160m Contest.

this project can't be done for a $10 bill and a little time, but it is within the capabilities of many clubs. With all preparations in place, we can erect and take down this two-element vertical array in a little under two hours, making it ideal for Field Day, 160m contests, and emergency operation (see **Photo A**).

This article will tell you how we of the TRW Radio club did it and with what results. First, however, here is a little background on how this project got started.

SOME BACKGROUND

I, W3CRI, began experimenting with aerial designs about five years ago when I bought Roy Lewallen's *EZNEC*, an easy-to-use, *Windows*®-orientated, aerial-modelling program. Although I have been licensed continuously for slightly more than a half century, I was inactive for many years and recently came back to active ham status – t a completely changed amateur radio vista.

Photo A: The authors operate various 160m contests from the shore of the inland Salton Sea, using a rental truck to transport their equipment, including the aerostat (balloon) to support the aerial.

Have you ever wished you could set up a low-emitting-angle vertical array for the long-wavelength bands? Work all states and a few foreign countries on 160? "Sure," you say, "I just happen to have a spare back 40 acres, an infinite supply of money, and hundreds of ground wires forming the counterpoise!" It's true that

As a teenager, I saved up my paper-route money to buy military-surplus gear, which I modified and put on the air mostly on 80 and 40m CW. In those days, stripping down a surplus chassis and building your own transmitter was fun and gave us an outlet for whatever creativity we could bring to bear. After waking up from a 30-year snooze like Rip Van Winkle, I found that amateur radio had changed completely. Rigs are almost 95% professionally built, and the technology no longer prizes 807 and 813 transmit tubes as it did back then. In fact, many hams may not even recognise these tubes!

After getting reacquainted with the hobby, I cast around for the modern equivalent of rig building with surplus parts. I found that there still were a lot of wire-aerial ideas waiting to be invented, so I happily set about my new amateur radio hobby! I experimented with fat dipoles, and fat deltas, mostly on paper, until I met Dave and Elizabeth Kunkee, members of TRW's radio club. Dave had bought a small aerostat (balloon) and had used it for several years to hoist a λ/4 vertical anchored by a mag-mount to the roof of his auto for the annual international 160m contest.

I persuaded Dave to loan the balloon to the club for the year 2000 Field Day. He agreed, and with it we hoisted an open-topped, corner-fed fat delta of my own design for 80m. It worked, but it wasn't clear that all that extra wire had much of an advantage over a simple λ/4 vertical and ground plane.

After Field Day, I went off to mull over why the delta didn't do much better than a λ/4 vertical. It should have because, as I later deduced, the two arms of the delta acted as a phased array with the bottom of the delta as the phasing line between them. However, if that was the case, maybe it would be better just to consider a vertical phased array instead.

HOW HIGH SHOULD IT BE?

Now vertical phased arrays are not new; two- and four-element vertical phased arrays are described in the ARRL's *Antenna Compendium*, for example. The wrinkle in this case was that we had only one point of suspension causing the two phased elements to 'lean' towards one another. Obviously, the higher the balloon, the nearer vertical the wires would be. The design question was, 'How high must the balloon be in order to get a decent front-to-back ratio?'. We'll answer this question in the following paragraphs.

Fig 1 shows a schematic of the balloon-borne, two-element phased array that formed the basis for a *NEC-2* analysis (*EZNEC 3.0* for *Windows*®).

While Dave's balloon might have worked, we all thought it was too small to give us adequate lift margin to support phased arrays. After some research we settled on the balloon described next.

The balloon, or aerostat, that the club bought is an aerodynamic lifting body buoyed by helium, the same type commonly

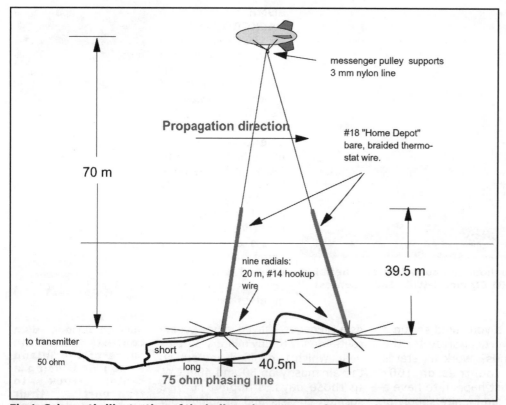

Fig 1: Schematic illustration of the balloon-borne, two-element phased array designed and flown for several contests and during the last Field Day in a scaled-down 80m version.

seen carrying advertising above large auto dealerships. Unlike a round balloon, this blimp structure is very stable in moderate to strong winds, because air flows around it without creating excessive vortices in its wake. Aerial Billboards Inc [1] built our aerostat out of 150-denier nylon coated with urethane. Its 18ft x 7ft volume contains 380ft³ of helium at full inflation, which takes about two-and-a-half helium cylindrical tanks filled with welding helium to a standard pressure. Although the balloon can be filled without a gas regulator, it is somewhat more risky to do so, and we highly recommend that you use a gas regulator [2] with the helium gas cylinders. As with all high-pressure gas cylinders, there is an element of risk in handling them, so be well aware of how to handle these gas cylinders safely.

There is a harness attached to the aerostat as shown in Fig 1 and **Photo B**. We used a pulley and swivel to attach the aerial apex to the balloon. For the most part, motions of the dirigible back and forth, as well as 'clocking' rotations, did not result in fouling of the aerial support.

The net lift of the balloon is about 16lb in still air and somewhat stronger with the wind blowing because of aerodynamic lift. Not shown in the drawing, but visible in Photo B , is a very important safety tether

Photo C: Bringing down the balloon after a successful contest. Note the size of the man (co-author W3CRI) compared with the aerostat, the technical name for a balloon of this type.

which, although slack, nonetheless would have prevented our balloon investment from taking off for Kansas had the aerial wire parted. Pulling down the balloon and deflating it requires careful effort (see **Photos C** and **D**).

I found that Home Depot sold a #18 braided copper wire used for some sort of ground strapping for low-voltage house (thermostat) wiring. A 42.1m length of this

Photo B: The balloon, or aerostat, in flight. The aerial lines are attached to the nylon via the first and third of the lines running up to the attachment point. The middle line is a 400lb test nylon safety tether.

Photo D: Co-authors KS4IS and W3CRI force helium out of the balloon by lying on it and pushing, a process that takes about 40 minutes to empty the gas bag. A vacuum cleaner would have been much quicker...

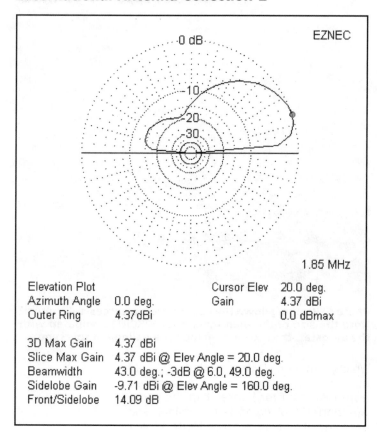

Elevation Plot

Azimuth Angle	0.0 deg.	Cursor Elev	20.0 deg.
Outer Ring	4.37dBi	Gain	4.37 dBi
			0.0 dBmax

3D Max Gain	4.37 dBi
Slice Max Gain	4.37 dBi @ Elev Angle = 20.0 deg.
Beamwidth	43.0 deg.; -3dB @ 6.0, 49.0 deg.
Sidelobe Gain	-9.71 dBi @ Elev Angle = 160.0 deg.
Front/Sidelobe	14.09 dB

EZNEC

1.85 MHz

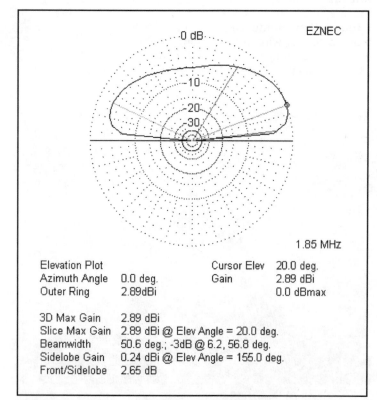

Elevation Plot

Azimuth Angle	0.0 deg.	Cursor Elev	20.0 deg.
Outer Ring	2.89dBi	Gain	2.89 dBi
			0.0 dBmax

3D Max Gain	2.89 dBi
Slice Max Gain	2.89 dBi @ Elev Angle = 20.0 deg.
Beamwidth	50.6 deg.; -3dB @ 6.2, 56.8 deg.
Sidelobe Gain	0.24 dBi @ Elev Angle = 155.0 deg.
Front/Sidelobe	2.65 dB

EZNEC

1.85 MHz

Fig 2: Comparison of front-to-back (F/B) ratio of aerial array at different altitudes. Note the significant loss of F/B ratio when the height is reduced by a factor of approximately 3/5, from 70 to 45m.

wire tied to a 3mm nylon line having a total length necessary to allow the balloon to fly at an altitude of 70m (230ft) formed one side of the vertical array 'triangle'. Flying the balloon at this height requires permission of the FAA. We found the FAA at our local airport very cooperative when we flew a reduced version of this vertical array for Field Day last June. I gave them several days' notice and received permission easily and well before Field Day. After 11 September, it is possible that it now may take longer for permission to be granted, so allow plenty of time to get the finer points correct.

As mentioned above, the balloon height of 70m for the 160m vertical array is not arbitrary, but was decided upon by setting up the aerial in *EZNEC* for various suspension heights. We chose each aerial base to be made up of nine radial wires (#14 insulated hook-up wire) each cut to 20m (65.6ft) long. (More about the radial choice below.)

We compared vertical radiation patterns for identical aerials suspended at several different altitudes (see **Fig 2**). It turns out from this study that nearly full vertical phased-array performance is recovered if the angle that the aerial makes with the ground is 74° or greater. However the fact that 70m is the right balloon altitude does not mean that 140m will give twice the performance. A little trigonometry will convince one that the cost of the added tether and support weight will offset any marginal gain increase.

THE SITE
Hoping for better conductivity to give us a low radiation angle and high efficiency, we chose our 160m contest site at the shore of a large inland salt-water lake in southern California called the Salton Sea (see **Fig 3**). The area is a broad salt plain about 200ft below sea level formed from an ancient inland sea that dried up millions of years ago. An accidental levee collapse filled this 14 x 7-mile-long lake in 1905. Presently, Salton Sea State Park occupies its eastern shore, where we flew the balloon for the *CQ* World-Wide 160m Contest and the most recent ARRL International CW 160m contest. For our purposes, the site is electrically quiet (S5 noise background on the vertical), unpopulated, flat, and right on the shore of the lake. In fact, the ends of some radials actually were in the water. The park

rangers were most cooperative and assisted us in setting up in an unused portion of a lakeside campground.

During the *CQ* WW 160 SSB Contest in February 2001, we brought along a network analyser and, after a bit of experimenting, we got it to work. Our team, now including club member Wayne Hogenkamp, KI6GM, measured the base impedance magnitude and phase angle separately at each aerial. **Fig 4** shows a bar graph indicating efficiencies for our two-element phased array over various grounds. According to our measurements of individual aerial base impedances at resonance, we expected an aerial efficiency at the site of 0.65 or better. According to the bar graph, our measurement suggested a soil type somewhere between very rich pasture land and salt water.

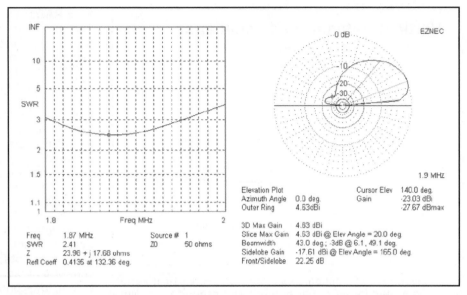

Fig 3: Calculated VSWR curve (left) and ideal vertical radiation pattern of aerial array over real, high-precision ground with moderately good conductivity (right). Measured VSWR in use was substantially better than predicted. (See text for details.)

AERIAL SPECIFICS

The two aerials are driven out of phase by a nominal 90°. (In fact, the *EZNEC* computation shows that the phase difference is more like 112.6° for the maximum front-to-back ratio at the operating frequency.) In our case, the $\lambda/4$ slanting 'verticals' are separated by $\lambda/4$ each. If each aerial radiates a nominally-cylindrical wave, the $\lambda/4$ spacing provides maximum reinforcement of the overlapping cylinders in the plane of the aerials in one direction and a near cancellation in the other. In other words, the phased array is end-fired. As it turns out, our no-tune (described below) phasing lines connecting each aerial are unequal in length.

Avoid a mistake that cost us a few QSOs the first time we used it – connect the phasing lines correctly. For example, if the aerials lie in an E - W plane and you wish to beam east, connect the easterly aerial with the long line and the westerly one with the short piece. Array direction can be selected from the comfort of the operating position with

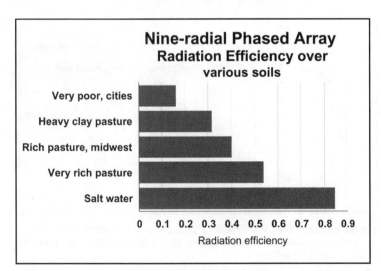

Fig 4: Our two-element phased-array aerial efficiency as computed by *EZNEC* over various soil types. Given 36.5Ω as the base impedance of a lossless vertical dipole, our measurement shows an efficiency of 0.65, which lies between 'very rich pasture' and 'salt water' as expected. Soil characterisations are those given in *EZNEC*.

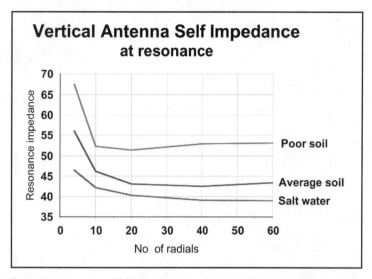

Vertical Antenna Self Impedance
at resonance

Fig 5: Resonant self-impedances of an isolated vertical aerial, shown as a function of radial number and ground type. Note the diminishing improvement above about 10 radials.

a switchbox and three DowKey coaxial relays.

There are several ways to achieve an out-of-phase feed from a common source. One is to use a quadrature-feed system shown in the *ARRL Antenna Book*, p8-14, Fig 17 [3]. This method will guarantee maximum front-to-back ratio at any frequency within the aerial's operating range, but requires tuning. For contesting, we sought a phasing method that requires no tuning, even at the expense of optimum front-to-back ratio.

Roy Lewallen's article 'The Simplest Phased Array Feed System . . . That Works' [4], has the answer. We've elaborated some on his ideas in Appendix A, on the *CQ* magazine website [5] as a companion to this article. For those mathematically-inclined hams (I'm one) interested in the definition and computation of the aerial mutual impedance and the answer to the question "Why are the phasing line lengths different?" refer to the appendix.

THE RADIALS
The last element of the aerial design to be discussed is the radial layout. Generally speaking, the self-impedance of an isolated vertical aerial decreases with added radials (see **Fig 5**). The desire is to have as low a base self-impedance as possible, indicating that non-radiative losses are at a minimum. As can be seen from the plots, there appears to a point of diminishing returns for radial numbers exceeding about 10. Although a study done in the 1930s for commercial broadcast verticals came up with the number of 120 radials, there appears to be no detailed justification for that number over different soil types. It is also clear from the plots that the basic soil type cannot completely be overcome. That is, a poor, low-conductivity urban soil will still yield a lower efficiency aerial array than very rich pasture land or salt water (see **Fig 6**).

An *EZNEC* computation for an isolated vertical having no resistive losses over a perfectly-conducting ground plane indicates a base impedance of about 36.5Ω. Consequently, the data shown in Fig 6 are easily converted to efficiencies by dividing the base impedances into 36.5Ω. Again, the payoff for more than 10

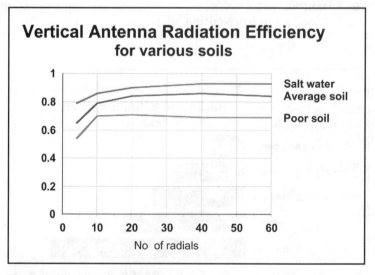

Vertical Antenna Radiation Efficiency
for various soils

Fig 6: Vertical aerial efficiency shown as a function of number of radials. Again, note that there is little benefit from having more than 10 radials.

radials is relatively small, and is worth the effort only if you are working QRP and need to make every milliwatt count. The curves do not cross so, according to this calculation, one cannot make up for poor

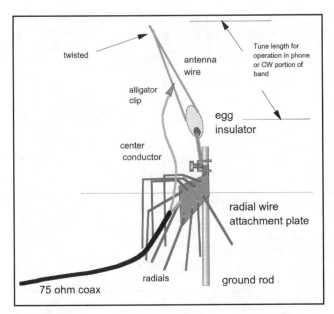

Photo E: The aerial, radials, and feed-line come together at this combination anchor/ground rod. See Fig 7 for additional details.

Fig 7: Details of the nine-radial attachment to the ground rod and aerial feed (see also Photo E). Aerial length may be fine-tuned by adjusting the length of the aerial loop through the egg insulator.

soil by lots of radials. This argument does not apply to a true ground plane, such as screening or a chicken-wire layout.

Thus, based on the curves above, we selected nine radials per aerial as being the best compromise between handling ease and aerial efficiency. We attached the radials to a ground rod and the aerial feed at the feed-point (see **Fig 7** and **Photo E**).

The VSWR performance of the array was quite a bit better than expected based on the *EZNEC* model. **Fig 8** shows a comparison of measurements made last January with the *EZNEC* prediction. We don't fully understand why this is so, but it may be that the random length of 50Ω feed-line partially compensated for some excess capacitive reactance presented to it by the aerial/phasing-line combination. Although we brought along an aerial tuner for the contests, we found that for the most part it was unnecessary.

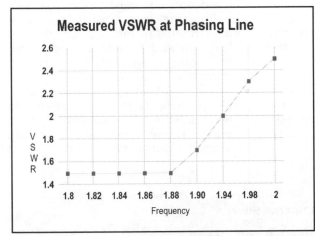

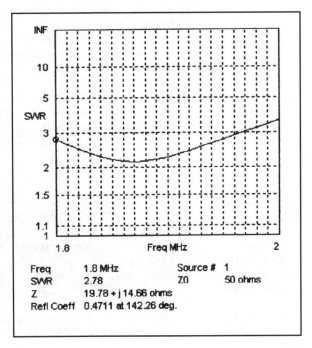

Fig 8: Actual versus predicted VSWR for 160m phased array. Graph on left shows actual VSWR measured with an MFJ VSWR meter. Graph on right is the *EZNEC* prediction for the same aerial. The authors are still not certain why the actual performance was so much better than predicted (but they're certainly not complaining!).

W6TRW Balloon-Supported Phased-Array Design

Balloon altitude:	70m (230ft)
Centre frequency:	1.87MHz
Phasing-line impedance:	75Ω
Feed-line impedance:	50Ω
Short phasing-line length:	53.41°
Long phasing-line length:	155.36°
No of radials:	9 per aerial
Radial wire size:	#14
Radial wire length:	20m (65.6ft)
Aerial length:	42.08m (138.06ft)
Aerial wire size:	#18 braided copper
Aerial ground spacing:	40.51m (132.9ft)
Ground type (model):	Real, high accuracy
Ground material (model):	'Good pasturage' to 'salt water'
Maximum front-to-back ratio (est):	25dB
Beamwidth:	43.3° (-3dB)
Gain:	4.44 dBi
Elevation angle for max gain:	<20°
Radiation efficiency, η:	$0.41 < \eta < 0.85$ depending on choice of ground conductivity

Table 1: Design parameters of the balloon-supported phased array that we successfully used in three 160m contests. A scaled version was also used on 80m for Field Day.

It can't be expected that the aerial array and phasing line will provide maximum front-to-back ratio over the entire 160m band. However, we found that we had good front-to-back behaviour except at the high band edge. (Note: This estimation assumes phasing-line lengths are constant in degrees, not in metres. Therefore, there may be an additional 5 to 10% droop in the front-to-back ratio for fixed phasing-line lengths.) Note that the peak F/B ratio is the highest for high-conductivity grounds as expected, because the ground-reflected aerial 'image' is the least attenuated. For the same reason, the radiation angle becomes lowest with the highest ground conductivity.

Table 1 shows the balloon-supported phased-array design parameters that we successfully used in three 160m contests and a scaled version for 80m for Field Day.

HOW DOES IT WORK?

Now that the design and theory have been fully explored, many will ask, "But how well did it work?". **Table 2** provides the answer.

We picked up a number of 'lessons learned' covering the details of our portable aerostat phased array. Among the many:

- Ensure that the aerial is carefully stored on a reel and wiped down with an oily rag after use. Kinks in the aerial wire are deadly and must be avoided.
- Roll up the ground wires in a hand-over-hand fashion, not around the forearm and thumb, to keep from producing snags that take time to unravel when in the field.
- Ensure that you use shrink-tubing sleeves over the joint between ground wires and the spade lugs at the ground plate. These wires take a certain amount of bending when deploying and

W6TRW 160m Contest Scores

Contest	Date	No Contacts	Points	WAS?	DX Worked
CQ WW 160 CW	28-29/1/01	465	73,580	Missed VT	S. America, Asia, Africa
CQ WW 160 SSB	23-24/2/01	419	53,940	No	6 countries
ARRL 160 CW	7-8/12/01	621	102,560	Yes	Japan, Australia, Carib

Table 2: Real-world performance of the balloon-supported phased vertical array in three recent 160m contests. The ARRL contest score was #1 in the Southwest Division.

will break free of the lugs at the most inconvenient time.

- The balloon is most vulnerable to damage during inflation and deflation. Be sure that you provide a ground tarpaulin on which to lay out the balloon when inflating it, and avoid walking on the balloon fabric at all costs! It is also helpful if the balloon is inflated away from buildings or other objects with sharp projections that could snag the balloon. Until the balloon is nearly full, it is easily buffeted by the wind and is the most vulnerable to damage. Once it is full, however, it becomes much easier to control and 'fly'.

- Be sure to bring down the balloon if the winds exceed about 30mph or are very gusty. At these speeds, a tether could part and the balloon be lost. Dave learned this lesson when his balloon nose-dived into a cactus patch at Anza-Boreego State Park during very gusty wind conditions.

It is also helpful to review the federal regulations governing balloons, kites, and so forth. These are contained in FAA Part 101, Subpart B – Moored Balloons and Kites. The source is Docket No 1580, 28 CFR 6722, June 1963, and the relevant paragraph is Sec. 101.15, 'Notice Requirements'. It has been our experience that the FAA is most cooperative, particularly when the balloon is more than 3 miles distant from an airport or heavily-travelled air corridor.

Finally, we want to emphasise that our successful 160m Balloon-Supported Phased Array is a TRW club project. While the authors did much of the design and construction, others offered help and encouragement, and the club underwrote the project costs! We couldn't have done it on our own. Look for us in the next 160m contest!

REFERENCES

[1] 426 Constitution Ave, Camarillo, California (800-700-5995).

[2] Our thanks to John Cheatham, KE6OJM, for donating a suitable gas regulator.

[3] The *ARRL Antenna Book,* 17th Edition, American Radio Relay League, 1994.

[4] *ARRL Antenna Compendium,* Vol 2, American Radio Relay League, 1989.

[5] Go to the January *CQ* highlights page at www.cq-amateur-radio.com/Jan.2003Highlights.html, then click on the appropriate prompt.

AN NVIS AERIAL

by Arnie Coro, CO2KK

Gale-force winds had already started and our hurricane emergency communications net was in full swing. Radar data was coming in, pinpointing the eye of the storm and the track it was following.

Signals from the portable station at the radar site were difficult to copy for almost every station participating in the net, except two who had installed permanent Near-Vertical-Incidence Skywave (NVIS) aerial systems just a few days before the official 1 June beginning of the hurricane season.

The portable station was also using an NVIS system of sorts, because Crescencio, CO4BM, had decided to place the λ/2 40m dipole really close to the ground, as the weather station personnel had told him that it was very likely that the Punta del Este site would receive the full blast of the hurricane that was rapidly approaching.

After the storm was over, many amateurs started to ask me questions about why the NVIS systems had performed so well, delivering really strong signals, plus another very desirable characteristic for emergency communications: much less QSB (fading) at around sunrise and sunset, as one would get with standard λ/2 dipoles installed at the typical 10 to 15m (30 to 45ft) above ground.

First used by broadcasters in the tropics, the NVIS aerial has now become a standard for close-range communications via the ionosphere. Because it points your signal nearly straight up (note the 'near-vertical' in the name), this type of aerial has become affectionately known as a 'cloud warmer'. It is an ideal system for emergency communications on the 80 and 40m bands, and will provide regular net control stations with an outstanding signal.

Interest generated by the effectiveness of the NVIS system during hurricane emergencies led to the design of the aerial shown in **Fig 1**, which may be installed using a single mast or tower, as the two legs of the folded dipole slope gently at a

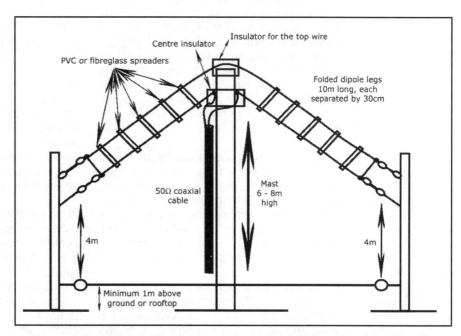

Fig 1: CO2KK's folded–dipole Near-Vertical-Incidence Skywave (NVIS), or 'cloud warmer' aerial for 40m. The horizontal line near the bottom (1m off the ground) is the reflector. If fed with open-wire line, the same aerial is usable on 30m, and a similar aerial can be built for 80m. It is excellent for short-range communications, as in emergency or traffic nets.

not-too-critical angle, so the long Dacron™ rope insulators can be tied to short masts or the side of a building or maybe a conveniently-located fence.

CO2KK'S NVIS FOLDED-DIPOLE-PLUS-REFLECTOR SYSTEM

At first glance, looking at Fig 1, you may ask, "Why use a folded dipole?". The answer is very easy. The CO2KK NVIS system uses a closely-spaced tuned-reflector element, which considerably reduces the feed-point impedance of the radiating element.

If you use a standard single-wire half-wave dipole, the typical feed-point impedance will go as low as 10Ω, and usually around 12 to 15Ω, depending on the local objects within the aerial's near field. By using a folded dipole element , the 10 to 15Ω impedance is quadrupled to between 40 and 60Ω, a very convenient value for using the aerial with a 1:1 balun and a 50Ω coaxial line. The use of the 1:1 balun is very important, as you don't want feed-line radiation to spoil your radiation pattern!

The CO2KK NVIS aerial can be built for permanent use by using fibreglass spreaders conveniently placed to keep the two wires that form the folded dipole at a constant spacing, and the 1:1 balun must be rated according to the power used by your station. I strongly recommend using an air-core balun, which can be homebrewed easily and will not saturate when running high power, as ferrite core ones tend to do.

Keep in mind that base stations operating during emergencies normally run near maximum legal power, even when using generators, as communications officials tend to agree that running the net control station at high power levels keeps the operating channel clear, something that is quite logical, to say the least.

Reports received over the past three years during which the aerial has been in operation show that the NVIS system aerial delivers a very strong signal during local daylight hours in the range from about 30 to 500km (20 to 300 miles), while its behavior during the ionospheric transitions that occur around sunrise and sunset make it particularly useful to keep communications running during emergencies.

No attempt was ever made to measure actual aerial gain, although the fact that it is a two-element Yagi array with a closely-spaced reflector could lead us to think that the NVIS Folded Dipole + Reflector should provide no less than 4dB gain over a standard λ/2 dipole installed at between 10 and 15m above ground level.

ADDITIONAL ADVANTAGES

The NVIS system has other advantages, too. Among them, there is one which is also particularly convenient for emergency communications systems, and it is the fact that signals coming in at low-incidence angles above the horizon are attenuated to an extent that makes reception of the desired high-angle signals much better – in other words, there is a definite advantage to installing the NVIS system, as the signals from nearby stations coming in at high-incidence angles are much stronger than those coming from DX stations.

In addition, the 7MHz system, using a folded-dipole radiator, can provide service on the 10.1MHz band (30m), if the aerial is fed using open-wire line, something that might be useful for running a digital communications net on that band during the hours when NVIS signals are available on 30m.

You can also build a similar system for 80m, but this would require a much higher mast, which could be difficult to keep up in the middle of a hurricane, although the NVIS 3.5 to 4.0MHz folded-dipole aerial would be ideal for Net Control Stations that operate systems handling regular (non-emergency) traffic.

WHAT ABOUT HIGHER FREQUENCIES?

NVIS systems are limited to operation at 10MHz or below due to the fact that even a very highly-ionised ionosphere will not support Near-Vertical-Incidence Skywave on higher frequencies. Very intense type-L Sporadic-E layers sometimes send back to Earth signals on frequencies as high as 20MHz, when the oblique incidence signals may propagate for brief periods on frequencies up to or even above 100MHz. However, these do not occur often enough for the aerials to be reliable above 10MHz.

Overall, the NVIS aerial should be strongly considered for any operator – such as an active traffic-handler or emergency communicator – who needs strong signals and reliable communications on 80, 40, or 30m with nearby stations within a range of 200 miles.

SUGGESTED READING

A Coro, CO2KK, Antena Acortada para 80 metros', *Revista Radioaficionados,* No 1, 1987, pp18/19.

A Preedy, G3LNP , 'A Compact and Effective HF Antenna', *HF Antenna Collection,* selected and edited by Erwin David, G4LQI, pp14 – 16, RSGB 1991 (reprinted 1994), UK.

D DeMaw, W1FB, 'Cloud-Warmer Antennas', *W1FB's Antenna Notebook,* pp81 – 83, ARRL, 1987.

J D Heys, G3DBQ, 'Half-Wave Dipoles', *Practical Wire Antennas,* Chapter 1, pp1 – 14, RSGB, reprinted 1991.

TUNING THE REFLECTOR ELEMENT

In a typical CO2KK type 'Folded Dipole + Reflector' NVIS system, the reflector wire is placed at not less than 1m (39in) above the ground, with 2m (78in) preferred.

The close proximity of the ground to the reflector element, together with the close asymmetrical proximity of the inverted-V-shaped folded dipole, makes it necessary to tune the reflector to resonance, using a lightly-coupled grid-dip meter. (See Feb 2000 *CQ* for 'The Grid Dip Oscillator', p22, and 'How to Build an LED Indicating Dipmeter', p26 – *Ed.*)

If you plan to operate the NVIS aerial on the 40m band, select the segment that is most likely to be used during either your regular net operations or during emergencies. In my case, the aerial's reflector was tuned for maximum gain at 7.1MHz, which was almost perfectly achieved by tuning it to a frequency 5% lower than 7.1MHz (6.745MHz).

The length of the very-close-to-the-ground reflector element will depend on so many variables that my advice is for you to deal with each aerial as a special case, and tune the reflector to a frequency 5% lower than the resonant frequency of the folded-dipole element.

WHAT ABOUT A THREE-ELEMENT NVIS BEAM?

Why not use the parasitic element as a director instead of a reflector? And... why not make the NVIS system a three-element beam shooting straight up?

The first question is not too difficult to answer: A reflector mounted close to the ground is easier to deal with, will provide the required gain and bandwidth, and can be more easily accessible for tuning than a director mounted above the driven element!

Making the NVIS system a three-element parasitic array will reduce the area of the ionosphere illuminated by the radiation pattern, something that is not desirable, as it will also reduce the effective service area of the aerial.

Making the NVIS system a three-element parasitic array will reduce the area of the ionosphere illuminated by the radiation pattern, something that is not desirable, as it will also reduce the effective service area of the aerial.

THE TVB: A TWO-SLOPING-WIRES-AT-AN-ANGLE HOMEBREW SIGNAL BOOSTER

by Arnie Coro, CO2KK

A single mast, two sloping wires plus two terminating resistors connected to ground, and an additional wire joining the resistors together will not take too much time to install (see **Fig 1**). Once installed, you will be the proud owner of a Terminated V-Beam (TVB), one of the most interesting wire aerials I have ever tested. Of course it is a directional aerial system, but it has the advantage that at least two of them can be installed from a single support structure without too much interaction between aerials pointing in opposite directions. Maximum radiation is in the direction of the centre of the two sloping wires.

WHY USE A TVB?

Such a simple, easy-to-install aerial is a nice option for contest stations, as it can be set up using a tall tree or a single easily transportable dielectric (non-conductive) mast.

The TVB aerial can be best described by saying that it is made using two sloping wire elements of a certain length, terminated by non-inductive resistors of the same value. The two wires spread out from the dielectric support structure at a certain specific apex angle (**Fig 2**), and that's one of the important parameters of this aerial system.

The feed-point of the TVB is located at the top of the mast, at the exact vertex of the two wire radiating elements. You can feed this aerial using a parallel balanced transmission line or a coaxial line but, in the case of coax, you must use a balun.

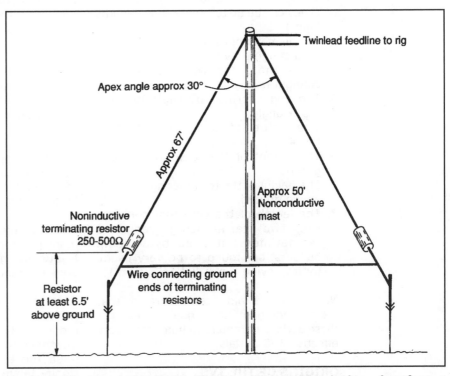

Fig 1: The Terminated V Beam (TVB) aerial uses two sloping wires from a centre feed-point to non-inductive terminating resistors at least 6.5ft above ground, with a third wire connecting the ground sides of the two resistors.

Some experimenters have tried using a metal tower or mast (conductive structure) as the support, and in that case results do change. There is a way of doing this which may be attractive for those who have a self-supporting tower or one with guy wires broken at appropriate length with insulators. The apex of the TVB simply is

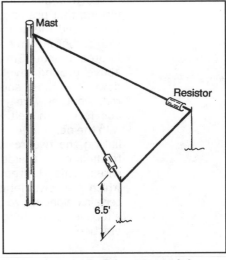

Fig 2: Side view of the TVB aerial.

moved away from the supporting structure a minimum of 1m (3.28ft), and then open-wire transmission line is installed horizontally until it reaches the tower, at which point you can install a balun and continue down to the shack using coaxial cable.

There are certain key TVB design parameters to consider:
1. The length of the radiating elements. (They can be up to several wavelengths long!)
2. The diameter of the radiating elements. (You can improve bandwidth by using more than one wire, or a cage configuration.)
3. The angle formed by the two wires (apex angle).
4. The value of the non-inductive terminating resistors.
5. The height of the feed-point above ground.
6. The height of the terminating resistors above ground.
7. The length of the wire that connects the two terminating resistors (sometimes not used by V-beam builders, but found to be very useful for improving the radiation pattern).

Now don't be afraid. I can assure you that the average ham can handle all seven of these aerial parameters to homebrew very effective TVB aerials.

ORIGINS OF THE TVB
Dr Jose A Valladares, now in his late 80s, was the aerial guru who introduced me to the TVB system way back in 1961, when he installed several of them at a commercial HF receiving station. I came to learn about the TVB one day while visiting that pre-satellite-era installation. I observed the sloping wires terminated with carborundum non-inductive resistors located at about 3m (approximately 10ft) above ground level, with a wire going down from those short masts to a ground rod. Another wire joined the two masts and formed a delta-loop-like structure, with the only difference being that the wire linking the two resistors was connected to their ground side, not to the sloping wires. This slanted-V configuration, in which the terminating resistors are at a certain height above ground, is much more effective, something that was proved in practice.

Dr Valladares told me that the great advantage he attributed to the V-beam configuration in general, and to this specific form of terminated-V, was its simple installation. He also stated that the flexibility provided by this aerial system was second to none, as he could install several of them using existing masts that supported other commercial receiving aerials such as the fishbone and the rhombics (the log periodic was not yet popular in the early 1960s).

For amateur radio installations, TVB aerials have an additional advantage in that the sloping wires respond to both the vertical- and horizontally-polarised waves when receiving and generate mixed polarisation when transmitting.

When you design a TVB aerial properly, technically-speaking it would be described by the aerial gurus as a travelling-wave aerial, so it will provide users with a rather large operating bandwidth.

The TVB aerial power gain will depend on many parameters, including the operating frequency, ground conductivity, height above ground of the apex, etc.

TRY ONE FOR 6m!
A typical TVB aerial for the HF bands will require a lot of real estate, as the elements may need to be up to a city block long or even more! However, with minimum sloping element lengths of the order of 20m (67ft), the aerial will work from 14MHz all the way up to 60MHz! The effective gain will increase as the frequency goes up, making this particular TVB configuration especially useful for the 12, 10, and 6m bands (see **Table 1** for design parameters).

You will have to choose the optimum apex angle but, in practice, angles between 60 and 30° will produce useful gain and directivity. If you want to favour the higher end of the aerial's frequency range, then reducing the apex angle is the way to go.

The terminating resistors connected to the near-ground end of each sloping wire must be non-inductive and capable of dissipating about 30% of the transmitter power if full-carrier modes of operation are used. For CW work, with a shorter duty cycle, the resistors may be smaller. For SSB, I have used resistors rated for 20% of the transmitter power without any signs of overheating problems after many months of constant use.

I have made my own non-inductive resistor assemblies in the 250 to 500Ω range by connecting series-parallel combinations of 2W carbon resistors. The actual value of the terminating resistors is not really important, according to my experimental work here at CO2KK, as the performance of my TVB aerials has proved to be essentially the same with terminating resistor values in that 250 to 500 and even up to 600Ω range.

Your best option for feeding this low-cost directional aerial is to use open-wire transmission line right to the shack, where a 4:1 balun will allow you to connect it to an aerial tuner.

START BUILDING!

Aerial experts will provide you with nice graphics to optimise the design of Terminated V-Beam aerials, and you can spend quite some time experimenting with different configurations. However, why not start to build the TVB for 12, 10, and 6m this weekend, and begin to enjoy operating on those bands with the aerial pointing in the most favourable direction.

My own north-oriented TVB sees a lot of action during the summer E-skip season, while the south-pointed TVB keeps me in touch with the many South American 6 and 10m operators during the twice yearly trans-equatorial propagation seasons.

Try the TVB aerial. It is easy to build, costs very little, and works well!

Wire length: 20m (approx 67ft)
Wire diameter: at least No 12
Apex angle: 30°
Height above ground of feed-point: 15m (nearly 50ft)
Height above ground of terminating resistors: 2m (about 6.5ft)
Value of terminating resistors: 300Ω (but you can use between 250 and 500Ω)
Feeder: 450Ω open-wire line to shack, then connected to 4:1 balun to tuner

Table 1: **Parameters for a practical 12, 10, and 6m band TVB that will also work (with somewhat less efficiency) on 20 and 15m.**

WHAT ON EARTH?

by Phil Harman, VK6APH

Most of us were brought up to believe that we need to have an extensive earth system in order to radiate an effective signal from a vertical aerial. Virtually all the aerial design books warn against operating low-band verticals with anything short of hundreds of buried radials accounting for miles of copper wire. However, what if there was another way to get a quarter-wave vertical to perform at peak efficiency with just a few, very short radials? From professional results and amateur experimentation, it is starting to look as if a half-mile of copper buried in your back garden may not be the only way to go. (Note that this discussion is about quarter-wave verticals, not the half-wave 'no-radial' verticals offered commercially – Ed.)

A BIT OF HISTORY
The concept of using the earth as part of an aerial system can be traced back to the early days of radio when Marconi was using very-long-wave communications (wavelengths of thousands of metres). These early experiments formed the basis of our heritage, and it was natural that we carry on the practice for wavelengths of 200 metres and down.

What's not generally recognised is that the shorter the wavelength, the less efficient and less appropriate it becomes to use the earth as part of the aerial system. To some extent, we have been led astray in carrying on long-wave practices into the short-wave region.

If radio had developed from the dipole-like aerial structures of Hertz who, in the pre-Marconi era, experimented with spark equipment on very short wavelengths, it is possible that the concept of using the earth as part of a tuned aerial (eg vertical at ground level) never would have caught on.

Several amateurs in the 1920s appear to have recognised the value of aerial systems not directly connected to the earth, and it is in this era that the 'counterpoise' approach appeared. It would seem that, over the years, amateurs in general have been using very long-wave techniques for short-wave radio and paying the price in terms of inefficiency and unpredictability. In fact, Jack Partridge, 2KF, who was the first British amateur to make contact with the USA on 200m, used an inverted-L aerial and a wire counterpoise some 7ft above the ground. The single-wire counterpoise remained popular in the 1930s until, largely due to the classic study of medium-wave aerials by Dr George Brown (the inventor of the ground plane, amongst other aerials, [and *not* the editor of this book]) using large numbers of buried radials, became the done thing.

Even George was not immune to outside infiuences, though, since it is often reported that his prototype ground plane actually consisted of two $\lambda/4$ radials. It was on the insistence of the marketing department that the first commercial ground-plane aerials used four radials – to make them 'look more symmetrical'.

WHY ON EARTH?
Why do we need an earth system for a vertical aerial anyway? Let's make our starting point for this explanation a vertical half-wave dipole in free space or, at least, far enough away from the ground that the latter has no effect (see **Fig 1**). The radiation resistance at the centre of the dipole will be 78Ω, and it will have the standard radiation pattern found in all the textbooks.

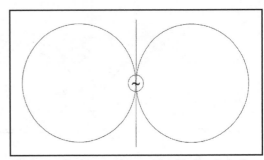

Fig 1: Radiation pattern of a $\lambda/2$ dipole in free space.

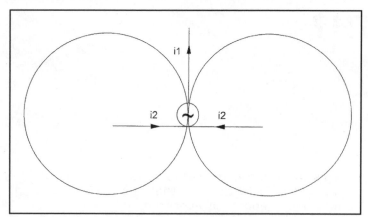

Fig 2: Radiation pattern of a ground plane in free space.

Now let's modify our vertical dipole by removing the bottom λ/4 conductor and replacing it with two λ/4 radials (**Fig 2**). Note that the radials are exactly λ/4 long at the frequency we are working on and areidentical in length.

In this case a current, I1, flows in the vertical element, and two equal currents,

each of I2, flow in the radials such that I1 = 2 x I2. Since the currents flowing in the radials are equal, and flowing in opposite directions, the radiation from the radials cancels out and all the radiation comes from the vertical element. Note that the radiation pattern has not changed, and at a distance you could not tell if the signal was coming from a vertical dipole or a ground plane.

Now, since the radiating element is only half the length of a λ/2 dipole, its radiation resistance must be a quarter of that of the dipole, which brings it to 20Ω and is independent of anything done to the radials, since these are non-radiating! Note that the radiation resistance is not 35Ω as is incorrectly reported in many aerial handbooks. We will see where this figure comes from later. Also note that the radials do not in any way act as a reflecting plane, since their fields cancel out in all directions; nor do they contribute to the angle of radiation.

In practice, we have a major problem using λ/4 radials, since length tolerances are always finite, making it impossible to maintain current equality whilst tuning through resonance. So, if λ/4 radials are not ideal, what's a practical alternative?

We have already seen that, if we can equalise the currents flowing in the radials, they do not radiate. It's logical, therefore, that since they don't radiate, they can be shortened to any desired extent without affecting the radiation resistance. If we shorten the radials, we need to bring them back to resonance by connecting a loading inductance at the centre of the radials (**Fig 3**). As long as the losses in the loading coil remain small compared with 20Ω, the efficiency of the system will remain high.

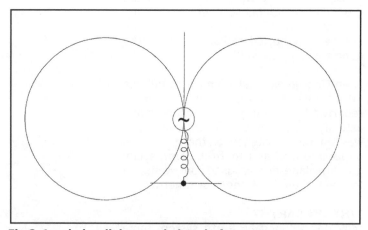

Fig 3: Loaded radial ground plane in free space.

We now bring the dipole down to earth (**Fig 4**). Shortly before reaching ground level, the aerial changes from a dipole to a monopole. Its radiation resistance rises to 35Ω (over a perfect earth) because of the mutual impedance between the aerial and its colinear image in the ground. The vertical radiation pattern broadens to one half that of a dipole and losses are incurred because of currents flowing in the (imperfect) ground.

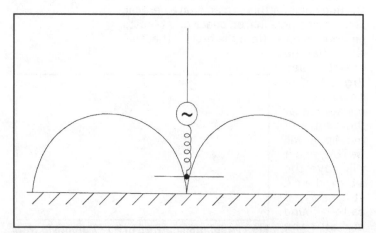

Fig 4: Loaded radial ground plane over perfect earth.

The variation of radiation resistance with height can be calculated by considering the aerial and its image as a colinear pair separated by the distance between the 'centres of gravity' of the current distributions. This gives the graph shown in **Fig 5**, which has been verified mathematically by VK2BBF [1].

As long as equal and opposite currents flow in the radials, then there is no radiation from them. No radiation means that there can be no current induced in the ground due to the radials, and hence no loss. It's for this reason that a single radial is ineffective: With a single radial there can be no equal and opposite current flow; hence the radial radiates and induces current in the ground, resulting in loss.

EFFECT OF THE EARTH

You might conclude from the foregoing that I am suggesting that the earth has no effect on the radiation performance of the aerial. As we shall see, this is certainly not the case. The point I am making is that hundreds of radials do work but are not necessary to provide the missing half of the dipole and do nothing to improve the efficiency of the aerial.

If you already have an extensive radial system, simply make sure they are each less than a quarter wavelength long and use a current probe to check for current equality.

In practice, the nature of the earth below the monopole has a very significant effect on its radiation pattern. The major influence on performance comes from the soil conductivity and dielectric constant, out to tens of wavelengths from the aerial's location.

The effect of the earth conductivity is shown in **Fig 6** where the radiation patterns over a perfect earth and typical earth are plotted. As can be seen, over a typical earth, radiation at low angles is reduced and the 'gain' of the aerial is lower.

In practical terms, there is little the user can do to improve the situation since, unless a radial system that extends tens of wavelengths away from the base of the aerial can be constructed, little improvement is possible. As noted by others, portable operation against the seashore, or on a boat, can provide spectacular performance.

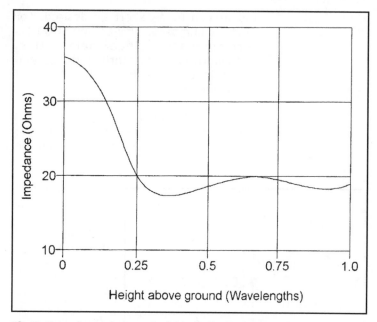

Fig 5: Base impedance of a l/4 vertical with height.

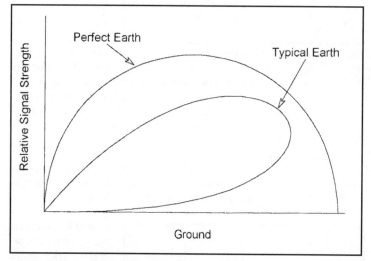

Fig 6: Effect of ground on radiation resistance.

In most cases, the vertical aerial system is best improved by constructing a two- (or more) element vertical array, at a cost a fraction of the equivalent horizontal beam. Even over a perfect earth system, our vertical will only have 6dB of gain over the theoretical free-space vertical. If we phase together two verticals, we immediately can achieve 5.3dB of gain regardless of the earth conductivity and, generally, at less cost and backache!

PRACTICAL SYSTEMS

It has been proved experimentally that, as long as the inductance of the loading coil is scaled accordingly, and its loss resistance is small compared with 20Ω, the radials can be as short as desired. For practical purposes, a lower limit of λ/12 is recommended, since below this, bandwidth is significantly reduced and there is no practical advantage of exceeding λ/8.

Note [2] describes the successful construction of a 14MHz vertical using two 60in radials and a common loading inductance of 3μH.

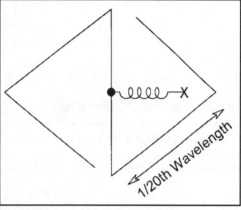

Fig 7: Compact radial system.

In its simplest form, the radial system can consist of nothing more than a horizontal wire or tubing, between λ/12 and λ/8 long, well insulated, mounted clear of any surrounding obstructions, and tuned to resonance by a single loading coil. For design purposes, a good starting point is a coil 3in in diameter, spaced the wire diameter, and as long as is necessary to give resonance – a 1in long coil will give 3μH of inductance.

If space is at a premium, the radial system can be folded as shown in **Fig 7** to form a very compact structure. A radial height of 3ft has been found to be quite adequate for use with 160 and 80m verticals.

When the loading coil becomes large and heavy, an alternative 'linear loading' may be used, as in **Fig 8**. Here, the necessary inductance is obtained from a length of wire mounted on insulators, as indicated.

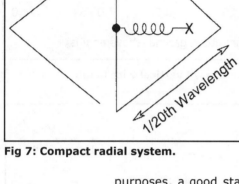

Fig 8: Linear-loaded radial system.

It is essential that the complete aerial system be tuned to resonance – using a grid dip oscillator (GDO), aerial analyser, or VSWR meter – by adjusting the loading coil or length of the linear loading element.

SUMMARY

I hope that, by now, you will at least be tempted to experiment with a loaded radial system before digging up the back lawn and burying miles of copper wire. In summary, radials:

1. act as one pole of a dipole, so as to provide a return path for the current flowing in the other pole;
2. reduce the current flowing on a coaxial feeder to prevent it from radiating;
3. allow a 'dipole' to be brought down to earth without having to dig a hole for the bottom element;
4. do not act as a reflecting screen;
5. do not have any effect on the radiation angle;
6. may be shortened to approximately λ/12 and brought back to resonance with a centre-connected loading coil;
7. (when resonant) have no effect on the radiation resistance of the aerial.

All in all, quite a non-controversial article! Now go out there and experiment!

NOTES

[1] 'The Feed Impedance of an Elevated Vertical Antenna', Guy Fletcher, VK2BBF, *Amateur Radio* magazine, Wireless Institute of Australia, August 1984.

[2] *HF Antennas For All Locations,* Les Moxon, G6XN, Radio Society of Great Britain.

THE MOTORISED CLOTHESLINE AERIAL - AN IMPEDANCE-TUNED AERIAL SYSTEM

by Robert Victor, VA2ERY

Remember Archimedes? He was the guy who jumped up out of his bath and went running down the hallway soaking wet yelling "Eureka!". That did not mean "Where are all the towels?", but rather, "I've found it!". What he'd discovered while slipping into his bath was a way to measure the volume of an object by dunking it into a tank of water, leading to the concept of specific gravity we still use today.

Archimedes discovered other stuff, too: π, the screw, and the inclined plane, to name a few. When he wasn't busy practising science, he was a philosopher and is quoted as having once said, "Give me a spot on which to stand, and I can move the entire Earth".

This brings me to impedance-tuned aerial systems and, more specifically, the 'Clothesline'. The Clothesline is an all-band, no-tuner, no-trap, no-loading-coil HF aerial that can cost as little as $20 or so to put up and will outperform almost any other multi-band dipole you can name.

I developed it by finding a different angle, a different "spot" to stand on, if you will, that allowed me to see a new approach to a conventional problem – how we match an aerial to a feed-line. Here's the low-down on impedance tuning and more specifically, the Clothesline aerial.

IMPEDANCE TUNING

Look at (A) in **Fig 1**. It shows a half-wave of radio energy distributed along a length of wire cut for λ/2 at that frequency. If this wire were 132ft long, we would say the aerial is resonant on 80m. Why resonant?

Because if we impose a signal of 3.5MHz on this aerial, we wind up with the maximum voltage points at the ends. This will be the case for any resonant dipole; the voltage will be at a maximum at the free ends.

The impedance at any point along an aerial is the ratio of voltage to current at that point. At our feed-point, in the middle, the voltage is lowest and the current is highest, so that's our point of minimum impedance – about 50Ω in this case. (Actually, the nominal feed-point impedance of a dipole is 72Ω, but let's just call it 50Ω for the sake of this discussion.)

Now look at (B) in Fig 1. Here we have the same piece of wire, only now we have voltage curves shown not only for the base frequency, but for a couple of harmonics as well. Let's say the base frequency is

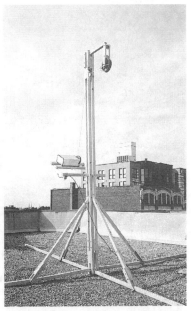

Mini-tower and drive unit at one end of the motorised clothesline aerial. The unit is self-supporting on the author's roof.

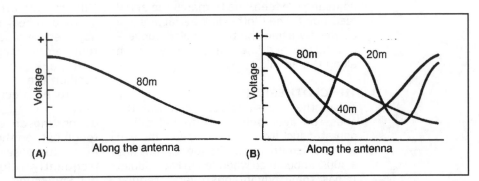

(A) — Voltage / Along the antenna — 80m

(B) — Voltage / Along the antenna — 80m, 40m, 20m

Fig 1: (A) This graph shows the voltage distribution of an 80m signal on a 132ft wire aerial. Note that the positive and negative peaks coincide with the ends of the aerial. Normally we would feed this aerial right in the middle, where the curve crosses zero. (B) Here's the same aerial with signals for 40 and 20m added. There are voltage peaks at the ends for each band – the aerial resonates – but the zero crossing points for 40 and 20 are nowhere near the middle.

The motor frame (lower right in photo) is hinged to permit tensioning of the drive belt. Tension is set by either shortening or lengthening the counter-balance lanyard.

3.5MHz and the harmonics are at 7MHz and 14MHz. You can see that the voltage peaks for the base frequency are at the ends as before, and the minimum is still in the middle. Voltage peaks for the harmonics are also at the ends (because they're harmonics), but the minima, which identify the 50Ω feed-points, are all over the place.

To run an aerial like this on more than one frequency, we have three choices: (1) live with the mismatches at different frequencies (by using a tuner); (2) adjust the feed-line to match the different impedances at each frequency (by using multiple feed-lines for instance); (3) physically move the feed-line to the right 50Ω impedance-matching point for each frequency.

An impedance-tuned system allows you to match your feed-line to your aerial by adjusting the feed-line to match the aerial feed-point. The Clothesline aerial lets you do this by using the third choice above— moving the feed-line to any point you wish along the aerial.

THE CLOTHESLINE

The Clothesline is a folded dipole with the ends run over pulleys. A folded dipole operates just like a conventional dipole in terms of length versus frequency, but has a 300Ω impedance when fed in the middle. It has some advantages over a regular dipole – it has a lower angle of radiation and it's much quieter on receive, both great for DX. The Clothesline uses these to advantage and more. Since we have a proper match on the base band and all

harmonics, we have a perfect match at all times and so can dispense with the tuner or traps and the associated losses that would otherwise be the case for most multiband dipoles.

The one disadvantage of the Clothesline (and hence the motivation to create a remote drive) is that you have to go to the aerial to tune it. Since I invented the Clothesline and first described it a couple of years ago in *QST* [1], I've received feedback from hundreds of hams who use it as their main aerial and don't find this a concern. It is true also that you can get one up in the air like this for about $20. (If you're planning on putting up any dipole, you should consider a Clothesline. It will only cost a couple of dollars more and open up all the other bands for the price of a yank on the feed-line. Note, too, that 'all the other bands' includes any harmonic of 160, 80, or 40 meters, which includes 6 and 2m!) However, I think I felt a responsibility as the aerial's inventor: I just had to try a motor drive...

DRIVEN TO A MOTOR DRIVE

Much of what is described here applies to a non-motor-driven Clothesline, so I recommend you read this, even if you're going to put up a manual version. Also keep in mind that I mention 40m as my base band, but you can put up one for 80 or even 160, if you have the space. If you decide to put up a motorised Clothesline, or already have one up that you want to drive remotely, you'll have some decisions to make. Here are some of the items I dealt with in executing my own installation, and the results of my experiments.

I'd already observed that the aerial seemed to peak on receive when properly adjusted for a particular band. I figured a remote drive might allow me to listen for that peak when tuning and help me position the aerial. This meant the drive had to be electrically quiet. I felt that getting a DC motor to run without generating an earful of hash would be tough but, on the other hand, an outdoor AC motor poses safety concerns and is frequently ruled out by electrical or building codes.

I thought I would need lots of torque to overcome the resistance of the pulleys and wire for shuttling in and out; my experience with the hand-driven version told me that the weight of the feed-line and consequent tension on the aerial might need a little oomph to overcome. Finally, reversibility was also required.

It looked like a DC gear-motor was going to be the practical choice. They are reversible, can be had with almost any amount of torque, and have the advantage that they are built with standard-size output shafts, a consideration when shopping for pulleys and drive-belts. I'd just have to deal with the hash as best I could. I bought a new gear-motor from Dayton Gearmotors. The unit I selected offered 50 inch-pounds of torque at 28RPM, giving me about a half-foot per second of wire travel at the pulley, which sounded just about right.

The easy way to control this motor is to use a centre-off, double-pole, double-throw (DPDT) switch right in the shack, which I did. However, as I also wanted to be able to run the motor while I was right at the aerial up on the roof, I added a second switch there. The schematic (**Fig 2**) was the result.

This setup is simple and achieves both local and remote control. Having motor control locally on the roof made adjustment of the aerial and feed setup a breeze. When was the last time you threw a switch and the feed-point came to you?

Here's where the work gets done! The author used a borrowed AC motor for the prototype, then switched to a safer DC motor for actual use outdoors.

CONSTRUCTION

My apartment rooftop had no really convenient attachment points for the aerial or drive unit, so I wound up building the mast you see in the photos. It was constructed to address a few different concerns. There's lots of wind up on my apartment roof, so a free standing structure (as this had to be) needed a wide base to stay vertical. The roof itself isn't designed for any significant freestanding loads, so weight was minimised, and the long foot-pads float the whole system and distribute the pressure over a wide area, which I figured would avoid any stress leading to leaks.

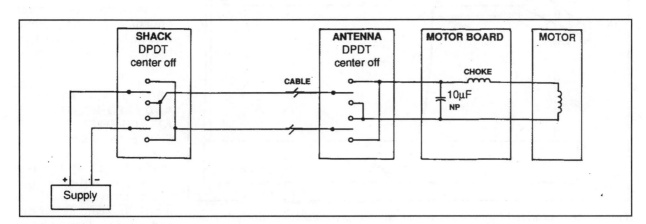

Fig 2: Schematic of the control circuit for the motorised Clothesline aerial, providing control from either the ham shack or the aerial itself.

The drive end pulley is mounted on a swing arm. This allows tensioning of the aerial and provides a counterweight to take up slack.

I mounted the aerial drive-end pulley on a swing arm using a stock hardware-store hinge to permit tensioning the aerial to take up slack and to provide for counterbalancing against wind and other miscellaneous forces. The pulley for the far end went into another mounting, this one hinged to permit it to swing from side to side as well as up and down, so it would align itself automatically with the aerial.

I strung the aerial wire over the pulleys, and here's something you'll want to know about. You want to get any residual twist out of the wire before you hang it up. If you don't, the aerial can wind itself up like a two-element Slinky!

One ham told me he tied one end of the wire to his lawn tractor and dragged it around his yard for a while; he said this worked great. Another (me) hung it in hunks over the edge of the building and shook it until his arms got tired.

I chose to mount the motor on a swinging frame bolted to the mast about four feet directly under the aerial drive-end pulley. I then ran a drive belt fashioned out of high-strength monofilament from the motor pulley up to the aerial pulley (see **Fig 3**). The drive belt and aerial wire both ride in the same groove in the aerial pulley; a little playing with the motor alignment keeps them from contacting each other.

It turned out that the weight of the motor and enclosure served well as a counterweight for the aerial, making for easy adjustment of the drive-belt tension. As you can see in the photo, the counterweight line is attached to the motor frame. Simply lengthening or shortening this line sets the drive tension, after which it remains relatively constant even as the motor swings up and down due to wind forces on the aerial. If needed for proper aerial tension, additional weight can be hung from the frame.

I recommend this setup, or something similar, no matter how or where you mount your own Clothesline. You're going to need some way of establishing and maintaining drive-belt tension and aerial tension, and you need to do so in a fashion such that changes in one don't affect the other. An alternative is to put the swing-arm pulley and counterweight on the far end of the aerial, while establishing drive tension to a fixed pulley at the near end.

CENTRE INSULATOR AND FEED-POINT ATTACHMENT

The centre insulator you see carries an idler pulley that rides along the top run, spaced vertically from the aerial wire tie-offs to match the diameter of the end pulleys. This spreads the weight of the insulator,

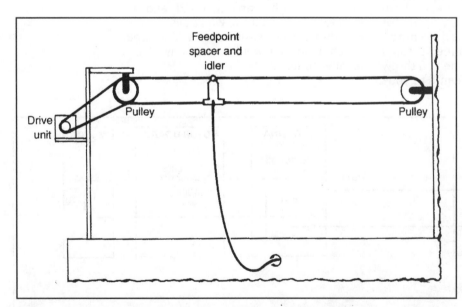

Fig 3: The motorised Clothesline aerial, showing connections of motor and feed-line. The feed-line must be long enough to reach from one end of the clothesline to the other.

balun, and feed-line equally between the top and bottom runs. Because tension is constant throughout the loop, the weight is shared perfectly, and the aerial runs remain perfectly parallel, even at low tension, no matter what the position or motion of the feed-point. This is important to conserve the folded dipole shape. If you don't do this, the runs will flop around and therefore your match will vary.

Once the whole system was up in the air and the motor was ready to run, I made an interesting discovery. With ball-bearing pulleys and the feed-line support system, the aerial, even under high tension, rolls like a breeze. A motor with a quarter the power of mine would have driven the system with ease.

The balun you see in the photos is a home-wound 6:1 and matches the 50Ω coax to the feed-point impedance of around 300Ω. Here you can get away with a more common 4:1 balun, but make or buy a 6:1 if you can, as it will do a somewhat better job. If you use a 4:1, consider using 75Ω coax as feed-line for a better overall match.

OPERATING WITH THE CLOTHESLINE

There's a word that describes operating a motorised Clothesline – fun!

My first experiments involved that oh-so-desirable quality of being able to peak the aerial on receive, and sure enough this works 100%. Throwing the switch to reel the aerial this way and that, while listening to either signals or noise, produces a smooth, reliable slope and peak of activity in the phones. Hit the peak and you're tuned! I checked this over and over on all bands, and it works like a charm.

The theory says that bands higher than the base band (in my case, 40m) have more than one feed-point. I had confirmed this with manual positioning of the feed-point; now the motor drive reaffirmed it with push-button ease. I noted no difference in the tuning slope or other behavior among the multiple feed-points on higher bands, which suggests that they're reacting just as normal dipole centre feed-points would.

There may be some directional effects in the selection of feed-points. Selecting an

Detail of the centre insulator and balun. Note that the upper section is fitted with a pulley through which the upper wire runs. This helps distribute the weight of the feed-line evenly and maintains a set separation between the sections.

off-centre point that places the long end of the aerial towards the transmitting station seems to improve performance in that direction. What with QSB and the like, it's hard to be precise, but I would say that I can improve reception (and presumably transmission) by two to four S-units with this technique, when my contact lies in a direction favoured in this manner.

Being able to pick the best point for reception while tuning the aerial on the fly is great fun, and it has really helped with some of the iffy ones. It brings back the days when having tuning savvy was better than good looks! I feel like I'm getting these benefits on transmit as well,

The pulley at the far end of the aerial pivots both side-to-side and up-and-down, automatically aligning itself with the aerial.

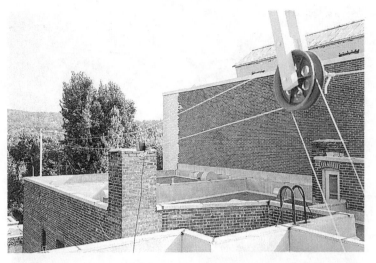

The whole lot! Note that the runs are kept perfectly parallel. This is maintained by sharing the feed-line weight between the top and bottom runs, as well as by the variable tension hinges at each end.

although I'm not sure how I'd be able to prove it.

Just like any other aerial, you will probably have to trim the Clothesline a little once it's up in the air. When you do, keep in mind that you're adjusting many bands at once. Take VSWR readings for all the bands on which you want to operate, and figure out what kind of adjustments you need to make on average to get things in order. Being able to flip that switch and take readings makes this very easy to do.

One more note on the switches: If you look closely at the schematic, you'll notice that the motor won't work if both switches are in the 'off' position. Here's how to set them up: for normal operation, you leave the switch at the aerial 'on' and use the switch in the shack to control the motor. When you want local control at the aerial, flip the aerial switch 'off', then go back and flip the shack switch 'on', and you'll have control from the switch at the aerial when you go back outside.

AND SO...

Motorising my Clothesline has been worth every penny and minute of effort. I have a trap-and-tuner-free multiband aerial that tunes at the flip of a switch, replaces four other dipoles with associated feed-lines, remote switches, and maintenance, is many dB quieter on receive, has a lower angle of radiation, and offers some directional and directable gain on most bands. It's rather more attractive and discrete, too, compared to all those other wires, feeds, and supports.

The tunable nature of the motorised Clothesline has permitted me to experiment with and optimise feed strategies, feed position, trim length, and noise pickup. I never really thought about this in the beginning, but this experimental facility has turned out to be one of the aerial's most valuable assets. I can't imagine how another aerial could have talked to me in such volumes, in so little time. My log book and 100W have smiles for miles.

Above all, the Clothesline is fun! Tuning the Clothesline has brought back those days when, as kids, we would peak preselectors, tweak trimmers, and sometimes even use a cupped palm held just so over a ganged capacitor to bring in the weak ones. It's so satisfying to just flip a switch and trim up the Clothesline and know that my aerial is perfectly tuned for that day, that band, and that contact. Ham heaven.

REFERENCE

[1] 'The Clothesline Antenna', *QST,* July 1998, p56.

ANOTHER APPROACH

Remember when I said that we can solve the impedance tuning issue two ways, by either moving the feed-line or adjusting the feed-line impedance? The Clothesline uses the first method, while a new aerial I've developed takes the second route – adjusting the actual feed impedance to match the aerial at different frequencies. This aerial, which is designed for portable HF rigs such as the Yaesu FT-817, is called the Miracle Whip, and it's being sold commercially by the company I work for, Miracle Antenna (I'm the Chief Designer). The aerial plugs into the back of the rig, covers HF and VHF, works DX off a tabletop (without a ground) and is only four feet tall!

A DOOR-LOOP RECEIVING AERIAL

by Ed Chicken, MBE, G3BJK

The tuned loop HF receiving aerials described here are intended for use indoors such as in a bed-sit or loft, where space is at a premium and the installation of a normal aerial impractical.

The loops are unobtrusive, effective, directional, and very easy to make using inexpensive hook-up wire. The wire loop aerial is simply wound on self-adhesive or self-suction plastic hooks stuck on whichever face of the door is convenient. This method of attachment avoids damage to the door itself, and the hooks can eventually be removed without trace.

Details are given for a range of aerials to cover the full short-wave band from 1.5 to 30MHz, and one for the 136kHz LF band. From the details given here, a loop can be selected for and tuned to the frequency band of interest. Also described is a simple but functional loop-signal amplifier, the output from which is taken via coaxial cable to the radio receiver.

ABOUT THE LOOPS

Strictly speaking, a 'loop' aerial has but one single turn, whereas a 'frame' aerial has two or more turns. Most of those to be described here are multi-turn and hence are actually 'frame' aerials. However, to call them door-frame aerials might be confusing because they are not wound around the door-frame, but on the door-face. So, for this article, they will be called loop rather than frame aerials.

And now to the directivity feature that makes the door-loop aerial unique. The response pattern of a loop aerial is a figure-of-eight similar to that of a dipole, but with one important difference. With a dipole aerial, maximum response is when it is broadside on to the signal, and minimum response when in-line. But with a loop aerial, minimum (not maximum) response occurs when it is broadside on to the arriving signal. Maximum pickup of received signal is when the plane of the door is in line with the signal. Similar to the dipole however, maximum and minimum responses are bi-directional. In other words, when a loop aerial is positioned for maximum received signal, the signal could be coming from either of two opposite directions. The same applies to a null.

This means that the all-round response of any loop aerial is obtainable by rotating it through no more than 135°. This is exactly what the door hinges provide free of charge, simply by opening or closing the door to give a nearly complete directional response from signal maximum to minimum. Elegant simplicity? Obviously, the realisable response pattern depends upon the extent of available door swing. A door that can swing through 180° will give a full response pattern, whereas if its swing is restricted to, say, 90° (as with my own), the pattern is also restricted, but only marginally, so don't be put off by that.

Regarding the diameter of a loop aerial, theory has it that, for optimum performance, the loop diameter must not exceed $\lambda/8$ at the highest frequency in use (ie 1.25m at 30MHz), so the standard domestic door fits that bill nicely. It should be pointed out, however, that these particular door-loop aerials are all of rectangular or square section, not circular, the different geometry being of no practical significance! Considering now the Q-factor of the loop, the use of thin PVC-covered stranded wire means that the Q cannot be as high as might be achieved by using thicker or more specialised wire such as Litz. In favour of a modest Q, however, the tuning of the loop is not critical, which means that the receiver can be tuned across an entire frequency band without having constantly to retune the loop. Furthermore, any loss of signal level due to a lower Q is more than made up for by the signal amplifier to be described later.

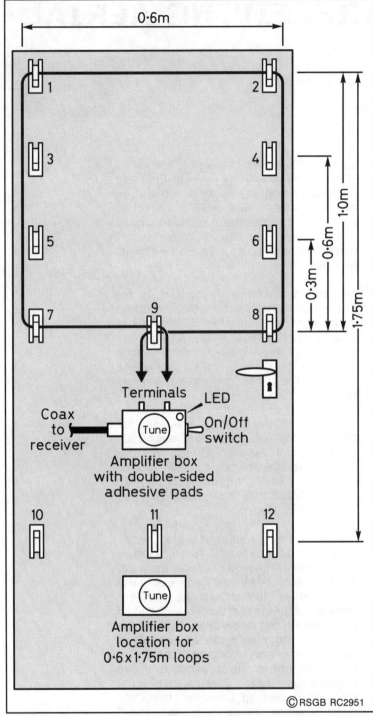

0·6m

1 2

3 4

5 6

7 9 8

0·3m
0·6m
1·0m
1·75m

Terminals   LED

Coax
to
receiver   Tune   On/Off
switch

Amplifier box
with double-sided
adhesive pads

10   11   12

Tune

Amplifier box
location for
0·6 x 1·75m loops

©RSGB RC2951

Fig 1: Disposition of hooks, amplifier and tuning capacitor on the side of a standard door.

loop inductance values is required to give the required frequency coverage. The HF loops described here have inductance values in the microhenry range, to be tuned by the 2 x 126pF AM sections of a low-cost miniature AM/FM tuning capacitor of the type used in transistor radios. Note that in this balanced loop arrangement, the two 126pF sections of the tuning capacitor are actually in series (not parallel) with the loop, hence the maximum capacitance swing is only 63pF. This limits the tunable frequency range for any one loop, but that could be doubled by using instead a 2 x 500pF tuning capacitor.

One must bear in mind that any loop aerial will have a self-capacitance determined by its dimensions. That self-capacitance, typically a few picofarads, will act in parallel with the loop's inductance to form a resonant circuit which will give the as-yet unconnected loop a self- resonant frequency. When a tuning capacitor is connected across the loop aerial, the loop's self-capacitance will act in parallel with the tuning capacitor, thereby changing its apparent value. So, a knowledge of the self-capacitance value can be useful when calculating the tuning range of a variable capacitor connected across a given loop-inductance. The self-capacitance of these HF loops was measured and found to range from about 6pF to 30pF from smallest to largest loop.

Approximate values of inductance to be expected from loops of different sizes and numbers of turns are shown in Table 1, based on the use of 7/0.2mm wire. It will be appreciated that these values can only be approximate because of the differences in door design, but they will be near enough for practical purposes. The tuning capacitor will make up for any modest differences in finished loop inductance.

There is, of course, no reason why heavier gauge wire such as 16/0.2 or 20/0.2 should not be used, especially for the HF loops as opposed to the 20-turn 136kHz loop, the limit being the size and strength of the support hooks. The inductance (and hence the tuning range) of the finished loop would not be markedly

Any wire loop, whether it be of one or more turns, constitutes an inductance which would need to be tuned to the frequency-band of interest. No normal tuning capacitor will have a big enough swing to tune any one loop across the entire short-wave band, which means that a range of

Loop size (m)	One turn		Two turns		Three turns		Four turns	
	L (µH)	f (MHz)	L (µH)	f (MHz)	L (µH)	f (MHz)	L (µH)	f (MHz)
0.6 x 0.3	2.4	*11.9 - 30.0*	8.0	*6.3 - 13.2*	15.4	4.4 - 8.7	24.3	*3.4 - 6.4*
0.6 x 0.6	3.2	10.2 - 24.3	11.1	5.3 - 11.0	23.0	3.5 - 6.2	39.0	3.0 - 4.3
0.6 x 1.0	3.9	8.6 - 21.2	15.3	5.6 - 8.4	31.0	3.0 - 5.2	52.6	*2.2 - 3.6*
0.6 x 1.75	7.0	7.0 - 16.2	23.1	3.5 - 5.9	47.8	2.3 - 3.6	83.7	*1.7 - 2.7*

Table 1: Showing the frequency ranges to be expected from different-sized loops, based on the use of 7/0.2mm PVC-covered hook-up wire and a 2 x 126pF variable capacitor.

different from that of the thinner wire and the extra cost would be negligible.

CONSTRUCTION

Assuming an average-sized wooden internal door of dimensions 2m high by 0.6m wide, the height of these loops has been restricted to 1.15m, to leave space at the lower part of the door face for the amplifier box and outgoing coaxial cable.

A maximum of 12 plastic self-adhesive or self-suction hooks is needed, the larger the better (especially for the 136kHz loop) because the smaller ones tend to break easily. Such hooks are readily available at very low cost from most hardware shops or street markets.

Refer now to **Fig 1** which shows the hook-method of winding for the loops. Decide which face of the door is to be used for the aerial, then stick the hooks on the door face. The hooks are numbered 1-12 in Fig 1. For HF use, all 12 hooks may be used but, for 136kHz, only hooks 1, 2, 10, 11 and 12 are needed. Be careful to position each hook with its open side facing up or down as shown on the drawing. Hooks 7, 8, 10 and 12 are inverted for ease of loop winding. Hooks 9 and 11 serve as fastening points for the wire tails of the various loops (and maybe even as a suspension point for the amplifier).

To decide on a loop size for a given frequency range, use **Table 1**. The figures in bold italics suggest that the entire short-wave band could be covered with five loop aerials, but that could be reduced to two or three by using instead a 2 x 500pF tuning capacitor. Once this size has been chosen, **Table 2** can be used to recover

Loop Size		Use hooks	Start/finish at hook number
Width (m)	Height (m)		
0.6	0.3	7, 5, 6, 8	9
0.6	0.6	7, 3, 4, 8	9
0.6	1.0	7, 1, 2, 8	9
0.6	1.75	10, 1, 2, 12	11

Table 2: Information on using the hooks shown in Fig 1 for loops of different sizes.

information about which hooks to use and where to start and finish the loop.

Fasten one end of the wire by a half-hitch or elastic band on the central fastening-hook (9 or 11), leaving a tail of about 75mm, then wind the chosen number of turns around the four hooks given in Table 2, and back to the fastening hook. Again, fasten the wire leaving a 75mm tail as before. Strip back the wire tails and connect them to the loop-terminals on the amplifier assembly. Your first door-loop aerial is now finished and ready for action.

Details of the amplifier for use with the loops are given in **Fig 2**, **Fig 3** and **Fig 4**. It is mounted on the door, together with the tuning capacitor, as shown in Fig 1.

136kHz DOOR-LOOP AERIAL

This long-wave aerial is offered as an experimental project. It has been included to embrace the recently-released amateur

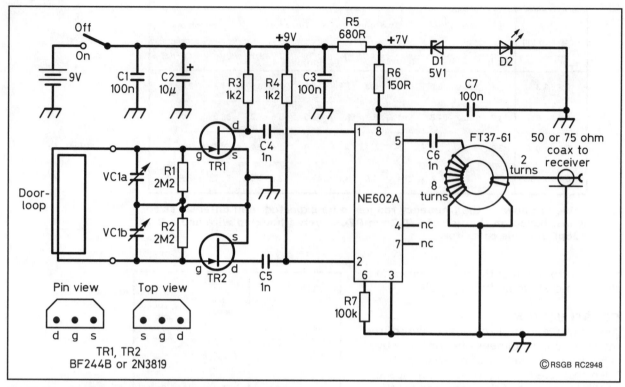

Fig 2: Circuit diagram of the loop aerial and amplifier.
Notes: (a) see Tables 1 and 2 for loop details;
(b) for HF use, VC1a, b = 1 x 126pF variable;
(c) for 136kHz use, VC1a, b = 2 x 500pF variable, and C4, 5, 6 = 10nF.

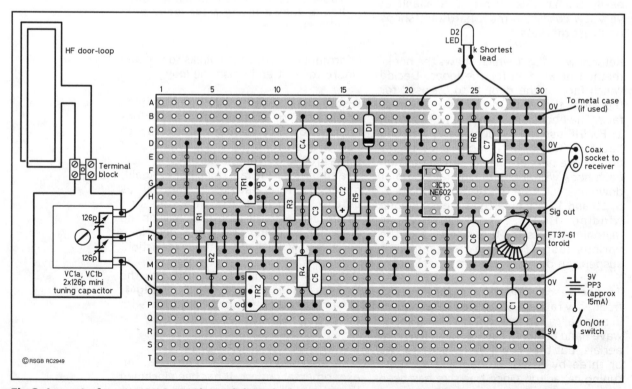

Fig 3: Layout of components on the stripboard, showing connections to off-board components.

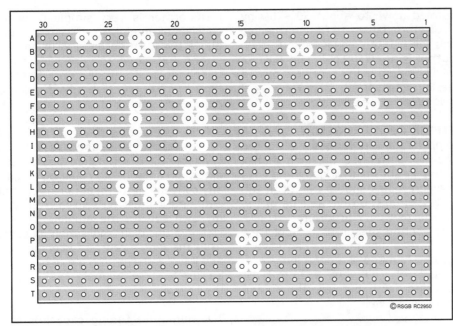

Fig 4: Showing the track-cutting positions from the track side.

band where the length of even a quarter-wave aerial would be about 550 metres. But first, a small change needs to be made to the loop-signal amplifier for use at this frequency. Because of the increased reactances of the three 1nF coupling capacitors C4, C5 and C6 at 136kHz, it is necessary to replace them by capacitors of value 10nF. Changes to the tuning capacitor, VC1, are mentioned later in this section.

The aerial consists of 20 turns of 10/0.1mm hook-up wire (equivalent to about four 25m reels) wound on hooks 11, 10, 1, 2, 12 and 11, to produce an inductance of about 1.8mH. To tune that 1.8mH to about 136kHz would require an effective parallel capacitance of 750pF. That figure would include the self-capacitance of the loop. Measurements indicate that the very narrow 136kHz band could be covered by using the same 2 x 126pF mini AM/FM tuning capacitor as used with the HF loop aerials, but with a 590pF capacitor soldered across each of its 126pF sections to give a tuning range of approximately 132 -139kHz. Alternatively, using a 2 x 250pF variable capacitor with 470pF padding capacitors would give a tuning range of about 139 -145kHz; a range of about 132 -158kHz is available from a 2 x 500pF variable with 270pF padding capacitors. Swinging the tuning capacitor through its range whilst listening to 136kHz on the receiver would soon let you know if the loop is tuning to that

frequency. The noise peak is quite pronounced.

LOOP-SIGNAL AMPLIFIER

The circuit diagram of an HF tuned loop and its signal amplifier is shown in Fig 2. The battery-powered amplifier uses two field-effect transistors in a balanced input configuration. This arrangement preserves the electrical balance of the loop about ground potential, and the high input impedance ensures that the Q-factor of the loop is not unduly damped. The RF gain of the FET input stage is quite low, but this receives a b--oost from the NE602 integrated circuit to give an overall signal voltage gain of at least 10 (20dB).

Power supply to the amplifier is from a PP3 9V battery at about 15mA. The transistors each take about 6mA and the NE602 draws about 2mA. The maximum voltage supply rating for an NE602 is 8V. It is therefore fed from a stabilised 7V supply, derived from the 9V rail by using a 5V1 Zener diode in series with a light-emitting diode. The LED also serves as a battery 'ON' indicator light. The NE602 is perhaps best-known as a double-balanced mixer/amplifier but, in this application, its internal local oscillator circuit is made inoperative by R7. The NE602 amplifier then acts in a cascode mode, with an output available at either pin 4 or 5. Either of these pins individually can be used to give an unbalanced output, with an output impedance of about 1500Ω. This is transformed down to about 50 -70Ω by means of a toroidal ferrite transformer, so allowing the use of coaxial cable to feed the output signals into a short-wave receiver. Although many receivers have a 50Ω aerial input socket, 75Ω TV coaxial cable would be quite suitable.

AMPLIFIER CONSTRUCTION

The component layout for assembly of the amplifier on perforated 0.1-inch matrix stripboard is shown in Fig 3, and also shows where holes should be cut in the copper tracks on the reverse side of the board. The use of a proprietary track-cutter (sometimes listed as a 'Spot Face Cutter') is recommended. It can save a lot of frustration and is a good long-term investment! Alternatively, a 3mm twist drill operated gently between thumb and forefinger works well.

The 4:1 turns ratio (theoretically 5:1 but 4:1 worked better) output matching-

transformer is very simple to wind. It consists of an eight-turn primary winding and a two-turn secondary, using single-strand PVC-covered wire such as from telephone cable, wound on a ferrite ring type FT37-61 (0.37in outside diameter, number 61 mix).

A twin section of screw-type electrician's terminal block is used for the loop connection. The finished board and its external components could be fitted into any convenient metal or plastic container, although it must be said in truth that in my own set-up, the amplifier assembly was left uncased and simply suspended from the loop's central fastening-hook... and it worked well! If a metal box is used, be sure to strap the metal to the 0V rail of the board.

The miniature tuning capacitor can be mounted on the front panel of the box, with its spindle protruding. Two M2.5 fixing

COMPONENTS LIST
Resistors
R1, 2	2M2
R3, 4	1k2
R5	680R
R6	150R
R7	100k

Capacitors
C1, 3	100nF, ceramic
C2	10μF, electrolytic, 25V
C4, 5, 6	1nF, ceramic (10nF for 136kHz use)
VC1a, b	2x126pF miniature AM/FM variable capacitor, eg Maplin AB11M

Semiconductors
D1	5V1 Zener diode
D2	Light-emitting diode, red
TR1, 2	BF244B FET
IC1	NE602A or SA602AN, double-balanced mixer

Additional Items
12 off	Self-adhesive/suction hooks
2 off	Screw M2.5 x 6mm
1 off	8-pin DIL socket
4 off	25m reel 10/0.1mm light duty connection wire
2 off	10m pack 7/0.2mm hook-up wire
1 off	Strip 2A terminal block, screw-type, eg Maplin FE78K
1 off	Ferrite ring type FT37-61
1 off	Vero stripboard, 0.1in hole spacing, 30 x 20 holes
1 off	Switch, SPST miniature
1off	PP3 battery
1 off	Connector for PP3 battery
1 off	Belling-Lee coaxial plug and socket

screws are required. Some tuning capacitors are sold complete with an extension spindle to accommodate a standard knob, which should be fitted. A tuning dial is not really necessary, because the loop aerial will simply be tuned by ear (or S-meter) for maximum signal strength on the frequency band in use.

A Belling-Lee (TV type) coaxial plug and socket would be suitable at the amplifier end of the coaxial cable, but a plug to suit the receiver's aerial socket should be fitted to the other end. Although its length is not critical, the coaxial cable should be kept as short as possible. The finished box can be secured to the door face by means of double-sided adhesive tape or pads, just below the loop's fastening-hook, or maybe even just hung on the hook itself!

USING LOOP AERIALS
Simply connect the coaxial cable between the loop-signal amplifier and the short-wave receiver's aerial socket, switch on the amplifier, tune the receiver to the frequency band appropriate to the loop aerial, and adjust the loop's tuning capacitor for maximum signal or noise level in the receiver. You can now use the receiver anywhere on that band without having to tune the loop again. If needs be, try opening and closing the door to peak the loop on any selected signal, or perhaps to minimise an interfering signal.

FURTHER READING
'An Introduction to Variable Tuned Circuits', G3PMJ, *RadCom* March 2001, pp34/5.
Backyard Antennas, by Peter Dodd, G3LDO (RSGB Shop).
HF Antennas for All Locations, by Les Moxon, G6XN (RSGB Shop).
Practical Antennas for Novices, by John Heys, G3BDQ (RSGB Shop).

A NOTE FOR THE ACADEMIC EXPERIMENTER
Although classical theory states that inductance is directly proportional to the number of turns squared ($L \propto N^2$), experience with these loops suggests that the power of N is nearer 1.8 than 2 ie ($L \propto N^{1.8}$ not N^2).

That might not seem much of a difference but take, for example, the 0.8m x 1.75m loop aerial whose 1-turn inductance was measured at 7µH. Now for this 20-turn loop of the same dimensions, its inductance should be 7µH x N^2 = 7 x 20^2 = 7 x 400 = 2800µH, compared with the measured value of 1800µH. This would equate to 7µH x $N^{1.853}$ = 7 x 257.5 = 1802µH. You would need to use the x^y function on a scientific calculator to check this. However, armed with that knowledge, it becomes easy to calculate what the inductance would be for a different number of turns on any one of the loops.

THE VERSATILE END-FED WIRE

by Peter Parker, VK1PK (now VK3YE)

A piece of wire of almost any length can be used as an aerial on the HF bands. However, just because an aerial can be made to work is no guarantee that it will perform efficiently. This article will initially concentrate on the half-wavelength of wire and its use as an effective multi-band aerial. Information on a simple aerial coupling unit and tuning indicator for use with these aerials is provided towards the end of the article.

LENGTH

It was mentioned above that the actual length of wire used in an end-fed aerial is not critical. However, some lengths are easier to use than others, particularly if multi-band capability is required. Also, very short aerials (significantly less than a quarter wavelength on the operating frequency) are inefficient, making it hard to put out a good signal.

A length of one quarter wavelength (ie 20m long on the 80m band) is commonly suggested. Though such aerials do work, an extensive ground system or counterpoise is required for best performance. Ground systems can require considerable time and effort to install and detract from the extreme simplicity of these types of aerial.

An alternative is to use a wire of one half-wavelength in length on the lowest operating frequency. An extensive earth system becomes much less important. Indeed, the author has had good results whilst using no earth at all. However, for certain other reasons (explained later) some earthing is desirable.

The aerial described here is 40m long, or a half-wavelength at 3.5MHz. As mentioned before, a substantial earth is not required. Because a half-wavelength piece of wire exhibits a very high end impedance at the operating frequency (and its multiples), some form of coupling unit between the transceiver and aerial is required. Its function is to transform efficiently the transceiver's 50Ω output impedance to the aerial's high feed-point impedance. Whether a wire aerial has a high or low impedance is important because it affects the type of coupling unit required, as well as the need for an earthing system.

So, what is the impedance of this aerial on bands other than 80m? We already know that a wire that is a multiple of a half-wavelength exhibits a high impedance at the feed-point. At 21MHz (15m) a 40m wire is approximately six half-waves long. On 28MHz (10m) it is eight half-wavelengths. Similarly, our wire is several multiples of a half wave on other HF bands such as 40 and 20m. This means that the aerial will always have a feed-point impedance appreciably higher than 50Ω and will not require much of a ground system on all bands. It is for these reasons that 40m is a good length for an end-fed wire aerial for the HF bands.

BENEFITS AND LIMITATIONS

Because it is fed at one end, people whose house is near one boundary of the block will probably find this aerial easier to put up than a half-wave dipole, which is fed in the centre. Another advantage of this aerial is that no separate feed line is required. This makes it particularly attractive for portable use as coaxial cable can be quite bulky.

What are the disadvantages of this type of aerial? The first is that it requires a matching unit to operate. Each time you change band you will need to adjust this for best impedance match between transmitter and aerial. Another risk with this types of aerial is the presence of RF in the shack. Nevertheless, these two problems are not insurmountable, and the end-fed wire is one of the most cost-effective multi-band aerials available.

69

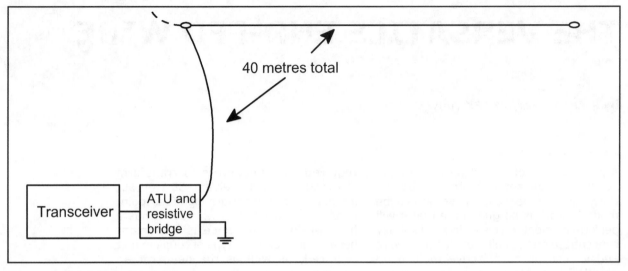

40 metres total

Transceiver

ATU and resistive bridge

Fig1. An end-fed aerial system.

ERECTION OF AERIAL

The aerial should be as high as possible, and arranged as shown in **Fig 1**. Have as much of the wire as you can running horizontal, or nearly so. However, if this is not possible, don't despair; your aerial will still work. The aerial is not particularly directional, especially on the lower frequency bands, so orientation is not that critical.

The type of wire used is also not critical. Medium gauge stranded insulated wire has given good service in the author's aerials. Ordinary egg-type insulators can be used to suspend the wire. As an alternative to purchasing these new, insulators can be made from short lengths of plastic water pipe or conduit.

Either trees, chimneys or specially-made masts can be used to support the wire. Two such supports are normally required for these aerials, unless your radio shack is on a second or third storey. In many cases the second support can be a tree in the backyard.

It is not necessary to climb this to mount the aerial; with a small lead sinker, a fishing line can be thrown over a convenient branch. The sinker is then removed and the line tied to the aerial's insulator. While observing the sag in the aerial wire, pull the fishing line tight. Then release it a little and tie it off at a convenient point. Some sag should be allowed for in wire aerials to allow for movement of the supporting branch in the wind.

Always observe the usual precautions about keeping the aerial away from power lines and public thoroughfares.

COUPLING UNIT AND RESISTIVE BRIDGE

The purpose of the coupling unit described here is to transform the transceiver's output impedance of 50Ω to the higher impedance of the wire aerial. Between the matching unit and the transceiver is a resistive aerial bridge that is switched in to aid the adjustment of the coupling unit. **Fig 2** is the schematic diagram for the complete unit.

An L-match circuit consisting of one adjustable inductor and one variable capacitor is used. This is simpler than most other aerial coupling units which require two or more variable capacitors, several inductors and possibly a switch. This simple approach is possible because the unit is only required to match a limited range of aerial impedances. The resistive bridge is used to show when the L-match is properly adjusted. Using it is similar to a standard VSWR bridge, in that you initially adjust the sensitivity control for full scale on the meter and adjust the L-match until the reading on the meter is zero (or close to it). However, the resistive bridge is unlike an VSWR meter in that it does not have a forward / reverse switch. Also, it cannot be left in line while transmitting. Further information on operating the resistive bridge is given later.

Because light weight was important, the prototype is housed in a commercially-

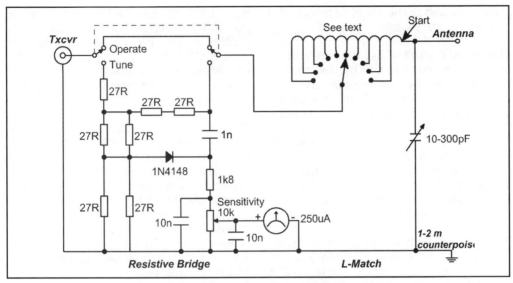

Fig2. Circuit diagram of the matching unit.

available plastic box. To accommodate the top of the Vernier drive, some plastic has had to be shaved off inside the top lid of the box.

An alternative is to cannibalise a variable capacitor from any valve broadcast receiver, or one of the older transistorised sets. Unless you are using very low power (a few watts), the small plastic dielectric types used in modem AM transistor radios are not really suitable.

Most variable capacitors that you'll see will have two or three sections or 'gangs'. Simply use only one gang and ignore the rest. The actual value of the variable capacitor is not important, provided its maximum capacitance exceeds 150 or 200pF.

A slow-motion drive and Vernier dial adds greatly to the appearance of the finished product and makes adjustment easier. However, if your budget is tight and you are unable to find suitable second-hand reduction drives, this part can be omitted.

The rotary switch used was a common wafer switch having 10 positions. The switch originally had several sections (wafers), so the unwanted ones were removed and the rear of the shaft cut to size. It is desirable to have a switch with as many positions as possible to allow more precise adjustment of the coil. These are suitable at low power levels, but the author has not tried them with 100W. If all else fails, an alligator clip and wander

lead will be just as effective as the switch, though somewhat less convenient to use.

The tapped inductor is the other main component of the L-match. The coil was wound on a piece of 25 - 30mm diameter plastic tube. Ordinary thin insulated wire was used in the prototype. The number of taps needed is always one less than the number of positions available in your rotary switch - thus the coil here has nine taps. To make a tap, simply remove about 1cm of insulation with a knife, form the bare portion of the wire into a hairpin loop, twist and solder. Hold the iron on the joint for only the minimum amount of time necessary to prevent the insulation melting off the wire.

Table 1 gives the coil taps used on the prototype. Note that the start of the coil is connected to the aerial socket and variable capacitor and the wiper of the

Switch position	No of turns from start of coil
1 (fully anticlockwise)	55
2	30
3	20
4	13
5	9
6	6
7	4
8	3
9	2
10 (fully clockwise)	1

Table 1: Tap position on the inductor (see Fig 2).

switch is wired to the aerial section of the 'Tune/Operate' switch.

The end of the coil whose taps are closest together should be nearer the switch. The reason for this is that these taps are likely to be used on the higher frequency bands, where the effects of stray inductance are more significant. It is also for this reason that all connections between the switch and the coil should be short and thick. The coil is attached to the bottom of the case with a pair of bolts, nuts and 10mm stand-offs, which can be made from an old straight-sided ballpoint pen.

Transceivers with rotary band switches normally have the lower frequency bands (eg 80m) near the anticlockwise end of the switch's rotation and the higher bands (eg 10m) selected when the switch is turned clockwise. Similarly, when you turn the VFO knob of your transceiver clockwise, the frequency selected will increase.

The controls on the prototype behave in a similar way. This is achieved by switching in the whole coil (which may be required on the low-frequency bands) when the rotary switch is turned to its fully anticlockwise position (position 1 in Table 1 above) and successively smaller portions of the coil as the switch is moved clockwise (position 10 in Table 1 above).

These smaller sections of the coil will be required when operating on higher frequency bands such as 10 and 15m.

The variable capacitor is configured in a similar way; as the reduction drive is turned clockwise, the capacitance is reduced, and the unit is tuned to a higher frequency. However, it is important to note that this cannot be achieved with some variable capacitors because a clockwise movement in the shaft increases rather than decreases the capacitance.

Most of the parts for the resistive aerial bridge are mounted on a piece of unclad matrix board, which is mounted to the case with screws and stand-offs.

Component values are not particularly critical except for the seven 27Ω resistors. The function of these resistors is to provide a reasonably constant 50Ω load for the transceiver when the L-match is being adjusted. For this reason, they will be required to dissipate a fair amount of RF power. Two-watt resistors were used in the prototype. This proved adequate for use with a 20W transceiver, provided the carrier was wound down to 5 - 10W and tuning-up was completed in a reasonably short length of time.

Many modem 100W transceivers can be wound back to produce the few watts required for this tune-up process. No accidents have been had with the prototype unit. However, if you routinely wish to use it with high power equipment, and have a habit of forgetting to wind the power back, it should be possible to replace each 27Ω resistor with four 2W 100Ω resistors to increase the unit's power handling capacity.

Do not be tempted to use wire-wound resistors - their power ratings may look attractive, but their self-inductance makes them unsuitable for a project such as this. The 'Tune/Operate' switch is a medium-sized DPDT unit. Again, this has given reliable service with 20W equipment. However, it might be wise to use a larger type if you intend to use this unit with 100W gear.

Other parts are not critical. The panel meter in the prototype was salvaged from a non-working CB transceiver. The scale was blanked out (using correction fluid) and a new one written over it with a ballpen. This operation calls for a fair degree of manual dexterity - it is easy to damage the meter movement if you are careless. If in doubt, leave the meter as is. The variable resistor could also be a salvaged item; in this case the volume control from a radio or a tape recorder will be fine.

A pair of binding posts was used for the aerial and earth terminals. Use colour coding to avoid confusion. The connection to the transceiver is either via a BNC or SO-239 socket.

Coaxial cable should be used between this and the transmitter section of the 'Tune/Operate' switch to minimise stray capacitance and inductance. Either RG-58 or RG-174 will be satisfactory.

ADJUSTMENT AND USE

Adjusting L-type couplers is simple. Set the inductance for maximum noise in the receiver. Then adjust the variable capacitor to obtain a further increase in noise. Apply a few watts carrier and switch to 'Tune'. Position the sensitivity control so that the meter is reading full scale. Adjust the variable capacitor for a dip in the reading on the meter. If it is not possible to get a zero reading, try a different combination of coil and capacitor settings until this can be achieved. At this point, the system is tuned up, and the unit may be switched to 'operate'. This step by-passes the resistive bridge and allows the full output from the transceiver to reach the aerial. Note that, when changing bands or making significant frequency changes within a band, this process should be repeated to assure full power transfer.

A counterpoise may or may not be required. Because the aerial is high impedance, adding one will not normally boost radiation efficiency or materially affect the settings of the L-match. However, in some cases, going without a counterpoise can cause RF to get back into the transceiver and spoil operation. A short length of insulated wire connected to the earth terminal of the L-match minimises this risk. One or two metres is usually enough.

IN CONCLUSION

In practice, the system described has proved easy to use, and represents a good way of getting multi-band operation from a single length of wire. There are no lossy traps or feed-lines, and the aerial is easy to erect. Medium-range SSB contacts have been made with this aerial on both 80 and 40m, with powers of between two and 20W. Though no detailed measurements have been made, performance on the lower bands seems to be roughly similar to a half-wave dipole at the same height.

FURTHER READING

1. Moxon L A, *HF Antennas for All Locations*, RSGB, 1982, p154.
2. *The Radio Amateur's Handbook*, ARRL, 1977, p599.
3. Cook R & Fisher R, *Amateur Radio*, May 1997, p20.
4. Butler L, *Amateur Radio*, Sep 1997, p15.

THE G8PO TRIANGLE SLOPER

by Ted Ironmonger, Cdr, RN (Retd), OBE, G8PO

Contacts with New Zealand via the long path on 80m have fascinated me for many years. The perplexing question as to whether propagation is by normal multi-hops, chordal hops etc, or even increased by 'antipodal focusing', has always been a compelling incentive for experiments with many friendly ZLs. Perhaps memories of the first-ever G-ZL contacts by G2DX and G2NM, way back in 1927, also drives me on. The aerials used for such observations at a favourable location near the sea have, in the past, been a relatively simple inverted-V, and a gamma-fed tower. However, with deteriorating sunspot activity creating even more interest in the lower bands, it became evident that an improved simple directional radiator was required to compete with the mushrooming LF Quads, Yagis, vertical arrays, etc.

INITIAL DEVELOPMENTS

Space limitations at G8PO precluded anything very elaborate, so a λ/4 sloper was investigated. The garden is 70x150ft with a 40ft tower, TH3 Yagi on top, and facilities to haul up wire aerials. The conventional arrangement was tried, ie coaxial feed to the top of the existing 40ft metal tower, the braid bonded to the top of the tower and inner conductor connected to approximately 66ft of wire sloping at 45° to the SW. Results were average for a sloper, with some gain compared to a permanently-rigged inverted-V reference, but the system was difficult to match. I felt this was due to the 'relatively' high impedance point at the base of the 40ft mast being earth, ie 40 ft down from the low impedance feed braiding connection -workable but not ideal. A further major problem was the need to lower the tower for installation and repairs.

Instead of connecting the braiding to the top of the tower, a separate 38ft wire conductor was used alongside the mast and the whole sloper hauled into position on a halyard. The 38ft vertical wire was spaced approximately 12in from the tower by fixing at the base and insulated from the ground. Results were similar to the tower connection, but the fitting arrangements were an advantage for experimentation and repairs. Matching was still a problem, however.

MATCHING TRIALS

In an effort to provide facilities for better matching, the spaced 38ft vertical wire was lengthened to approximately 66ft (as for the sloping element) and the 28ft extension run horizontally near ground level, approximately 12in above ground to the rear of the mast. The coaxial feeder was cut to a half-wavelength on 3.5MHz, allowing for its velocity of propagation. This is approximately 88ft for the present sloper. With the above arrangement, satisfactory matching was achieved by lengthening or shortening the wire elements and checking SWR at the shack. This may appear tiresome, but is, in fact, a most simple and effective method - a low SWR can be achieved with patience and neither a balun nor an ATU is required. On-air checks with ZL indicated that progress was being made, but I still felt a better configuration could be developed.

FURTHER INVESTIGATIONS

Various handbooks were consulted to ascertain how a sloper really works [1, 2] and the following came to light. Firstly, some directivity is obtained by sloping the wire in the direction required, and this holds good even when the radiator is only a quarter-wave long. Secondly, from W6SAI's *Antenna Handbook* [2], a quarter-wave sloper can be considered as a 'tilted', one-radial ground plane. It should be noted that such a ground plane has maximum radiation in the direction of its simple radial. Deductions from the foregoing indicated the directivity could, perhaps, be due to a combination of factors:

(a) maximum radiation in the direction of the slope;

(b) some radiation from the direction of the 'built-in' tilted ground plane's radial element, which could possibly be modified to advantage.

I wondered whether these two directional properties (if they both exist!) could be made to add by element rearrangement. It was not possible to tilt both the wire elements (the sloping and vertical sections) - this had appeared as a possible way of combining the directional properties of each. However, another compromise was found.

FINAL ARRANGEMENT

Over the past year, the triangle sloper has been used daily on 80m and results at this QTH have been satisfying and interesting. **Fig 1** indicates the latest arrangement at G8PO. The system detailed gives some gain, due to the slope of the aerial, but provides additionally:

(a) improved front-to-back ratio due to the part-vertical fanning which could offset the need for a metal mast;

(b) further gain due to the elevated radials per part horizontal fanning. 3. Much improved matching and broad banding due to the combination of horizontal and vertical fanned radials.

The fanned radials can be of small gauge insulated wire, so as to be less visible and more easy to manoeuvre. They should be tethered at the bottom right angle position to a 12ft spreader fastened to the mast or to ground posts - their lengths are not critical, but obviously slightly longer than the original central right-angle radial.

CONSTRUCTION HINTS

All radials must be paralleled at the top and at the directional end of the system as shown. If left open-circuit at the directional end (as was first tried at G8PO) matching will be tricky due to four more variables being added. Paralleled, the system is broad-band and matches like a

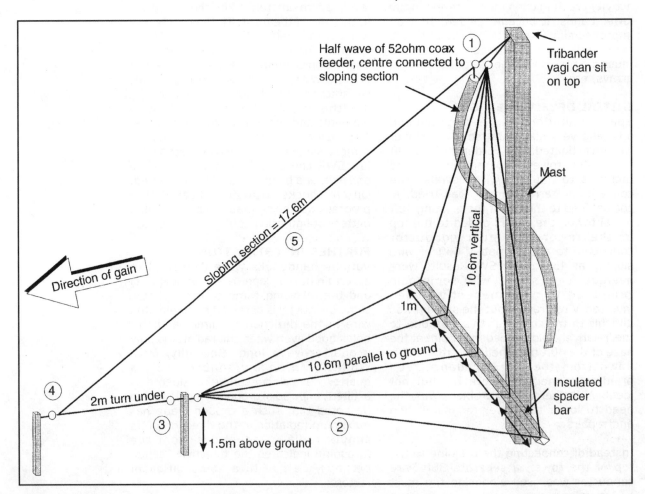

Fig 1: The G8PO fanned triangle sloper.

dummy load without an ATU. Three wires per fan will also work well. G3XPH kindly investigated the fanned radial broad-banding effect and his perusal of many aerial handbooks indicated a liking to 'Bind Café' and 'Bow Tie' dipoles – or, at least, using half of such aerials. The system is also perhaps comparable to half of the jaws aerial [3] turned through 90°. The jaws aerial performance, once again, was based on elevated radials, and I still feel this is an area worthy of more investigation.

REFERENCE AERIAL

An inverted-V reference aerial is permanently rigged on the same mast as the 'Triangle Sloper'. Both aerials are fed with half-wave coax feeders, and the separation of feed points is approximately 2ft; some interaction must take place, but checks indicate degradation is minimal. Both feeders come away at right-angles to the triangle sloper elements. For receive comparison tests, I monitored the Portuguese commercial station CTP (3782.9 kHz) which is roughly in the ZL long-path direction and a useful indicator. A low take-off angle is required for this station at midday, and the signal is invariably stronger on the sloper - often +12dB.

MAST INTERACTION AND RADIALS

The 40ft metal mast is top-loaded with a three-element all metal Yagi. Readers may wonder what part this plays in the triangle sloper's performance. This is not known, it is not easy to remove for a trial! However other stations have used normal slopers hung from wooden masts and they have performed satisfactorily (see pages 133-37 of [2]). I am aware that the metal structure must have some effect - a computer simulation would show that it affects both performance and feed impedance. However, unlike a 3.8MHz gamma-fed tower - where top loading for resonance, with a 40ft mast, is a big advantage, this is possibly not the case with a triangle sloper. Many users are certain that a top-loading Yagi is essential

in similar circumstances (ELNEC checks indicate this). However, see the section on 'ideas and suggestions' with regard to this. Ground radials were tried with the triangle sloper, but many tests with ZL indicated they gave no improvement. Note the voltage and current distribution in **Fig 2**; this is most interesting - perhaps the experts should analyse it?

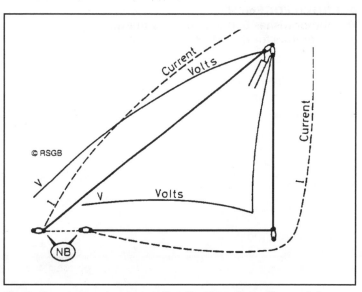

Fig 2: Current and voltage distribution along the aerial.

SAFETY CONSIDERATIONS

Protection is recommended at point X (Figs 1 and 2), as the RF voltage here can be very high and dangerous. I am not aware of many other aerials where one can put fingers across both ends of the driven element!

CONCLUSIONS

The normal sloper is an effective, simple, directional aerial, but the triangle arrangement appears to give an improvement in performance - perhaps 3dB of gain and a lower angle of radiation although this is difficult to measure. However, reports from ZL are most encouraging; after 14 days of use in October 1992, many ZLs on 80 m were asking over the air "what has happened at G8PO?" - the signal had apparently improved significantly!

IDEAS AND SUGGESTIONS

Readers might like to try one or more of the following: (a) try the triangle at different heights and in different related shapes; (b) experiment with possible multi-band operation, eg where harmonically, the feed point becomes low; (c) try a 40/80m trapped inverted-V in a semi-triangle sloper configuration. It could possibly work as a triangle on 80m and a normal sloper on 40m; (d) if both wooden and top-loaded masts are available on site, rig a triangle sloper on each and compare the results; (e) try the sloper on a self-supporting metal rotating device, on one of the higher bands.

ACKNOWLEDGEMENTS

The author wishes to thank the very many 80m operators for their time and patience in reporting and commenting on the triangle sloper trials. In particular ZL1BOQ, ZL1CCR, ZL2JR, ZL2SN, ZL2APW, ZL3GS, ZL4AP, ZL4BO and, last but not least, ZL4KF.

REFERENCES
[1]   *The ARRL Handbook*, ARRL.
[2]   *The Radio Amateur Antenna Book*, by W6SAI and W2LX.
[3]   *RadCom*, Nov 1984.

THE DOUBLET DE-MYSTIFIED

by Brian Horsfall, G3GKG

The doublet is the most versatile and trouble-free all-band aerial for use on the amateur HF bands. My own installation is shown in the photograph.

It offers the facility to achieve perfect matching, ie an SWR of 1:1 (or, as I prefer to express it, zero reflected power), with high forward power efficiency, anywhere in the entire HF spectrum. Add to this the fact that, provided its inherent balance is maintained by feeding it from a properly-balanced matching unit, it also gives maximum immunity against interference, either incoming or outgoing. It is obvious why, wherever space considerations allow, experienced operators eventually abandon all other compromises and/or gimmicky aerial solutions, and adopt the simplicity and perfection of the doublet.

The doublet at G3GKG.

BASIC INFORMATION

In its simplest and most all-round efficient manifestation, it consists merely of two equal lengths of wire, forming a top section of any convenient length, coming together in the centre, with spacers attached, so as to create a similarly random length of twin feeder. For maximum efficiency as a radiator, the actual length of the top section does, of course, matter and it should be at least equal to an electrical half-wavelength at the lowest frequency of intended use (so that the current maxima will then be in the top, rather than in the feeder). If space is restricted, bending the ends down (by no more than 90°) will have very little effect on the efficiency. Similarly, height above ground and orientation will be determined by whatever will fit the location and, on the lower frequency bands at least, will have little influence on the effective polar diagram; for inter-G working it's the signal that goes *upwards*

that counts.

Whatever the individual lengths of the top section and the feeder, the natural fundamental resonance of the system as a whole is determined by the length, L (**Fig 1**), measured from either end of the

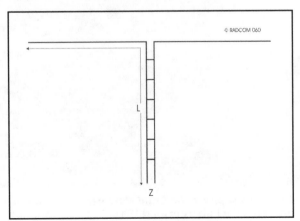

Fig 1: The basic doublet configuration.

aerial to the bottom of the feeder. It will, of course, be at a much lower frequency than the required band, but that is of no practical consequence. The noteworthy fact is that the impedance, Z, at the feed-point, ie at the bottom end of the twin feeder, will also depend on this same length. Neither the impedance at the centre of the top nor the nominal impedance of the feeder are of any real significance.

Actually *at* the resonant frequency, the impedance 'seen' by the transmitter or ATU, would be purely resistive and low in value but, at all other frequencies, the feed-point resistance itself is increased and reactance is introduced. As the operating frequency is moved away from resonance, both the resistive and reactive components of the impedance increase more and more rapidly (the reactance being capacitive (-j) if the frequency is lowered and inductive (+j) if it increases) until a frequency is reached where the total impedance is at a very high value (thousands of ohms) and, again, becomes purely resistive. Beyond this maximum, the sign of the reactance (j) suddenly reverses and the impedance decreases, quite quickly at first and then more gradually, until it is again low and purely resistive when, L is equivalent to three-quarters of one wavelength ($3\lambda/4$). At still higher frequencies, there will be any number (and parts) of such cycles.

So, if the doublet is to be used over a wide range of frequencies, the feed-point impedance in the shack, at any given frequency, may comprise any combination of resistance and reactance. It is important to realise that, at all frequencies, there will be standing waves along the entire length of both aerial and feeder. The only constant factor is that, at the far end of each half of the aerial there will be a voltage maximum and the standing waves could be plotted right back from there to the feed-point. Moreover, nothing done in the way of tuning or impedance matching at the bottom of the feeder will affect either the standing waves or the actual impedance at that point. The purpose of the matching circuit is to convert that balanced, random impedance so that the transmitter sees it as an unbalanced, resistive load of, say, 50Ω. If both the feed arrangement and the disposition of the two halves of the aerial maintain a true balance, the currents on the two legs of the feeder will always be in anti-phase and radiation from them, and pickup of any external interference on them, will cancel out.

My own doublet is constructed using just two 83ft (25.3m) lengths of heavy-duty, stranded, PVC-insulated wire, the centre of which is shown in the second photograph. The two outside ends are completely sealed against water ingress and the nearer 15ft (4.8m) of the two legs form the feeder, which comes right into the ATU; thus there are no joints or connections exposed to the weather.

BALANCED MATCHING

Although the two extremes of impedance mentioned in the above discussion correspond to the situations often referred to as requiring 'current feed' on the one hand and 'voltage feed' on the other, it is quite possible to make a matching unit that will cope with any

The method used to support the bend. The centre insulator is a bit of DIY improvisation, being the hub from an NAB reel-to-reel tape spool. The spacers are likewise, using the packing pieces employed by plastic window installers.

combination of reactance and resistance to be found in any aerial which is suitable (ie long enough) for the band in use, provided the physical attributes of the actual components used are adequate. For several years, I have been using an aerial matching system (ATU) which I devised in about 1993, only to discover subsequently that, although generally neglected, it had appeared in print at various times as far back as 1955, and probably very much earlier. I have also more recently noticed that the same circuit appears to be quite a favourite of Pat Hawker, G3VA.

The basis of this design, shown in **Fig 2**, is a sort of linkcoupled, balanced π-coupler that does not require any tedious setting of taps on the coil. It uses one variable capacitor, C1, to tune the network and a second one, C2, to 'tune out' any reactance at the feed point and match the overall impedance effectively performing the functions of both the second capacitor and the movable taps of the well-known ARRL circuit. The two controls do interact but it is very easy to obtain a perfect match by rotating them alternately.

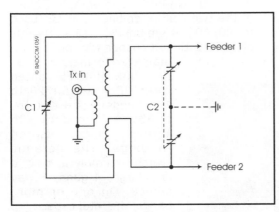

Fig 2: The matching unit.

Tuneup initially using low power; rotate each control until a decrease is observed in the reflected power (or SWR) reading. Then continue, slowly, in order to reduce reflected power to a minimum. With practice (and safe-cracker's fingers in some situations, see the next paragraph), it is possible to obtain zero reflected power, coincident with maximum forward power.

In general, the lower the impedance of the load the more capacitance will be required in C2 and, as the two capacitors

are effectively in series as regards resonating the inductor, the lower will be the capacitance of C1. For either capacitor, the lower the capacitance when loaded, the higher will be the voltage across it at any given frequency and power. Also, the lower the reactance in the load, the broader will be the tuning it is only with very high impedance and highly reactive loads that the tuning becomes quite sharp and critical.

PRACTICAL CONSIDERATIONS

There are three possible arrangements of the two variable capacitors. Either C1 or C2 can be a twingang type with the frame earthed, to provide a centre about which the feeders are balanced, or both can be single-gang types, completely isolated from earth so that the whole of the secondary circuit, including the aerial system itself, is floating. In virtually all amateur installations, the aerial will be more or less unbalanced anyway so there is a strong argument for using the floating method and letting the whole aerial/feeder system find its own 'balance'. (In either case, high-value resistors should be connected to earth from each side of the feeder to prevent static voltage buildup.)

C1 will need to be fairly wide-spaced, but of reasonably low capacitance, whereas, provided steps are taken to avoid the higher feed-point impedances (at or near voltage maxima), C2 can often be an oldfashioned, close-spaced receiving type. It might be advantageous to use a twingang capacitor, with or without the earth connection to the frame, so that the two sections are in series (so as to double the voltage rating) but that, of course, reduces the capacitance swing to half that provided by one section. In any event, at the lower frequencies, particularly if the feed-point is at or near a current maximum (low impedance), the value of capacitance required can be quite high necessitating either a multigang component with the sections in parallel, extra fixed capacitors to be switched in, or both. (However, the voltage rating of those particular fixed capacitors could be relatively low.)

It is well worth giving some consideration to the total length of the feeder/aerial combination so as to avoid both extremes of feed-point impedance. However, if the

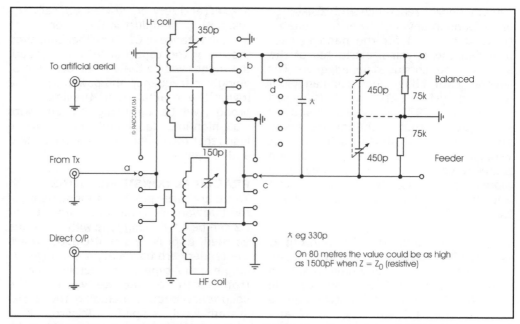

Fig 3: Schematic circuit of G3GKG's 'all-band' ATU. See the text for details of the two coil assemblies.

aerial is intended to be used on all the amateur HF frequencies, it might well prove virtually impossible to avoid having a high impedance (and hence voltage) feed-point on one or more bands. Rather than going to extremes with ridiculously wide-spaced capacitors and switches when using relatively high power, there is a useful dodge which has, in fact, sometimes

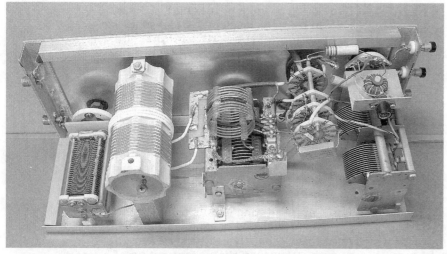

Inside view of the ATU. The toroid/ switch assembly (top right) is to cater for an alternative, aperiodic feed directly to the receiver.

been proposed as the *sole* method of matching. That is, to add a few extra feet of feeder, which could be 300 or 450Ω, plastic type (rolled up in the shack) to be

inserted in series on the troublesome band(s).

AS USED AT G3GKG

Fig 3 shows the ATU that I use. An inside view is shown in the photograph. Details of the two coil assemblies are: LF (used for 80, 60 & 40 m bands) – (9 + 9) turns of 16SWG tinned copper wire on 2.25in-diameter former, with 3-turn link of PTFE-coated wire; HF (used for 20 to 10m bands) – (4 + 4) turns of B&W 1.75-in stock with 1-turn link between windings. The ceramic switch assembly a, b, c, d is a large, 4-gang, 6-way device. On one or more bands, the total capacity of C2, required to suit the particular aerial, is made up by switching in an extra fixed capacitor, the value of which is determined to suit the aerial by temporarily substituting a variable capacitor, and using low power. C2 itself needs only to be capable of providing coverage of each of the individual bands. The design could be simplified somewhat by using single-section tuning capacitors for both C1 and C2, when the frames would have to be well-isolated from the chassis/earth.

Even when using a twin-gang variety, C2 should be treated similarly so as to give the option of balanced or floating output, as in my circuit.

This 'all-band' model uses only two coils to cover from 80 to 10m and avoids switching the 'hot' ends by having separate tuning capacitors for each inductor. The low frequency coil is wound on one of those old Eddystone ceramic formers with ribs which determine the turn spacing at about 1 turn's width. The two main windings are spaced as far apart as the former allows, so that there is a gap about an inch wide between them in which the link is close-wound using thicker, PTFE insulated wire. Even at that, the coupling is closer than it needs to be and indeed, *must* be kept fairly loose so as to minimise capacitive coupling (which can produce in-

phase current in the feeder). For virtually complete elimination of the capacitive effect, an earthed Faraday shield around the link could have been arranged.

TWO-BAND VERSION

This is a 40/80m tuner, shown in the photograph, in which the only switching is performed by a ceramic, 2-pole switch which just adds the padding capacitors across *both* variable capacitors on 80m. By that expedient, the single-gang, wide-spaced variable capacitors are reduced to reasonable values and the only 'earth' connection is to the high value static bleed resistors.

It uses a slightly smaller ceramic former from one of the TU 6 type of wartime tuners and an optimised number of turns, 11 + 11, with a 3-turn link. To avoid trying

The two-band version of the ATU, interior view.

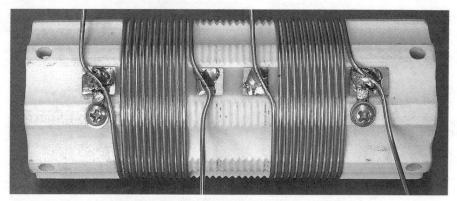

Securing the coil windings in the two-band version.

to drill holes in the ceramic, and to provide anchor points for the inner ends of the windings, I devised a method I hadn't tried before, but which worked very well (see the photograph). It consisted of preparing a strip of fibreglass PCB cut to fit closely into one of the flutes in the former, with all the copper removed except for lands used as anchor points. It is fixed in place by solder tags held under screws using the two existing threaded holes in the former. The ends of the main windings are soldered to the copper anchor points on the PCB, leaving sufficient extra wire to form the connections to the capacitors.

A strip of thin polythene sheet (cut from the lid of a redundant 'Tupperware' box!) was wrapped around the interwinding space and held in place with polythene adhesive tape before winding the link over it using heavy duty, PTFE-insulated , silver plated stranded wire. The ends of this winding were twisted together before slipping a short length of heat-shrink tubing over them, as close to the former as possible, and applying a thin coat of acrylic varnish to fix it in place.

[I did a bit of experimenting using some of the larger iron-dust toroidal cores, eg T 300-2, for the inductor and had very promising results, which I passed on to the late G3IPZ. Dave developed the idea very successfully for even larger units, working on 40, 80 and 160m, but I'm afraid his findings died with him.]

Having somewhat alleviated the problem of finding suitable variable capacitors, the next problem, although possibly less acute, may now be in finding appropriate fixed components. There are numerous types of capacitor available which claim to have high kilovolt ratings, but *beware* - a lot of them (eg the big ones to the left in the photograph, and the one in the top right corner of photo 6) are meant only to be used in pulse applications and will soon break down if subjected to the sort of high RF voltages likely to be encountered here. Other types (the ceramic disc and 'doorknob' types shown) may or may not stand the voltage strain, but are only

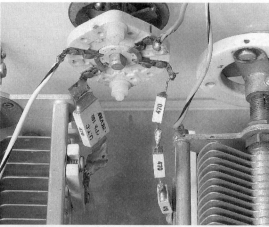
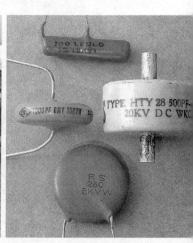

Capacitors. Left and centre: suitable types. Right: the ones to avoid.

intended for coupling and decoupling situations and are prone to large capacitance changes with temperature.

I have in the past had some unfortunate experiences with the old, wartime, moulded mica capacitors, from the American TU units (y'know, the ones we used to swear by!) rated at up to 5kV. On examination, I found the internal construction to be of an appalling standard, but there are now occasionally to be seen mica ones of more recent manufacture, with voltage ratings up to 3kV. Some of these do seem to be suitable, at least for medium-power units but one or two, even of the 3kV ones, have expired spectacularly when used at the full legal limit.

I am told that the tuning capacitors now being used in the so-called 'smart tuners' are rated for RF up to 6kV and come in a large range of fixed, binary-related values required by that application. I have no knowledge regarding the type of construction or, more importantly, where to obtain them.

The best ones to look out for are the large 'mushroom' types of capacitor specifically designed for RF and rated at about 10kV, made by Plessey and TCC among others, which come in values between 10 and 1300pF to my knowledge, but I've only found them at rallies, usually amongst the silent key 'junk'. They are ideal for any power up to at least the legal limit but, by the time you get up to 1000pF or so, they are *huge*. Another glazed-ceramic-encased type, which I have used in both my ATUs, came in two sizes, rated at 1kV and 2kV **RF**. They are very stable, produce no perceivable heat at full power and give no trouble whatsoever; the only two snags are that I only ever came across them once, at a rally some years ago (I think on Birkett's stand) and the only values were around 500pF, so parallel or series combinations are usually required.

THE HALF-WAVE INVERTED-L FOR 80m

by Greg Smith, ZS5K

THE commonly used 80m DX aerials, such as the delta loop, grounded vertical and loaded Yagi are difficult or impossible to erect on a typical small city plot, as they all take up much more space than is usually available. The grounded vertical itself does not take up much ground space but, to be effective, it needs an extensive radial system which does. Other aerials, such as the inverted-V, are not effective for long-haul DX unless erected at greater than a half-wave elevation.

Being keen on low band DX, and with limited space, I decided to try to find an aerial which would be reasonably effective, but which I *could* fit into a limited space. An idea which came to mind was the half-wave vertical. This aerial has a high feed impedance, so does not need an extensive ground system, and is obviously vertically-polarised, giving the required low radiation angle. However, erecting a full half-wave for 80m is also impractical for many people.

Having access to the *Antenna Optimizer* software package, from Brian Beezley, K6STI, I decided to see what performance was predicted for a half-wave inverted-L structure. I have a fibreglass tower which allows a vertical leg of about 16m, and a tree, about 25m away, with a height of around 10m. I therefore modelled an aerial with a 16m vertical wire, and a 19m wire gently sloping down to 10m as shown in **Fig 1**.

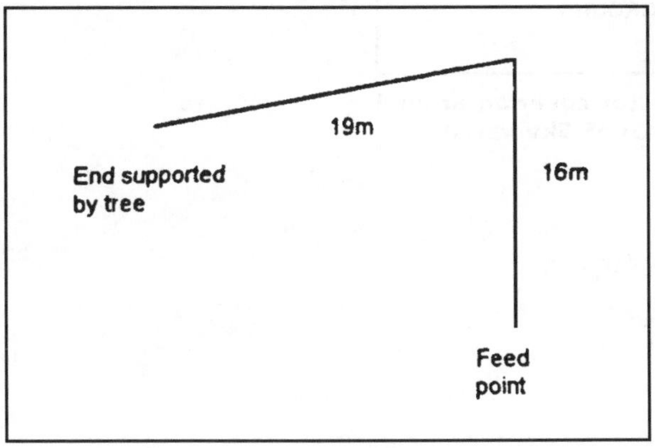

I decided to go for a total length of 35m, which is not quite a half-wave, to prevent the resistive part of the impedance from rising to an impractical value. *AO* predicted the impedance to be 766 + j2361. The horizontal radiation pattern predicted was almost omnidirectional, and a significant amount of energy is radiated at lowish angles in the vertical plane. This is assisted by the fact that the current peak is at the highest point of the aerial, instead of close to the ground. The predicted radiation pattern is shown in **Fig 2**. A suitable matching unit is shown in **Fig 3**.

The component ratings specified are sufficient to cater for the legal power limit in this country. If variable capacitors of this rating are not available, then fixed ones could be used, but tuning up is then less convenient. One plan is to use low-voltage rating capacitors for tuning, and then to measure the values arrived at, and replace them with fixed-value high-voltage types.

For grounding, I used two 16mm diameter by 1m long copper plumbing tubes driven into the ground. The ground resistance using this method should be less than 100Ω, resulting in a sufficiently high ground efficiency.

Results on the air have been very satisfying. Clearly this type of single-element aerial will not compete with phased verticals with good radial systems or Yagis at 40m height, but I have had no problem in working all seven continents on a regular basis, and with good reports.

Any queries or comments would be welcomed by the author at gregsmi@iafrica.com

Fig 1. The inverted-L structure.

19m

End supported by tree

16m

Feed point

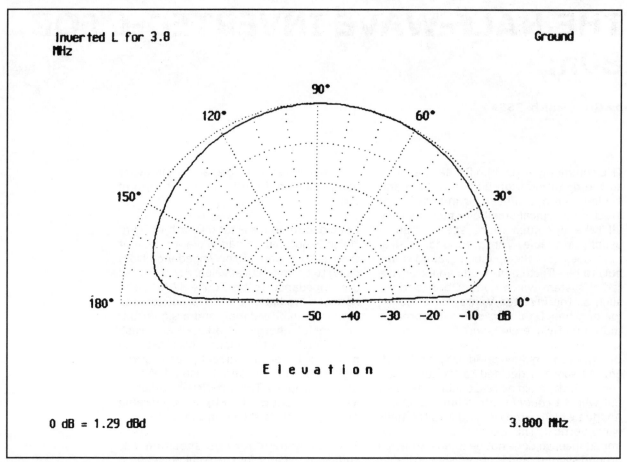

Fig 2. The predicted polar diagram.

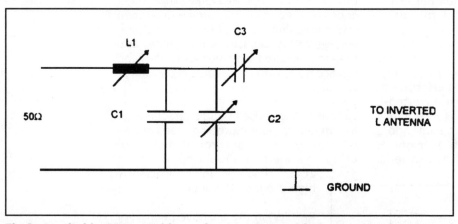

Fig 3. A suitable 50Ω matching unit. L1 - trapped inductor covering around 8μH. C1 - 100pF 2kV fixed. C2 - 100pF 2kV variable. C3 - 30pF 5kV variable.

ACKNOWLEDGMENT
My thanks are due to John Fielding, ZS5JF,
for assisting with this article.

THE SKELETON SLOT VHF AERIAL

by Peter Johnson, ZL4LV

THE skeleton slot aerial for 2m was featured in RSGB publications about 40 years ago and proved very popular. Many were built by amateurs world-wide, including myself, with seemingly good results.

In essence, the aerial array consists of two six-element Yagis stacked 5λ/8 apart, the main feature being the driven element, which can be described in two ways:

(1) as two half-wave dipoles folded so that the ends of the upper and lower conductors are connected in parallel;

(2) as a slot aerial, ie a slot cut in a sheet of metal, but with most of the surrounding metal removed. Hence the name 'Skeleton Slot'.

The feed-point is the paralleled dipole ends via a delta-matching section. The main feature of this type of driven element is that it is relatively broad-band and thus non-critical, the rest of the aerial being a conventional Yagi.

In the absence of any comparisons, the skeleton slot aerial I built many years ago seemed to give good results. The aerial also had some use on the earlier satellites and, whilst the performance seemed to be good, I had the feeling that some features were not as good as they might be. The front-to-rear ratio was not very great and, when tracking a satellite, there seemed to be more pick-up on an overhead pass than there should be.

So much for history. Coming forward in time to the present, the availability of aerial design computer programs has taken the guesswork and gut feeling out of the design of aerials. There are several programs available from various sources.

About two years ago I purchased a copy of the *YO6.5 Yagi Optimizer* and *AO6.5 Antenna Optimizer* by Brian Beezley,

K6STI, as advertised in *QST*. The minimum computer needed to run these programs is a 386 with maths co-processor. Aerial design programs such as these are not for the beginner and a good understanding of aerials is necessary to make best use of the features provided. With these programs you can analyse the radiation pattern, the impedance match of an existing aerial and, as the name implies, optimise the aerial to certain parameters defined by you.

The *YO* program is specifically for Yagis, including stacked arrays of two Yagis, and the *AO* program will analyse all aerial types, including Yagis, but with a size limit. The main difficulty with the *AO6.5* program is feeding the data to the program, since it has to be in the form of a text file describing the aerial in three-dimensional terms. The *YO* is not so bad, as it has a simpler system for data entry. The *AO* text file description takes some time to get the hang of, but there are several example files included which do help.

My first significant attempt with these programs was the design of a seven-element Yagi for 6m using the *YO* program for which it is easier to load the data. In fact, I modified an existing file which the program allows you to do.

Before starting the optimization process the required parameters were entered. These were: gain, front-to-rear ratio and matching.

The front-to-rear ratio is not the same as front-to-back; front-to-back can give an almost complete null at 180°, but with significant side lobes. Front-to-rear gives a reduction of side lobes over a full 180° to the rear. This reduced pickup is important at my location to reduce interference from the local TV transmitter.

Several matching options are available within the program, so as well as the desired impedance, I selected a T-match to 200Ω.

While the calculation of the pattern plots and impedance match for an existing aerial is quite fast, the optimisation process may take some time, as it is a trial-and-error process. Using my 100MHz Pentium, the process was spread over two days.

The aerial was built to the design and the results were excellent. There was no need to adjust the match, it was as predicted. On-air tests were done using my existing five-element Yagi in a direct A-B comparison. The new aerial's temporary set-up was only about 6m high, whereas the existing five-element was at a height of about 8m.

The results: the gain was only slightly greater than the existing aerial, which was as predicted. However the front-to-rear ratio was a vast improvement and it was

While the *YO* program can model stacked Yagis, it will only handle conventional driven elements, (including dual-driven element types). It was not possible to model the Skeleton Slot array and this is where the *AO* program comes in. As mentioned earlier, it is necessary to input the data as a text file, describing each element size and position in the form of x, y, z coordinates. The program will handle physical dimensions, but for the optimisation process to take place, each component that can be varied has to be allocated a symbol (as in algebra) where the original dimension is entered in a table at the start, eg D1 = 36in. There is not space to cover the full details of the process, but I must admit that it took some time, and many error reports before the data was accepted. A further feature of the program is that it draws a three-dimensional picture of the aerial which can be rotated and zoomed for closer examination to show errors that may have

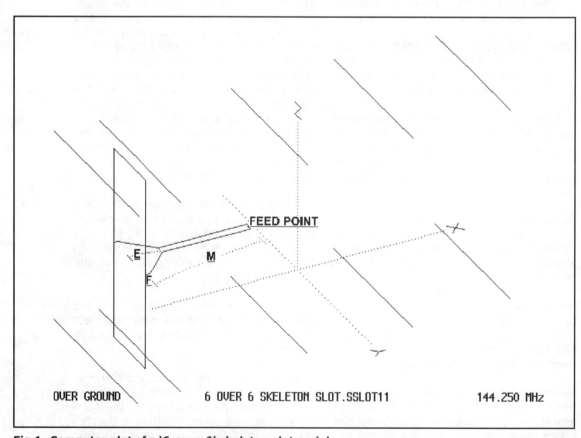

Fig 1. Computer plot of a '6-over-6' skeleton slot aerial.

now possible to copy signals that were completely unreadable on the original five-element because of the rear noise pick up.

passed the text entry stage. See **Fig 1** for an example of the computer-generated drawings.

First, I did some practice on some simpler aerial types before attempting the slot array, and a good selection of aerial types for study are included with the program.

The dimensions fed into the program were those of my existing skeleton slot, which I thought were those given in the 1962 *RSGB Handbook* (see later). The only difference was the method of feeding the slot-driven element, where I had added a quarter-wave matching section. I wanted to retain this slot element, as I had the sections already made with aluminium welded joints. I should also mention at this stage that the program will model matching sections. When the data was finally loaded, the graphs of the original design were plotted and they confirmed my suspicions about the poor front-to-rear pattern and excessive high-angle pick up. Note that this is modelled for 'above ground', since the program gives the option of a specified height above ground, or in free space.

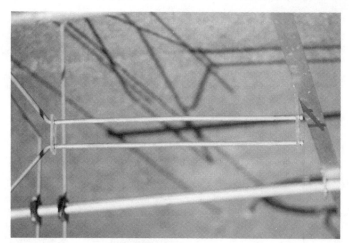

The quarter-wave matching section.

The next stage was the optimisation process, where the variable parameters were: the length and position of the reflector and directors, the boom-to-boom spacing and hence the proportions of the slot and the proportion of the Y and

The skeleton slot in business!

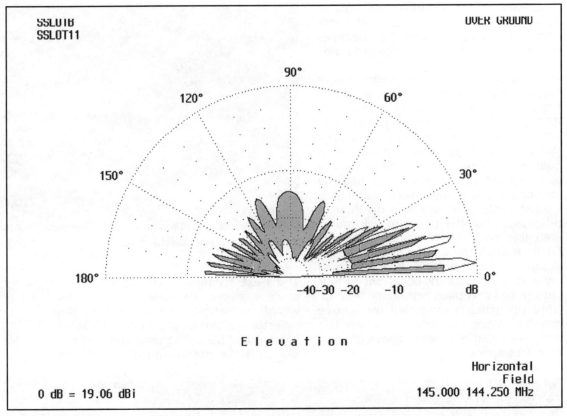

Fig 2a. Plots of ZL4LV's original aerial (shaded), with the optimised plot overlaid.
(a) Elevation view; (b) Plan view.

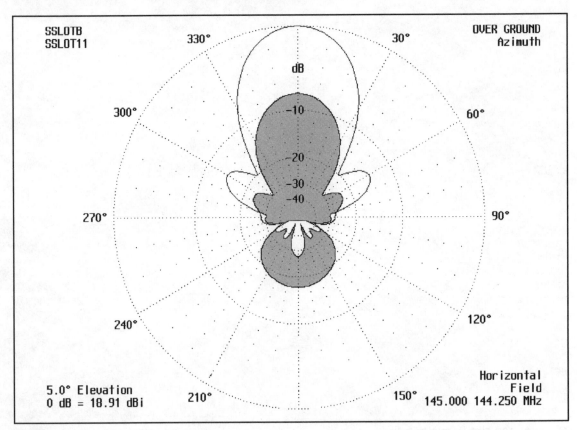

Fig 2b.

quarter-wave matching section. In other words, all the dimensions. I also specified the frequency range for the lower part of the 2m band, as this DX portion is where my interest lies.

The program includes the facility to weight the priorities of the gain, front-to-rear, and match parameters as percentages but because it is not possible to achieve optimum performance of all features, some compromises are necessary. For example, optimising for maximum gain will normally give a poor front-to-rear ratio and excessive side lobes, and an undesirably-low input impedance The optimisation process took many hours, spread over several days, and the changing parameters were displayed on the screen as the optimisation proceeded. I halted the procedure at times to vary some feature.

Eventually, after about some 25,000 models, the ultimate design was reached. The resultant plot is shown in **Fig 2(a)** and **(b)**, with the original version plot overlaid. As you can see the overall pattern has been improved significantly. The physical results of the optimisation were a small extension of the boom, the first director now being closer to the driven element but, interestingly, the size of the slot and hence the boom-to-boom spacing showed only minor changes from the original,so these variables were disabled and returned to the original dimensions as the optimisation proceeded.

When I first started to prepare this article, I assumed that the skeleton slot I was using was that as originally published by the RSGB. However, on checking the dimensions, I found that this was not so and I cannot now recall from where they originated. However, since the computer program was now ready, it was a relatively simple matter to feed the original set of dimensions into the program. The resultant performance was very good, not at all bad for some 40 years ago, well before the availability of computer design programs.

I have given this information to illustrate how these aerial design programs can take an inferior design and convert it to one that is very much better, as well as improving an already good design.

A further comment with regard to the pattern plots where the stated gain will seem to be rather higher than normally expected. The program has the choice of either the theoretical isotropic aerial or a dipole as reference, and these plots used the former. The main reason for the apparently high gain is brought about by ground reflections, where the height of the aerial above ground influences the radiation pattern. Different heights produce an array of lobes at different angles. The programs do allow for modelling in free space where the true theoretical pattern is displayed, but I chose to model the aerial at the height I expected to use it, since this is the realistic situation.

CONSTRUCTION

An existing skeleton slot aerial was available and so was dismantled and rebuilt to the new design. Where necessary, I lengthened the elements by adding extensions to the ends and each joint was coated with electrical jointing paste to prevent corrosion. It would have been preferable to use new materials but it goes against the grain to waste aluminium. The boom also required lengthening and this was done in a similar manner. In the original construction, the elements had been mounted by passing them through holes drilled in the boom but, in this new design, the elements were to be isolated so length correction was unnecessary. Insulated mountings were machined from plastic with the hole for the boom slit at the base to allow a clamping screw to grip it firmly. The elements passed through a hole drilled near the top edge and were locked in position with a self-tapping screw. Since it was not possible to use this mounting feature on the already-built slot element, these mountings were changed to an open groove. **Fig 3** shows the essential dimension of the mounting insulator.

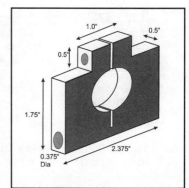

Fig 3. The element mounting block.

My apologies for retaining Imperial dimensions, but the original design was given in this form and the materials used in the construction are still Imperial-sized. However, the program has provision for either measurement system. Also, when constructing components to accurate dimensions, conversions can add to the possibility of errors, eg 10mm is not exactly $^3/_8$in.

RESULTS

This is the most difficult part to evaluate with any degree of accuracy. The first test was impedance matching for which I had available a Rohde and Schwarz Polyskop. This is a wide-band sweep generator with a built-in display. By itself this instrument can be used to show a relative match to good accuracy, but I have found I can achieve better results by using a return loss bridge (a type of VSWR indicator) to feed the display. The slot matching section was designed to give a balanced terminal impedance of 200Ω. A 4:1 balun was made using a half-wave coax section and, using the Polyskop, this was confirmed as working correctly. The design frequency of the array was 144.25MHz and when checked via the balun it showed an almost perfect match from 143-145MHz, indicating the broad-band nature of the slot-driven element.

I am still evaluating the on-air performance. The existing slot array is still in position and available for an A-B comparison. The results with the 6m aerial make me confident that an equivalent performance improvement will be achieved.

The programs will model the aerial's performance either in free space or above an ideal ground, which is not what you will find in the normal suburban section. Also included with these aerial design programs are two others - one that

---

Frequency = 144.250 MHz, dimensions in inches.
35 6061-t5 wires (6061-t5 is an aluminium alloy); wires are the number of elements and matching section components.

dia=0.375	element diameter
r=19.78845	reflector half length
dl=18.93056	director 1 half length
d2=17.6535	director 2 half length
d3=18.14537	director 3 half length
d4=17.26315	director 4 half length
s=8.157777	spacing driven element to reflector
sd=2.449892	spacing driven element to dl
sl=33.74707	spacing driven element to d2
s2=58.78832	spacing driven element to d3
s3=82.42427	spacing driven element to d4
w=7.5	horizontal part of slot, half width
h=22.375	vertical part of slot, half height
m=28.75	quarter-wave matching section, plus 'e' and 'f'
c=1	half centre-to-centre spacing of match section
e= 7.625	x-axis length of Y section, plus 'f'
f=1	short joining section between Y and slot element
ht1=240	above ground to lower boom
h2=(ht1+2h)	above ground to upper boom
h3=(ht1+h)	height of feed-point

This optimisation uses 15 segments and is for 200Ω impedance and the above results are the optimised dimensions as calculated by *AO6.5*.

The original dimensions were entered against these variables. Following this table in the actual program, a detailed description of each element and its position is entered, but this is too detailed to show here.

NOTE: The program uses element half-lengths. These must be doubled to give the actual element length. The element spacing and matching sections are listed as above. All dimensions are in inches.

Table 1. Dimensions of the revised 6-over-6 skeleton slot aerial over ground, as calculated by the *AO* program.

analyses the effect of guy wires on the radiation pattern, the other that analyses the effect of the ground below and in the area away from the aerial. The ground can range from excellent (sea water) to poor (rocky) and the ground profile can be varied from flat to whatever your location has. The mouse is used to shift the reference line to show the effects of rising or falling slopes, obstructions etc at defined distances from the aerial in the direction of interest. This program is quite fascinating to play with, as there is almost instantaneous redrawing of the radiation pattern as the surrounding ground profile is changed; rising obstructions and/or sudden changes in the height of the ground modify the radiation pattern from the flat ground ideal.

The use of these computer aerial design programs has completely revolutionised the design of aerials, so it is now possible to produce an aerial with the features you require in a predictable manner; the guesswork has been removed and you know what you will get. There is a further advantage in that it has eliminated the cut-and-try processes of the past.

However, you still have to do the mechanical construction, but the end result is a working aerial.

THE SPIDERBEAM

by Cornelius Paul, DF4SA

My favourite way to play radio is on portable, outdoor operations, field days, and DXpeditions. I definitely needed a lightweight aerial, and the Spiderbeam was developed to fulfil that need (see **Table 1**). It yielded the following benefits: it should be lightweight (5.5kg) and have a small packing size (1.20m). These make transportation a lot easier, even more so because a light mast and rotator are sufficient. The aerial also presents low wind resistance.

Contrary to most boom-to-mast plates, which position the aerial on one side of the mast, the Spiderbeam is mounted exactly at its centre of mass. Antenna weight and vertical torque moment are optimally applied to the mast and rotator which means the load on these parts is reduced and makes it easier to raise the mast.

Setting up the aerial on site is greatly simplified because it can be carried and put up by a single person; it goes where you would never drag along a heavy conventional design of tribander. This makes it easy to select the most favourable location with the best radiation conditions.

The visual appearance is low-profile, which makes it easier for the neighbours to

Ural Contest Group setting up their own local WRTC-style competition. Each of these single-operator stations used a Spiderbeam and 100W. (Photo: UA9CDC)

Operating frequencies	14.0 – 14.35 MHz
	21.0 – 21.45 MHz
	28.0 – 28.8 MHz
Feeding	Single coaxial cable
Continuous HF power	Maximum legal
Weight	5.5kg
Dimensions (length x width)	7.0m x 7.0m
Turning radius	5.0m
Transportation length	1.2m
Rotator requirement	TV rotator

Table 1: Spiderbeam general data.

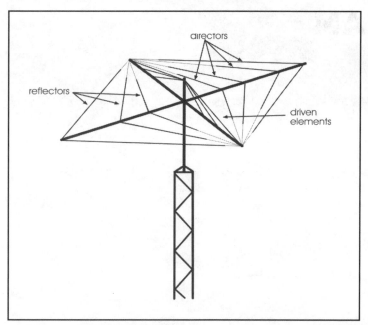

Fig 1: Spiderbeam schematic diagram.

my requirements, so I decided to start development myself.

After countless simulation runs, the Spiderbeam eventually evolved. The problems were mostly mechanical. The aerial had to be lightweight but sturdy; it had to be waterproof, have repeatable electrical parameters no matter how often it was put up and taken down, and should be easy to assemble with as few tools as possible. In the end it was a great pleasure to see the last prototype survive the heavy storms during my activity from CT3EE (*CQ* WW CW 2002).

The development is now completed and I have written a detailed step-by-step *Construction Guide* (details are given later) which is available free from me by e-mail (PDF file, 23 pages, 600KB). Thus, while the following text will not provide every constructional detail, it will give a general insight into the aerial design and constructional methods.

BASIC ANTENNA PRINCIPLE

The Spiderbeam is a triband Yagi for 20, 15 and 10m. It consists of three interlaced wire Yagi aerials strung on a common fibreglass spider. These are - three-element Yagis for 20m, and 15m, and a four-element Yagi for 10m. In contrast to a regular Yagi, the director and reflector elements are V-shaped.

The driven element is a multi-band fan dipole for 20, 15 and 10m, ie three individual dipoles connected at their centre feedpoint. The feedpoint impedance is 50Ω, fed through a W2DU-type current choke balun, making a very simple and robust feeding system. No phasing lines or matching devices are needed (see **Fig 1**).

The wire lengths and mounting dimensions of the parasitic elements can be found in **Table 2** and **Fig 2**.

Please note that the specified wire lengths

accept, should you erect it as your base station aerial. The Spiderbeam is much lighter than other beams with comparable performance, making handling much safer.

Assembly is straightforward, user-friendly and non-critical; when assembling the aerial for the first time, ensure that the wires are cut to exactly the correct lengths. The mounting distances of the elements are not critical. No complicated or fragile parts are involved. The tuning procedure requires only a VSWR bridge and can be done in 10 minutes.

HISTORY

Five years ago, the Spiderbeam was just a dream. I was not convinced by the exaggerated claims by the mini-beam manufacturers of gain, front-to-back ratio and bandwidth. One day I stumbled on an aerial design called a 'bow-and-arrow-beam' (or 'Bird-Yagi' after its inventor Dick Bird, G4ZU). It is a three-element Yagi using director and reflector elements bent into a V-shape. Nowhere in the literature could I find a multi-band version to meet

Band (m)	Reflector (cm)	Director 1 (cm)	Director 2 (cm)
20	1054	984	- - -
15	700	648	- - -
10	526	488	488

Table 2: Parasitic element lengths.

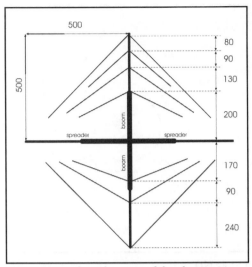

Fig 2: Mounting the parasitic elements.

The wire lengths and mounting dimensions of the driven elements can be found in **Table 3** and **Fig 3**.

Band (m)	Driven element (cm)
20	2 x 497
15	2 x 342
10	2 x 261

Table 3: Driven element lengths.

are only valid for bare wire of 1mm diameter! Other wire types (especially insulated wire) will result in different element lengths because of the change of velocity factor caused by the insulation. The same is true when mounting insulators at the wire ends, as they will also cause a change of the effective electrical wire length.

It is very important to cut the wires precisely to the specified lengths. Even an error of one centimetre will make a difference. Therefore it is also essential to use a wire type which does not stretch. I am using copper-clad steel wire (Copperweld®, DX-wire®). The first versions of the Spiderbeam were built using normal (soft) enamelled copper wire. Each time when assembling and dismantling the aerial, some elements had stretched up to 10cm. In turn, the resonant frequencies of the wire elements change, resulting in a deterioration of the radiation pattern, especially the front-to-back ratio. See the *Construction Guide* for further details.

The single dipoles of the driven multi-band dipole must be vertically spaced correctly, see Fig 3. The further apart they are spaced, the less is the mutual interaction, as with any multi-band-dipole. The distance between the highest dipole (20m) and the lowest dipole (10m) should be around 50cm. It is also important to keep the 10m dipole a few centimetres away from the fibreglass spreaders, otherwise the VSWR will change a lot when the spreaders get wet from rain.

Because the feedpoint impedance of the aerial is already very close to 50Ω, no impedance transformation is necessary, but a balun between the aerial and the coaxial cable is needed. This can take the form of a simple coaxial cable choke.

The simplest coaxial cable choke is constructed by coiling up a few turns (5-10) of coaxial cable right at the feed point. The performance of such a choke is highly dependent on the operating frequency, the coaxial cable used, and the diameter and height of the coil.

A much better solution is the coaxial choke developed by W2DU [*QST*, March, 1983]. Take a piece of thin coaxial cable and slip a number of ferrite beads over the outer plastic jacket, which effectively stops current from flowing on the braid (outer

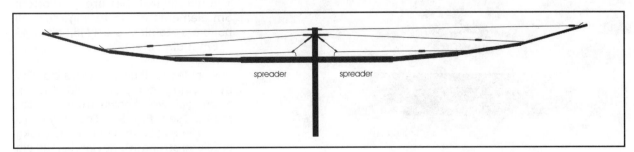

Fig 3: Mounting the driven element.

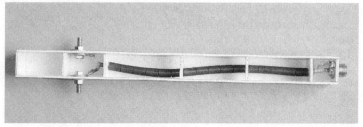

The coaxial cable choke.

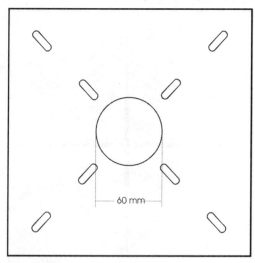

Fig 4: (b)

conductor), resulting in a good match of the balanced aerial to the unbalanced coaxial cable. Using a piece of Teflon cable makes such a coaxial cable choke easily capable of handling 2kW continuous HF power.

After preparing the coaxial cable choke as described above, it is mounted into a suitable piece of weatherproof plastic 'U'-section. One end of the cable is connected to a SO-239 coaxial socket, the other end to two stainless steel M6 bolts. These connections are then made water-tight with epoxy. A piece of flat plastic panel is glued on top and serves as the lid of the box. The choke is shown in the photograph.

The balun housing has a second function - it will be strapped to the aerial mast, thus serving as a stable mount for the feedpoint. The driven elements are then connected to the M6 bolts.

A few words are needed regarding the mechanical design of the aerial. The heart of the construction is the centre joint made from aluminum sheet metal and tube: **Fig 4**.

The long slots make it possible to slide the aluminum tubes in and out and thus accommodate diameters of vertical masts from 30 to 60mm. Many push-up masts have top sections smaller than 60mm. With the long slots, the tubes can always be positioned in a way that the mast is perfectly pinched between them. Hence most of the load that normally stresses the U-bolts is transferred to the tubes. U-bolts are necessary only to prevent the aerial from rotating on the mast.

With this construction, it is possible to use a wide range of vertical mast diameters without compromising stability. This means more flexibility when putting up the aerial.

Most boom-to-mast plates put the aerial on one side of the mast. With the centre joint described here, the mast goes right through the centre of mass. Aerial weight and vertical torque momentum are optimally applied to the mast and rotator, which means the load on these parts is reduced.

The fibreglass tubes are the bottom 5m elements of 9m fishing rods. All bolts are stainless steel M6 bolts (M6 = 6mm diameter).

The spider itself gets its extra stability by guying it completely within itself, a concept well known from sailboat masts (see **Fig 5**). The guys are Kevlar lines (1.5mm diameter, 150kg breaking strength). Kevlar has the big advantage of not stretching at all, so

Fig 4: (a) The centre joint; (b) the aluminum plate.

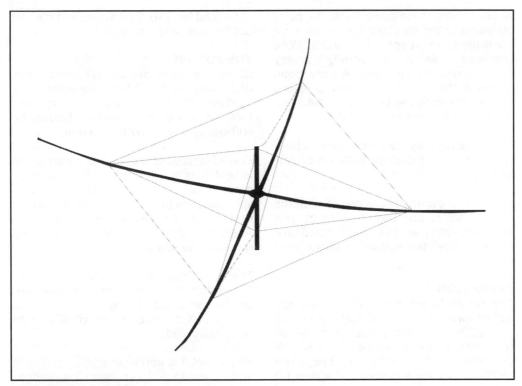

Fig 5: The basic spider.

the guy-lines always stay as tight as you pulled them during assembly.

It is a good idea to use sailors' hitches for fastening the guy-lines, so they are easy to untie when dismantling the aerial (see **Fig 6**).

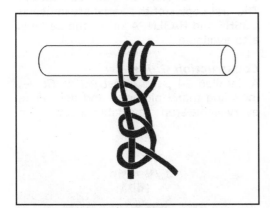

Fig 6: Round turn with half-hitches.

Attaching the wire elements to the spider is quick and easy, using cable-ties. Short pieces of polyamide hose are used for stress relief at the bending points and also to cover the joints between the wire ends and the fishing line insulators.

All the tools necessary for assembly are two spanners for M6 nuts, some cable-ties, and some sticky tape.

For transportation, all the wires and guy-lines are wound onto a big spool (in the most appropriate order for assembly). Such a spool could be found in kite stores.

Many further details can be found in the step-by-step *Construction Guide* mentioned above.

ANTENNA PERFORMANCE & TECHNICAL DATA

The aerial was developed using the *NECWires* software by K6STI and the free software, *4NEC2*. During the test phase, the aerial was put up at 10m height in an open field and was been measured extensively. It was found that the wire (DX-wire 1.0mm, black enamelled) had a unity velocity factor, ie the lengths derived from the computer model could be used directly in the real world. It also became clear that the covering of the element tips (4cm-long pieces of 8mm-OD polyamide hose, filled with epoxy) affected the resonant frequency of the wire elements; it drops by 100 to 200kHz. Of course, this effect must be taken into account when transferring the simulated wire lengths to reality!

After applying these corrections, the polar diagrams of the aerial were measured on all bands, in steps of 100kHz. The shareware *Polar-Plot* by G4HFQ is a very suitable tool for this job. A very good match of the computer-predicted values to the measurements was found. The values are summarised in **Table 4**.

These are roughly the same data as for a typical modern tribander with a 6 or 7m-long boom.

Diagrams showing the calculated patterns at 10m height and the changes of gain and F/B ratio across each band are available from the author's website (see below).

OPERATION
The Spiderbeam has fulfilled all my expectations in practical use. Since the year 2000 I was lucky enough to go on tour with it for all three *CQ* WW CW Contests (9H3MM, CS7T, CT3EE). The CS7T activity even resulted in a new EU record in the 100W class (my favourite class, especially for portable operation). During the CT3EE activity I also experienced phenomenal pile-ups, but unfortunately the heavy storm resulted in a power failure before the contest was over. Therefore I was very pleased (and the pain was eased a bit) by the fact that the Spiderbeam had survived the storm.

All in all, having a lightweight aerial that can be put up at the best suitable location has proved to be a very good concept.

The specified wire lengths are a good compromise for CW and SSB operation. For single-mode operation it is, of course, very easy to use one set of wire elements optimised for CW and another one optimised for SSB, thus squeezing the last decibel out of the design.

THE FUTURE
Of course there are always more ideas and plans for the future, for example a lightweight stack of two Spiderbeams (where a normal tower should be sufficient), and a WARC version.

One advantage of this style of construction is that it is not limited to the tribander described here. Once the supporting structure has been built, other wire aerial designs can be tried easily and cheaply. Apart from the wire elements, everything remains the same.

There are also different ideas regarding the bending of the elements. For example, on the same supporting cross, a Moxon beam, an X-beam or a bent HB9CV could be constructed.

All you need is aerial simulation software and a few ideas! For some inspiration, W4RNL's web site can be recommended to anyone interested in aerials and simulation.

MORE INFORMATION
Further information and pictures can be found on the author's website. Several helpful radio amateurs from other countries have kindly translated the *Construction Guide* to their languages, and an e-mail reflector has been set up. The first copies of the aerial are in use at G3SHF and HA3LN. A kit for the aerial is also available.

Construction Guide
A detailed 24-page *Construction Guide*, including many pictures, and describing every single step is available directly from

Band	Forward gain in free space	F/S ratio (dB)	F/B ratio (dB)
20m	6.5 dBi (4.3 dBd)	12	15-20 across band
15m	6.6 dBi (4.4 dBd)	15	18-25 across band
10m	7.2 dBi (5.0 dBd)	18	20-30 across band

Table 4: Performance data.

the author. If you are interested, please e-mail df4sa@contesting.com to receive this *Construction Guide* as a free pdf. If you do not have Internet access, ask a friend who has, to download it and print it out for you.

THE KIT

A complete kit of parts is available from the author. It costs 300 Euros plus shipment, which is 25 Euros to the UK.

The box is 115 x 20 x 20cm, weighs around 8kg, and is shipped by regular mail.

Please remember that the author is not a big manufacturer. In fact, this is a secondary project which creates a lot of work for him.

Contact him by post or e-mail regarding payment details.

Website details

DX-Wire

www.dx-wire.de

4NEC2

www.qsl.net/wb6tpu/swindex.html

Plotting software

www.g4hfq.co.uk

DF4SA website

www.qsl.net/df4sa

E-mail reflector

http://groups.yahoo.com/group/Spiderbeam

W4RNL

www.cebik.com

THE GM3VLB MINI-DELTA

by André Saunders, GM3VLB

I had been searching for a compact beam which could be easily and quickly assembled for portable operations from Scottish islands, because time wasted assembling a complex station on an island means that many lose the chance of a QSO with that island.

We must assume that if a station is calling you, he/she can hear you (not always the case nowadays of course, when 'listening' means, for some, watching the DX Cluster listings on a monitor and then calling blind, whether you can hear the DX or not!). Let's be honest, a compact beam is unlikely to give you more than 3dB gain – equivalent to half an S-point at the other end. Is it worth the effort?

However, these thoughts did not stop me experimenting. Having done all my DXing, in my previous life as 5Z4KL, with quads or loops, I dug out my old 1970 bible, *All About Cubical Quad Antennas* by the late Bill Orr, W6SAI. I had built and worked /P with half-size loaded two-element quads, but had rejected them due to the narrow bandwidth and initial tuning problems. However, my 1964 edition of the ARRL *Antenna Handbook* made passing reference to half-wave loops. I decided to investigate these further.

THE HALF-WAVE LOOP
First of all, let me say that theoretical information on the half-wave loop seems to be very hard to come by. A search through some two dozen antenna books at a recent radio rally, produced only *one* reference of any substance (and this originated from the ARRL *Antenna Handbook*).

A half-wave loop is formed by bending a simple half-wave dipole into a loop, the circumference of which is thus a half-wavelength long. The loop can be any shape, from square (with each side $\lambda/8$) to circular (of radius $\lambda/4\pi$). In the case of the square loop, there are two possibilities

– the closed loop, as in **Fig 1**, or the open loop, as in **Fig 2**, in which the side opposite the feed-point is *open* at its centre. The current distribution is similar to that along a half-wave dipole. In Fig 1, the input resistance at the feed-point A is high (a few thousand ohms) as the current is minimum at A and maximum at B. In the case of the open loop (Fig 2), the current is maximum at A and minimum at B. The input resistance is therefore low and of the order of a few ohms. Unlike the simple dipole, there is no direction in which radiation is zero. This results in the gain of the half-wave loop being about 1dB less than that of a dipole (-1dBd), but having a front-to-back ratio of some 4 to 6dB in the direction of maximum radiation which, for both configurations, occurs in the plane of the loops and in the directions shown by the arrows. Such a half-wave loop would therefore normally be mounted horizontally.

If there are any readers who are dab hands with *EZNEC* or similar, the author would be most interested to see the radiation pattern of such an open horizontal half-wave loop in the horizontal plane, referenced to a simple horizontal dipole at the same height. As stated above, the loop can be any shape. It occurred to me that a square loop requires four spreaders whereas a triangular (or 'delta') loop requires only three. This could be an advantage for /P operation. The 'open' configuration input resistance is too low

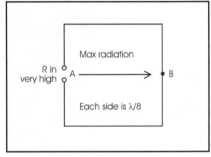

Fig 1: The closed half-wave loop.

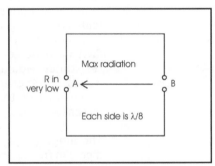

Fig 2: The open half-wave loop.

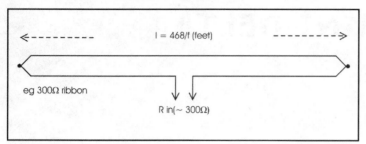

Fig 3: A simple folded dipole.

to match 50Ω coax directly. Either some form of matching must be used, or the input resistance must be raised. It occurred to me that a folded dipole does precisely that.

THE FOLDED DIPOLE
Simple form

One or more extra conductors half a wavelength long are added in parallel with the original dipole – see **Fig 3**. The input resistance is raised by the square of the number of conductors. For example, if the folded dipole has two conductors, its input resistance rises from 72Ω to around 300Ω. (with three conductors, the input resistance would be 72 x 9, ie around 650Ω). Another useful feature is that the bandwidth of the folded dipole is also increased, relative to a simple dipole.

The length, *l* (ft), of a simple horizontal dipole in free space is given by the formula

$$l = \frac{492}{f},$$

where *f* is the desired resonant frequency in megahertz (MHz). In practice, due to end-effects, the actual physical length is reduced to 468/*f*. If, instead of open-wire line, the folded dipole is made from solid twin-conductor line such as 300Ω TV ribbon or perhaps from 'figure-of-eight' electrical flex, loudspeaker or bell wire,

the velocity factor, k, of the line should be taken into consideration as follows.

Modified folded dipole

The overall length of the folded dipole remains 468/*f*, but the length of the shorted parallel section is reduced by the velocity factor, k. The length of this section is therefore given by 468k/*f*. See **Fig 4**.

I used the MFJ-259B Antenna Analyser to determine the velocity factor of the figure-of-eight clear lighting flex/loudspeaker wire used in the prototype mini-delta beam, and found it to be approximately 0.71. The length of the 'shorted' section is thus

468 x 0.71/*f* = 332/*f*, leaving 136/*f* for the end sections (68/*f* at each end).

THE FOLDED DIPOLE HALF-WAVE LOOP

If, instead of bending a simple dipole into a loop (the input resistance of which drops from 72Ω to a few ohms), we take a folded dipole and bend that into a loop and, if its input resistance, now of some 300Ω, drops by the same order of magnitude, it should become a fairly good match to 50Ω coax. This was my reasoning. My knowledge of antenna theory is very limited and I would be happy for anyone to shoot me down in flames! However, the results obtained seem to suggest that this simplistic reasoning works.

Lengthening effect of the loop

As W6SAI explains in his book on quad antennas, bending a dipole into a loop actually has a lengthening effect (there is no end-effect in this case). Although he suggested that the electrical or free-space wavelength (492/*f*) is increased by a factor of 1.028, my own experiments have suggested an empirical value of 1.024. Applying this to the free-space length produces the figure of 504/*f* for the overall length of a closed half-wave loop. If the velocity factor is now applied, the folded section should have an overall length of 358/*f*, while each end-section is increased to 73/*f*. These are the design figures I have used.

The 'Delta' design

As stated earlier, the delta configuration (named after the capital letter 'D' [Δ] in the Greek alphabet) was chosen, because it reduces the number of supports from four to three, for only a

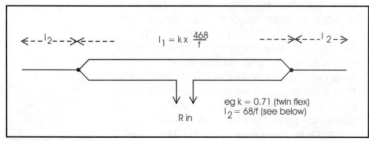

Fig 4: A 'modified' folded dipole.

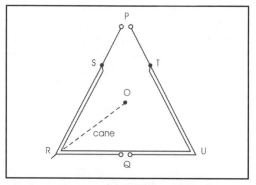

Fig 5: A folded dipole half-wave loop.

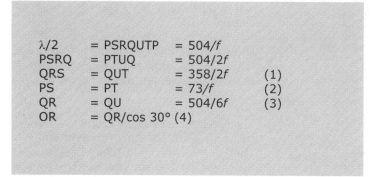

$$\lambda/2 \quad = PSRQUTP \quad = 504/f$$
$$PSRQ \quad = PTUQ \quad = 504/2f$$
$$QRS \quad = QUT \quad = 358/2f \quad (1)$$
$$PS \quad = PT \quad = 73/f \quad (2)$$
$$QR \quad = QU \quad = 504/6f \quad (3)$$
$$OR \quad = QR/\cos 30° \quad (4)$$

EXAMPLE

The dimensions for the GM3VLB mini-delta beam for 20m (14.175 MHz) are calculated as follows:

From (1), length of twin-flex needed = 2 x 358/(2f) = 25ft 3in (i)

From (2), length of single flex needed = 73/f = 5ft 2in (to the nearest inch) (ii)

From (3), distance to spreader from feed-point = 504/(6f) = 5ft 11in (iii)

From (4), minimum spreader length = 504/(6f.cos 30°) = 6ft 10in (iv)

In practice, these dimensions are modified slightly to allow for final tuning *in situ* and to allow other loops (in the case of a multi-band beam) to 'fan in' to a common feed-line connection point (via a 1:1 balun). As with all antennas with shortened radiating elements, the bandwidth will be less than that of a full-size beam. I measured this to be about 240kHz with a centre frequency of 14.175MHz - a very acceptable figure for such a small beam. Those who regularly operate CW in the lower reaches of the band allocations, will find that only minor length adjustments are required at the open end. Setting the desired resonant frequency is extremely simple.

relatively small increase in support length. Each spreader is less than seven feet long – very short for a 20m antenna! An individual loop is shown in **Fig 5**. In the diagram, Q is the feed-point. In the formulas that follow, *f* is the design frequency.

INITIAL TEST RESULTS

As I operate largely on or about the IOTA frequencies (CW and SSB), I adjusted the resonant frequency of the prototype version of the 20m mini-delta to 14.150MHz. This was done with the mini-delta loop mounted only five feet above the ground on a light aluminium pole replacing the parasol of a patio table. At resonance, an MFJ-259B Antenna Analyser indicated a VSWR of 1:1, indicating zero reactance and an input resistance of 50Ω. The measured bandwidth was about 240Hz (earlier tests on a very much 'Heath Robinson' five-band prototype, had produced very similar results). Raising the loop to 15ft above ground produced only a very slight rise in the resonant frequency and no change in the input characteristics. At this height, several QSOs showed no discernible difference in signal strength at the DX end, when compared with my 20m

inverted-V dipole 30ft up at its apex. At the receiving end, there was a barely discernible drop of about 2dB on the mini-delta.

CONSTRUCTIONAL HINTS

A suitable central support should be manufactured. For portable use, this could be a triangular piece of wood or plastic with four tubes to take, say, three garden canes and the short support for the feed-point and balun. Some sort of bracket to take a vertical mast is also needed. The design of this central support is left to the ingenuity and junk box of the individual constructor.

Small cable ties are used to attach the mid-point of the folded element for each band, to a suitable circular insulator as shown in **Fig 6** (such as a 'slice' from $1\frac{1}{4}$in rigid plastic gas or

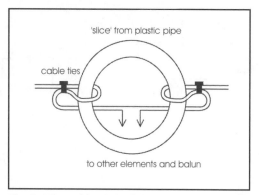

Fig 6: The midpoint of the folded element.

water pipe, or a car exhaust rubber O-ring).

Distances QR' and QT' should be measured from the O' ring and points R' and T' marked (permanent marker or whatever) on each element.

The spreaders should be around 7ft overall to begin with, to allow for adjustments. They can be trimmed later. They should be measured from the centre of the support and marked for each band.

EXTRA LENGTHS
PS and PU are increased from $73/f$ by an amount $5/f$ to $78/f$ (corresponding to approximately 2in to 4in, depending on the band). An extra 2in of folded element section (1in for each side) is allowed for wrapping round the ring, after which one side of each element is split and all elements are then tied together and connected by short flying leads to the 1:1 balun. The middle loop (15m for a five-band beam) is an equilateral (equal-sided) triangle, but minor allowances must be made to the other elements to allow them to fan out. **Table 1** summarises these allowances and all other relevant dimensions for a five-band mini-delta beam.

FEED-POINT
The loop is a balanced antenna system and is therefore fed via a 1:1 balun. In its simplest form, this consists of a trifilar winding on a short length of ferrite rod salvaged from a scrapped transistor radio. This is mounted in a small ABS plastic box held securely at the end of a suitable support OQ' (eg wooden dowelling or similar insulating material). Its length OQ' (ie from the geometrical centre of the beam to the centre of the ring) is calculated as follows: OQ' = Q'R' tan 30° = 2ft $3^1/_2$in.

In practice, the support rod OQ' is made slightly longer.

To construct the balun, take three 16in lengths of 20 or 22SWG enamelled copper wire (ideally different colours), twist together about 10 times and wind seven turns onto a 2in length of ferrite rod. Make short connections between the windings as shown in **Fig 7**.

The output of the balun consists of short tails passing through the box to a two-terminal connector mounted on its lid. This connects to the common feed-points. A 3ft length of RG-58U coax is soldered to the balun input, taped to the balun support

Design f (MHz)	QRS = QTU = $358/2f$	QR = $504/6f$	OR = QR/cos30°	Extra for fan-out	Q'R' (QR + extra bit)	SP = UP = $73/f$	Extra $5/f$ to adjust f	SP' = UP' = $78/f$
14.175	12' 7^1/2" (+2")	5' 11" (+1")	6' 10"	1^1/4"	6' 1^1/4"	5' 1^3/4"	4"	5' 4^1/4"
18.110	9' 10^1/2" (+2")	4' 7^1/2" (+1")	5' 4^1/4"	^{1}/4"	4' 8^3/4"	4' 0^1/2"	3^1/2"	4' 2^1/4"
21.225	8' 5^1/4" (+2")	3' 11^1/2" (+1")	4' 6^3/4"	0"	4' 0^1/2"	3' 5^1/4"	3"	3' 7"
24.940	7' 2" (+2")	3' 4^1/2" (+1")	3' 10^1/2"	^{1}/4"	3' 5^3/4"	2' 11"	2^1/2"	3' 0^1/2"
28.300	6' 4" (+2")	2' 11^1/2" (+1")	2' 5^1/4"	^{1}/2"	3' 1 "	2' 7"	2"	2' 8^1/4"

Table 1: All dimensions and 'allowances' for the five-band mini-delta beam.

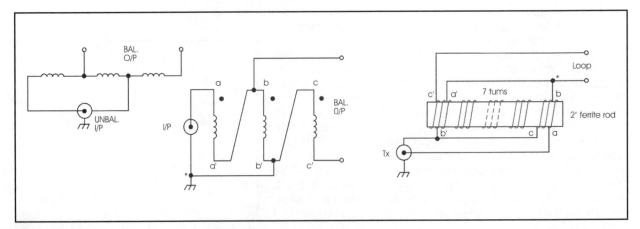

Fig 7: Balun details. * Soldered connections

'boom' and terminated in a 50Ω BNC female in-line connector. This allows connection to an antenna analyser or to the feed-line.

ANTENNA ADJUSTMENT

Short lengths of nylon fishing line or similar are attached to the loop ends, P, and the lengths of PS and PU are adjusted until resonance occurs at the desired point in each band. If desired, the beam may be rotated in the horizontal plane. The overall appearance of the beam is shown in **Fig 8**, with dimensions given in Table 1.

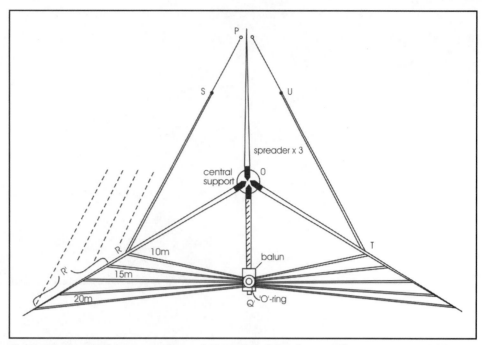

Fig 8: The overall construction of the mini-delta beam. The support at Q' is not shown. See Table 1 for element dimensions.

THE NEIGHBOURS'LL NEVER KNOW!

A compilation of ideas for aerials that won't be noticed

TAKE THE TUBE

A problem arose from a blind operator who mentioned how difficult putting up an aerial could be if you were living in a block of flats with a resident warden and a controlling authority. Here is one solution to his problem that has proved to be very useful.

The components are two lengths of 2.5in bore rainwater downcomer, each 3m long, plus about 40m of 16, 14, or 12SWG enamelled copper wire. **Fig 1** provides details. When buying the tubing from a DIY store, get a colour match to the house rainwater piping, together with six brackets to fix the tubing to the house wall. The tubing has a socket at one end. Cut one socket off one tube.

The idea is to wind an amount of wire onto the tubes, to form a resonant aerial on 40m. Most reference books tell to you in effect to suck it and see. On that basis I started with enough wire to make an 80m half-wave dipole and gradually reduced the windings to not more than 70 turns on each length. Those get you close to resonance, but definitely having enough left over for trimming to tune. You can, if circumstances are really difficult, put the aerial inside the tube, which will be fixed to the wall as though it is a working drain. Mine is wired on the outside because that was easy to do and has remained so because, from 50ft, you cannot see it. Make small wire anchoring holes at the tube ends to just clear the socket. Fix one wire end and simply wind the length on at about 3cm spacing by rolling the tube up the wire. Wind the wire on and spread it evenly afterwards, by slackening and tightening with two hands, finally pulling the ends hand-tight.

At the centre, bridge the socket in a 'Y' shape of twin feeder to the middle of the aerial and take that to a Z-match by your transceiver, but use a dip meter to provide the signal. The aerial will peak outside the band, so now you can choose to cut some wire off from either the outer or inner ends, and then re-stretch the coils to match the tube length. If you do not have a dip meter, cut 10 turns off each half of the aerial. This will resonate close to the middle of the 40m band and will also work very well on 80m. To form capacitor hats, I have soldered two pieces of double-sided copper board, each about as big as a postcard, at the outer ends.

The results are about two S-points down on a dipole at 40ft high, and this from an aerial which is almost totally shielded by the building. It is at the inside corner of our house, with one wall facing south-west and the other south-east, but I can work all over the UK from 20 miles south-west of Glasgow, even through the house to the rear. To test the aerial, one evening at about 9pm I called people around the coastal fringe. Not only did I make good contacts, but

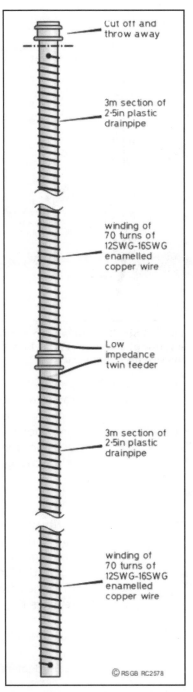

Fig 1. How to make a helically-wound 40m dipole on a drainpipe.

- Cut off and throw away
- 3m section of 2·5in plastic drainpipe
- winding of 70 turns of 12SWG-16SWG enamelled copper wire
- Low impedance twin feeder
- 3m section of 2·5in plastic drainpipe
- winding of 70 turns of 12SWG-16SWG enamelled copper wire
- © RSGB RC2578

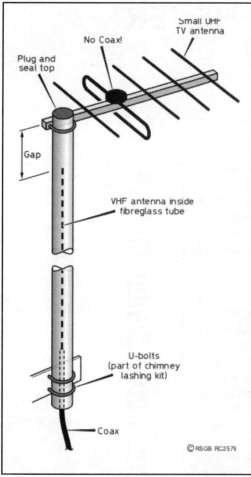

Fig 2. This TV aerial isn't connected to anything! The real aerial is a VHF vertical, inside the support tube.

in the middle of calls heard a New Zealander talking about what he had just had for breakfast. Clearly the aerial has potential.

Given a particular situation, I would shrink or stretch the aerial vertically to fit the soffit of the house and bring the lower end to about 1ft off the ground. But also, having tried its appearance and the reaction of neighbours to it, I would also erect it in full view in the most useful radiation position. Once up, the aerial looks just like all the other drain pipes and only close inspection shows that water does not run in this one.

Alan Lovegreen, GM4FLX

DUMMY TV AERIAL (1)

A VHF vertical aerial can be mounted inside a fibreglass tube *that appears to be* supporting a normal TV aerial (see **Fig 2**). From ground level, no-one is likely to notice the fact that the coax that emerges from the bottom of the support tube never reaches the aerial at the top!

Suitable tubing, about 1¼-1½in diameter, can be purchased from some amateur radio dealers.

DUMMY TV AERIAL (2)

An almost vertical long-wire aerial can be made from TV coaxial cable, terminated in a real TV aerial [1] that is supported by fibreglass tube. It is necessary to keep the coax a respectable distance away from the chimney lashing kit (see **Fig 3**) and any metal guttering on its way down to ground. The braid of the TV coax should be shorted to its inner close to ground level

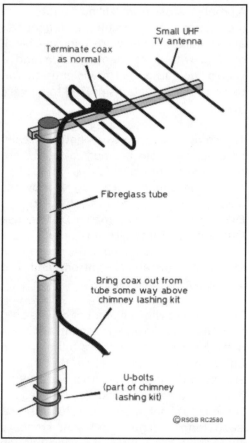

Fig 3. Keep the down-lead clear of the chimney lashing kit.

(**Fig 4(a)**), then attached to the coax from the shack in the normal way or, ideally, a remote ATU (**Fig 4(b)**). With this type of aerial, a decent earthing system will certainly pay dividends, and who's to know what wires are buried beneath ground?

TACTICAL OPERATING

Working DX from a restricted location isn't easy, but it is quite possible. One of my aerials consists of a 33ft length of wire taped down the drain pipe, with a couple of radials wedged between the cracks in

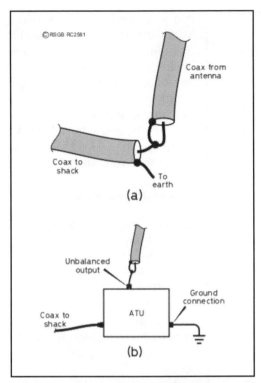

Fig 4. (a) Connection of the dummy TV aerial's down-lead direct to coax. (b) Connection via a remote ATU.

the patio. This resonates on 40m, and I use an ATU to get it onto 30m. I also have a 15m dipole. The same tuner allows some sort of service on 17, 12 and 10m. 1999 saw 258 DXCC entities worked using these two aerials. My current all-time total is 305 entities with these simple wires and never more than 90W.

May I share with readers some experiences of mine, which have helped when DX has been my objective?
- Plan your operating times around 'grey line' conditions, when propagation can favour your location.
- If possible, steer clear of weekends, when competition is fierce.
- Small stations have much more success on CW and PSK31.
- Plan activity at those times of year when paths favour you. For example, on 18MHz, JA / ZL favours the UK around 1000 UTC in January. Try much earlier and you will have too much competition from continental Europeans, who have been in the daylight longer. Also, 40m can be excellent to the Caribbean and Central

America an hour or two after sunrise, when the rest of Europe has lost propagation.
- If you want to work a particular DXpedition, it is just as important to know when their finish date as their start date. Call towards the end of their operation, not on the first day when the pile-up is full of high-powered stations.
- Contests provide an opportunity for less competitive stations to work DX. Remember, it is in the interest of contesters to pull the weak ones through.

Neil Carr, G0JHC

DUMMY CLOTHES LINE
How many neighbours would complain about a clothes line? Not many, so why not take advantage of the fact?

A low dipole from a clothes post to somewhere on the house isn't likely to attract much attention, especially if you leave pegs permanently dotted along its length!

STEPS TO SUCCESS
Load up an aluminium ladder which is propped-up against or hung on wall brackets, inconspicuously (but very well) insulated and fed against a good RF earth. Alternatively, run a G5RV around the soffit / fascia boarding of the dwelling, with the feed concealed behind the surface [2]. The best idea I have heard of was a series of dipoles in the format of the commercial CobWebb, which - on non-operating days - was actually used as a rotary clothes drier [3].

Howard Walton, M0CMG

TRUSTY TOROIDS
There is a simple solution to operating from a terraced house in a conservation area. A tried and tested technique is a toroidal aerial, sited at any convenient place on the premises. Such aerials were detailed in *RadCom* April & May 1994, and are shown in **Fig 5** and **Fig 6**.

The simplest form of toroidal aerial is formed from the combination of a single air-cored toroidal coil, spaced an inch or

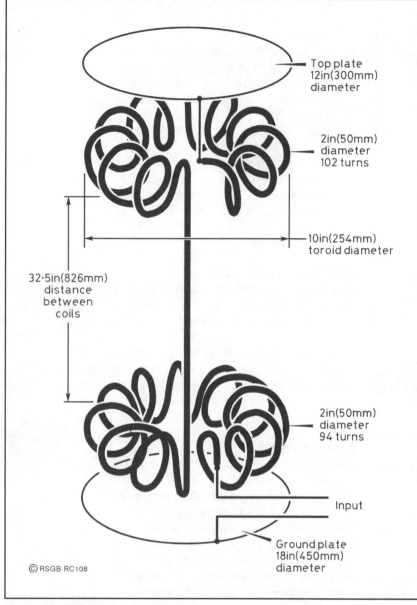

Top plate
12in(300mm)
diameter

2in(50mm)
diameter
102 turns

10in(254mm)
toroid diameter

32·5in(826mm)
distance
between
coils

2in(50mm)
diameter
94 turns

Input

Ground plate
18in(450mm)
diameter

© RSGB RC108

Fig 5. G2AJV's 80m toroidal aerial.

full-sized beam, but it certainly gives me access to the world. For nearly a decade, I have been using a 2in-high double-toroid as a 2m aerial on the roof of my car. I still have a few toroids scattered in various parts of the house for 1.8, 7 and 21MHz, and would be delighted to demonstrate any of these in QSO.

Roger Jennison, G2AJV

REMEMBER THE JOYSTICK?

When I moved into sheltered housing some 13 years ago, I really thought that it was the end of my transmitting days. However, after settling-in at my one-bedroomed flat on the ground floor, I began to weigh-up the pros and cons.

I dug out my old Partridge Joystick 8ft 6in vertical, with 40ft of single wire feeder. Spread around the bedroom and tuned with the Joymatch tuner, together with my old KW2000B transceiver, it gave me much pleasure on SSB / CW on all bands. However, I had to be careful not to interfere with the internal alarm system when operating on full power.

Although I was fairly happy with this, it presented problems for my cleaner and I was always conscious of BCI / TVI problems, so one day I tried a trick that I had done before at a previous poor location. This involved using the braiding *only* of my 2m vertical's 45ft feeder, via the Joymatch - a sort of inverted L. On all bands - with good SWR readings - it works a treat! I have cards from JA, ZS, W, VE, ZD9, OY, etc. Of course I go back to conventional feeding when I use the aerial for VHF.

F C P Flanner, G3AVE

two above a conducting sheet. A sheet of aluminium about 2ft-square is ample for the purpose (it reflects a contra-wound image of the coil and acts as the grounded terminal for the outer of the coax). The inner conductor of the coax is connected to one end of the toroidal coil via a small preset capacitor. In some cases a small parallel capacitor may also be required to obtain a perfect match.

I have had many DX phone QSOs on 21MHz with a toroid sitting on the washing machine in the kitchen on the ground floor of my house. It doesn't blast out like a

50Ω

© RSGB RC114

Fig 6. A horizontal toroidal dipole for 80m, with the toroids spaced about 3ft apart.

EDITORS' NOTES

[1] Don't try to use it to receive TV, as well as transmit!

[2] Fine if your guttering is plastic, but not recommended if it is metal.

[3] Adequate safety precautions required.

THE NJQRP SQUIRT

by Joe Everhart, N2CX

At one time, 80m was one of the more highly populated amateur bands. Lately, it has become significantly less popular because much DXing has moved to the higher frequencies and many suburban lot sizes are too small to accommodate a full 130ft, $\lambda/2$ aerial for the band. That's unfortunate, because 80m has lots of potential as a local-communication band - even at QRP levels. The recently published 'Warbler' PSK31 transceiver can serve as a great facilitator for close-in QRP communication without much effort [1]. What's really needed to complement the Warbler for this purpose is an effective aerial that fits on a small suburban plot. Because PSK31 (which the Warbler uses) is reasonably effective, even with weak signals, we can trade off some aerial efficiency for practicality.

WHAT'S A HAM TO DO?

I investigated a number of aerial possibilities to come up with a practical solution. One intriguing candidate is the magnetic loop. Plenty of design information for this aerial is presented in the *ARRL Antenna Book* and at a number of Web sites [2, 3]. To obtain high efficiency, however, the loop must be 10ft or more in diameter and built from ½in diameter (or larger) copper pipe. The loop needs a very low-loss tuning capacitor and a means of carefully varying it, because of its inherently narrow bandwidth. Another configuration, the DCTL, may be a solution, but it's likely not very efficient [4].

An old standby aerial I considered is the random-length wire worked against ground. If it is at least $\lambda/4$ long (a Marconi aerial) or longer, it can be reasonably efficient. Shorter lengths are likely to be several S-units down in performance and almost any length end-fed wire needs a significant ground system to be effective. Of course, you may not need much of a ground with a $\lambda/2$ end-fed wire, but it's as long as a centre-fed dipole.

Vertical aerials don't occupy much ground space, but suffer the same low efficiency as the end-fed wire if they are practical in size.

Probably the easiest aerial to use with good, predictable performance is the horizontal centre-fed dipole. Unfortunately, as mentioned earlier, the usual 80m $\lambda/2$ dipole is too large for many lots. But all is not lost! The dipole can be reduced to about $\lambda/4$ without much sacrifice in operation (see the box – 'Compromises'). Furthermore, if the dipole's centre is elevated and the ends lowered-resulting in an inverted V - it takes up even less room. This article describes just such a dipole: the NJQRP Squirt.

V FOR VICTORY

You can think of the Squirt as a 40m, $\lambda/2$ inverted-V dipole being used on 80m. **Fig 1** is an overall sketch of the aerial; The photograph shows a completed Squirt prior to erection. The Squirt has two legs about 34ft long separated by 90° with a feed-line running from the centre. When installed, the centre of the Squirt should be at least 20ft high, with the dipole ends tied off no lower than 7ft above ground. This low aerial height emphasises high-angle NVIS (Near-Vertical-Incidence Skywave) propagation that's ideal for 80m contacts ranging from next door out to

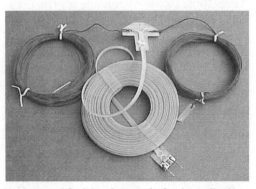

An assembled Squirt ready for installation.

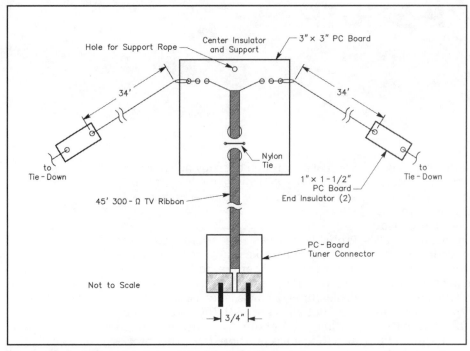

Fig 1. General construction of the 80m Squirt aerial.

For instance, the end and centre insulators (see Fig 1) are made of $^1/_{16}$in-thick scraps of glass-epoxy PC board. For the aerial elements, I use 21SWG or 23SWG insulated hookup wire. Although this wire size isn't recommended for use with fixed aerials, I find it entirely adequate for my Squirt. Because it's installed as an inverted-V aerial, the centre insulator supports most of the aerial's weight, making the light-gauge wire all that's needed. The small-diameter wire has survived quite well for several years at N2CX. This is not to say, of course, that something stronger like 16SWG or 14SWG electrical house wire couldn't serve as well.

The 300Ω TV ribbon can be purchased at many outlets including RadioShack and local hardware stores. Once again, if you want to use heavier-duty feed-line, do so. The only proviso is that you may then have to trim the feeder length to be within tuning range of the Squirt's aerial tuner.

The End-Insulators
I used $^1/_2$ x $1^1/_2$-in pieces of $^1/_{16}$in PC board for the Squirt's two end-insulators. As with everything else with the Squirt, these dimensions are not sacred; tailor them as you wish. If you use PC board for the end-insulators, you have to remove the copper foil. This is easy to do once you've got the knack. Practice on some scraps before tackling the final product. The easiest way to remove the foil without etching it is to peel it off using a sharp hobby knife and needle-nose pliers. Carefully lift an edge of the foil at a corner of the board, grasp the foil with the pliers and slowly peel it off. You should become an expert at this in 10 or 15 minutes. Drill $^1/_8$in-diameter holes at each end of each insulator for the element wires and tie-downs.

Tuner Feed-Line Connector
The tuner end of the feed-line is terminated in a special connector. Because

150 or 200 miles - and that's where 80m shines! With the Squirt's centre at 30ft and its ends at 7ft, the aerial's ground footprint is only about 50ft wide.

One nice feature of a λ/2 centre-fed dipole is that its centre impedance is a good match for 50Ω or 75Ω coax cable (and purists usually use a balun). Ah, but the Squirt is only λ/4 long on 80m, so it isn't resonant! Its feed-point impedance is resistively low and reactively high. This means that feeding the aerial with coax cable would create a high VSWR, causing significant feed-line loss. To circumvent this, we can feed the aerial with a low-loss feed-line and use an aerial tuner in the shack to match the aerial system to common 50Ω coax cable. I'll have more to say about the tuner later.

I use 300Ω TV flat ribbon line for the feed-line. Although a better low-loss solution is to use open-wire line, that stuff is not as easy to bring into the house as is TV ribbon. Using TV ribbon sacrifices a little transmitted signal for increased convenience and availability. If you feel better using open-wire line, go for it!

USING AVAILABLE MATERIALS
It's always fun to see what you can do with junkbox stuff, and this aerial is one place to do it. See the 'Parts List' for information on materials and sources [5].

the TV-ribbon conductors aren't strong, they'll eventually suffer wear and tear.

This connector provides needed mechanical strength and an easy means of attaching the feed-line to the tuner. In addition to some PC-board material, you'll need 4 - 5in of 19SWG to 14SWG solid, bare wire. Refer to **Fig 2** and the accompanying photographs for the following steps.

Take a $1\frac{1}{8}$ x $1\frac{3}{4}$in piece of single-sided PC board and score the foil about $\frac{1}{2}$in from one end; remove the $1\frac{1}{4}$in piece of foil. Now score the remaining foil so you can remove a $\frac{1}{8}$in-wide strip at the centre of the board, leaving two rectangular pads as shown in Figs 2(B) and the photograph. Drill two $\frac{1}{16}$in-diameter holes in the copper pads spacing the holes about $\frac{3}{4}$in apart. Drill two $\frac{3}{8}$in holes at the connector mid-line about $\frac{5}{8}$in apart, centre-to-centre, to pass the feed-line and secure it.

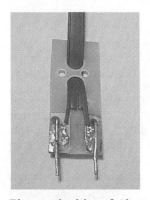

The pad side of the home-made feed-line to tuner connector.

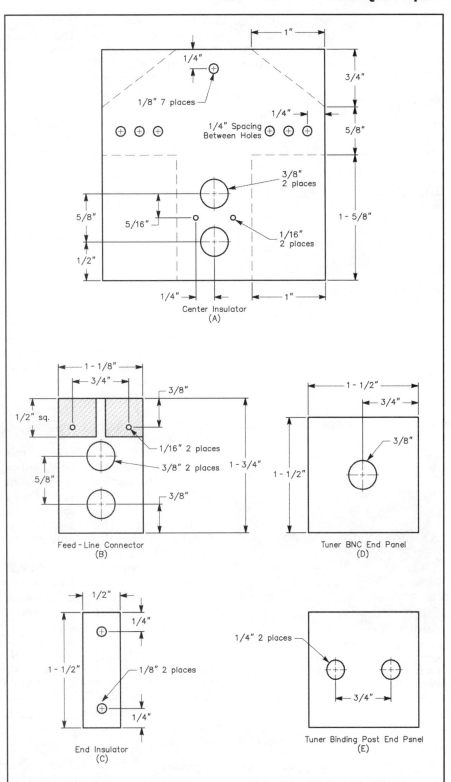

Fig 2. Hole sizes and locations for the various PCB pieces. See Note 5.

Cut two pieces of 19SWG to 14SWG wire each about 3in long. Pass one wire through one of the $\frac{1}{16}$in holes in the connector board and bend over about $\frac{1}{4}$in of wire on the non-foil side. Solder the wire to the pad on the opposite side and cut the wire so that about 1in of it extends beyond the connector. Repeat this procedure with the second wire.

Next, strip about 2in of webbing from between the feed-line conductors and loop the feed-line through the two $^3/_8$in holes so that the free ends of the two conductors are on the copper-pad side. Strip each lead and solder each one to a pad. You now have a solid TV ribbon connector that mates with the binding-post connections found on many aerial tuners. The photo shows the connector mated with a Squirt tuner.

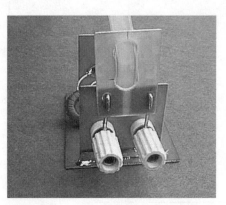

Here, the feed-line to tuner connector is shown attached to the binding posts of the Squirt aerial tuner.

Centre Insulator

Strip all the foil from this 3in-square piece of board. Use Fig 2(A) as a guide for the hole locations. The top support hole and the six wire-element holes are $^1/_8$in in diameter; space the wire-element holes $^1/_4$in apart. The feed-line-attachment holes are $^3/_8$in diameter spaced $^1/_2$in apart, centre-to-centre; the two holes alongside the feed-line-attachment holes are $^1/_{16}$in-diameter. These $^1/_{16}$in holes accept a plastic tie to secure the feed-line.

I trimmed the insulator shown in the photograph from its original 3in-square shape to be more aesthetic. Your artistic sense may dictate a different pattern.

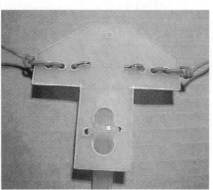

View of an assembled centre insulator fashioned from a 3 x 3in piece of PCB from which all the foil has been removed.

Bevel all hole edges to minimise wire and feeder-insulation abrasion by the glass-epoxy material. You can do this by running a knife around each hole to remove any sharp edges.

PUTTING IT ALL TOGETHER

The Squirt is simple to assemble. Once all the pieces have been fabricated, it should take no more than an hour or two to complete assembly. Begin with the centre insulator. Cut each of the two element wires to a length of about 34ft. Feed the end of one wire through the centre insulator's outer hole on one side, then

loop it back and twist around itself outside the insulator to secure it. Now loop it through the other two holes so that the inner end won't move from normal movement of the wire outside the insulator.

Repeat the process for the other insulator/wire attachment. Separate several inches of the TV-ribbon feed-line conductors from the webbing; leave the insulation intact except for stripping about $^1/_2$in from the end of each wire. Pass the TV ribbon through both $^3/_8$in holes. Strip a $^1/_2$in length of insulation from each dipole element, then twist each feeder wire and element lead together and solder the joints. It might be prudent also to protect the joint with some non-contaminating RTV or other sealant. Finally, loop a nylon tie through the holes alongside the feeder and tighten the tie to hold the feeder securely. A close-up of the assembled centre insulator is shown in the photograph. Attach the end-insulators to the free ends of the dipole wires by passing the wires through the insulator holes and twisting the wire ends several times to secure them.

So that the aerial / feed-line system can be tuned with the Squirt tuner, the 300Ω feed-line needs to be about 45ft long. If you use a different tuner, you may have to make the feed-line longer or shorter to be within that tuner's impedance-adjustment range.

TUNER ASSEMBLY

This tuner (see **Fig 3** and the photograph) is about as simple as you can get. It's a basic series-tuned resonant circuit link-coupled to a coaxial feed-line. At C1, I use a 20 to 200pF mica compression trimmer acquired at a rally (you do buy parts at rallies, don't you?), although almost any small variable capacitor of this

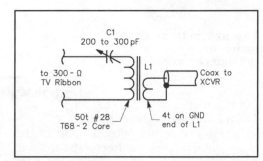

Fig 3. Circuit diagram of the Squirt aerial tuner. See the 'Parts List' for details.

This Squirt tuner prototype uses a 2 x 3in piece of PCB for the base plate, two $1^1/_2$ x $1^1/_2$in pieces for end plates, and a $^1/_2$in square piece as a tie-point for the toroid and tuning capacitor.

value should serve. The inductor, L1, consists of 50 turns of enamelled wire wound on a T68-2 iron-core toroidal former. An air-wound coil would do as well, although it would be physically much larger. The photograph shows the tuner built on an open chassis made of PC board. My prototype uses several PCB scraps: a 2 x 3in piece for the base plate, two $1^1/_2$ x $1^1/_2$in pieces for each end plate (refer to Fig 2); a $^1/_2$in square piece (visible just beneath the capacitor in the photograph) is glued to the base plate to serve as an insulated tie point for the connection between the toroid (L1) and tuning capacitor (C1). The tuner end plates are soldered to the base plate to hold a pair of five-way binding posts and a BNC connector at opposite ends. L1 and C1 float above electrical ground, connected to the TV ribbon. One end of L1's secondary (or link) is grounded at the base plate and the coax-cable shield. The hot end of L1's secondary winding is soldered to the coax-connector's centre conductor.

TUNER TESTING

C1 tunes sharply, so it's a good idea to check just how it tunes before you attach the tuner to an aerial. You can simulate the aerial by connecting a 10Ω resistor across the binding posts. If you use an aerial analyser as the signal source, a $^1/_4$W resistor is suitable. But if you use your QRP transmitter, you need a total resistance of 8 to 10Ω that will dissipate your QRP rig's output, assuming here it's 5W or less.

Four RadioShack 271-151 resistors (two series-connected pairs of two parallel-connected resistors) provide a satisfactory load if you don't transmit for extended periods. Or, you can make up your own resistor arrangement to deliver the proper load. Adjust C 1 with an insulated tuning tool to achieve an SWR below 1.5:1.

Once the tuner operation is verified using the dummy aerial, it's ready to connect to the Squirt. Tuning there will be similarly sharp, and a 2:1 VSWR bandwidth of about 40kHz or so can be expected as normal.

A MULTI-BAND BONUS

Although the Squirt was conceived with 80m operation in mind, it can double as a multi-band aerial as well.

PARTS LIST
Squirt Aerial

1	3 x 3in piece of $^1/_{16}$in-thick glass-epoxy PC board for the centre insulator.
2	$^1/_2$ x $1^1/_2$in pieces of PC board for the end-insulators.
1	$1^1/_8$ x $1^3/_4$in piece of PC board for the feed-line connector.
2	34ft lengths of 21SWG (or larger) insulated hookup wire.
1	6in length of 17SWG (or larger bare) copper wire; scrounge scraps from your local electrician.
1	45ft length of 300Ω TV ribbon line.

Squirt Tuner

1	2 x 3in piece of PC board for base plate.
2	$1^1/_2$in-square pieces of PC board for end plates.
1	$^1/_2$in-square piece of PC board for the tie point.
1	200pF to 300pF (maximum) mica compression trimmer.
1	T68-2 toroid core.
2	5-way binding posts.
1	55in length of 27SWG or 30SWG enamelled wire.

Note: You can use $^3/_{16}$in-thick clear Perspex for the Squirt's end- and centre-insulators. Commonly used as a replacement for window glass, Perspex scraps can be obtained at low cost from hardware stores and window repairers.

The simple Squirt tuner is designed to match the aerial only on 80m. However, a good general-purpose balanced tuner such as an old Johnson Matchbox or one of the currently popular Z-match tuners (such as an Emtech ZM-2) will give good results with the Squirt on any HF band. The Squirt prototype was recently pressed into service at N2CX on 80, 40, 30, 20 and 15m for several months. It worked equally as well as a similar aerial fed with ladder line. Although no extensive comparative tests were done, the Squirt has delivered QRP CW contacts from coast to coast on 40, 20 and 15m and covers the East Coast during evening hours on 8m.

Build one! I'm sure you'll have fun building and using the Squirt!

NOTES

[1] D Benson, NN1G, and G Heron, N2APB, 'The Warbler - A Simple PSK31 Transceiver for 80m', *QST*, Mar 2001, pp37-41.

[2] R D Straw, N6BV, *ARRL Antenna Book* (ARRL, 1997, 18th ed), pp5-9 to 5-11.

[3] www.alphalink.com.au/~parkerp/nodec97.htm; www.home.global.co.za/~tdamatta/loops.html

[4] home.earthlink.net/~mwattcpa/antennas.html

[5] Full-size templates are contained in *squirt.zip* available from www.arrl.org/files/qst-binaries/

COMPROMISES

One of the unfortunate consequences of shrinking an aerial's size is that its electrical efficiency is reduced as well. A full-size dipole is resonant with a feed-point impedance that matches common low-impedance coax quite well. This means that most transmitter power reaches the aerial minus only 1dB or so feed-line loss. However, when the aerial is shortened, it is no longer resonant. A *NEC-4* model for the Squirt shows that its centre impedance on 80m is only about 10Ω resistive, but also about $1k\Omega$ capacitive. This is a horrendous mismatch to 50Ω cable, and feed-line loss increases dramatically with high VSWR. The Squirt uses 300Ω TV ribbon for the feed-line, with an inherently lower loss than coax, but it's still appreciable. Calculated loss with 300Ω transmitting feed-line is about 7.7dB (loss figures are hard to come up with for receiving TV ribbon) so the feed-line used doubtless has more than that.

Although this sounds discouraging, it's not fatal. You have to balance losing an S-unit or so of signal against not operating at all! Consider that the Squirt, even with its reduced efficiency, is still better than most mobile aerials on 40 and 80m. So for local communication (a low-dipole's *forte*), using PSK31 and the Squirt is quite practical.

If you don't already have an aerial, the Squirt's a good choice to get your feet wet when using PSK31. Once you get hooked, you'll probably want a better aerial. If you have the room, put up a full-size dipole; you'll see the improvement right away. If you can't do that, use a lower-loss feeder on the Squirt, such as good-quality open wire.

THE SUPER SLOPER

by Roger Sparks, W7WKB

You can imagine my surprise when *ELNEC* [1] revealed that a parasitic element can be combined with a long wire to form a whole family of directional aerials. There on my screen, I was looking at useful combinations not found in that bible of aerials, the *ARRL Antenna Book*. I had been exploring combinations of full-wave parasitic elements with wire arrays. How far off-centre can I slide a parasitic element, I wondered? 'A lot' was the answer coming from *ELNEC* and later confirmed by *EZNEC*. As I offset a closely-spaced (0.015 to 0.046λ) parasitic element by λ/8 to 5λ/8, a whole family of aerials appeared (see **Fig 1**).

I call the configuration a 'Super Sloper', because the pattern resembles that of the well-known sloper, but it is greatly enhanced (see **Fig 2**). Super Slopers provide gain in the direction from the tall to the short pole. The amount of gain depends on aerial length, or more exactly, on the number of half-wavelengths in each element.

Like slopers, Super Slopers require two supports, one tall and another shorter. At my station, and in this article, I considered only non-conductive supports. Other builders can explore the possibilities of Super Slopers suspended from metal towers. Super Slopers are very inexpensive to build (if you already have suitable supports). They require only wire and a few feet of PVC pipe. Unlike slopers, Super Slopers have high feed-point impedances. A matching network is required when feeding a Super Sloper with a 50Ω line. The result is a broadband, low-Q aerial (**Fig 3**). Don't think of this as just one aerial, but rather a whole family of aerials, one for each half-wavelength added.

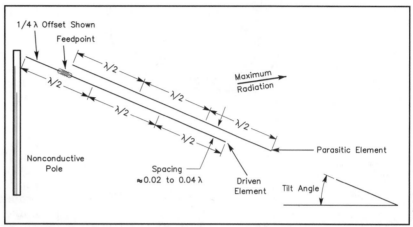

Fig 1. The Super Sloper, showing nomenclature. This is a 3λ/2 model. See Fig 7 for constructional details.

TECHNICAL CONCEPTS

If you just want to build an aerial, skip ahead to the 'Practical Aerials' discussion. Those with a technical inclination can continue here, and they may even want to take a look at the discussion of long-wire aerials in the *ARRL Antenna Book*. An aerial is called a long wire if it is one wavelength or longer. The radiation pattern can be described as the surfaces of two opposed cones that are coaxial with the wire and have their apices meeting at the feed-point. The apex angle becomes smaller and the lobes grow stronger as aerial length increases. An azimuth plot of radiation pattern for single long-wire aerials over ground shows four principal lobes at low radiation angles. There are two principal lobes, in one direction, when the aerial is terminated in a matched. resistive load.

ELNEC shows that a parasitic element added to a single long-wire aerial creates a unidirectional radiation pattern similar to that created by a resistive termination. Energy eliminated from the back goes into useful forward gain. The parasitic element can be tuned as either a director or a reflector [2]. Experience with Yagis (and many other applications of parasitic

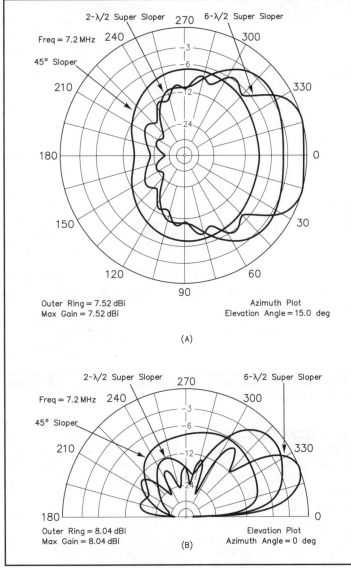

Fig 2. Azimuth (A) and elevation (B) plots for a 45° sloper,
2λ/2 (λ/4 offset, spaced 0.04λ, low end 0.119λ above ground),
and 6λ/2 (λ/4 offset, spaced 0.015λ, low end at 0.066λ above
ground) Super Slopers. The high end of each is λ/2 high.

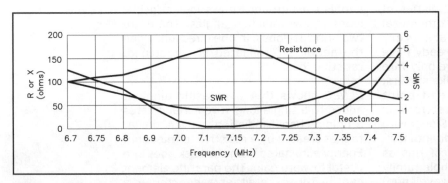

Fig 3. A plot of impedance and VSWR against frequency for the 2λ/2 aerial
described in Table 6, placed as described in Fig 6. The data source is
NECWIRES 1.5 (see [3]).

elements) led me to believe that all parasitic elements must be nearly a half wavelength long and located within the span of the driven element. That concept is completely incorrect. Parasitic elements can be any resonant length and offset from the driven element, as long as there is adequate coupling between the elements.

Here's how Super Slopers produce front-to-back ratio (F / B) and gain. The best F / B results from a 180° phase shift between the currents in the driven and parasitic wires, as seen from a distant location where a pattern null is desired. A phase difference of 180° means that the signals completely cancel each other, if each element delivers equal signal strength. A phase shift of 90° is possible with a λ/4 offset, and the remaining 90° phase shift can come from the tuning (length) of the parasitic element. If the fields cancel in one direction, they will reinforce in some other direction, to produce gain. By increasing the phase angle of the current in the parasitic element, the angle of maximum cancellation can be moved. This is particularly useful in Super Slopers, because the principal lobes of long wires lie at some small angle to the direction of the wire. From **Table 1**, notice that the current in a resonant parasitic element has about -144° to 156° phasing, which is about right for correct reverse-lobe cancelling.

If we want each element to deliver equal signal strengths to a distant location, nearly equal currents must flow in both the driven and parasitic elements; the coupling between elements must be very close. Table 1 suggests the approximate spacings for currents to be equal within ±10%. (The aerial also has gain at closer spacings because gain is affected less by unequal currents than is F / B.)

DESIGNING A SUPER SLOPER

When placed near (and parallel to) the ground, Super Slopers show twin-lobed azimuth patterns with a null, often 10dB or greater, on the axis of the wire. This centre null can be filled by tilting the wire, with the low end in the direction of the null. **Fig 4**

Aerial Length(λ)	Spacing (λ)	Phase angle (°)
0.5	0.046	-156
1.0	0.030	-147
1.5	0.023	-144
2.0	0.018	-142
2.5	0.015	-142
3.0	0.015	-144

Table 1: Spacing and phase angle for various aerial lengths. At the spacings listed, the current in the resonant parasitic element is equal to driven-element current ±10%. (Derived from *ELNEC*, under free-space conditions, λ/4 offset, at 7.1MHz.)

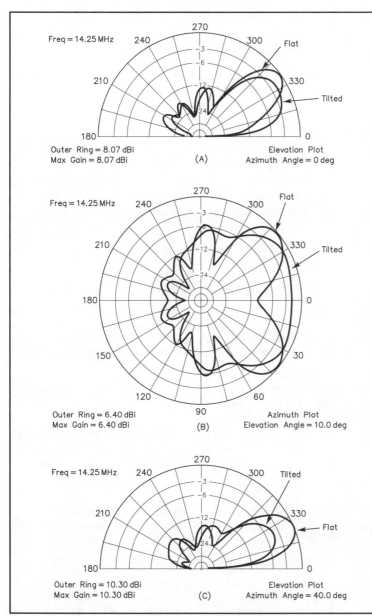

Fig 4. Patterns of a 3λ/2 aerial with 0.36λ offset and spaced 0.04λ, orientated flat at λ/2, compared with one sloping from λ/2 to 0.045λ. (A) shows the elevation patterns at 0°. (B) shows the azimuth pattern. (C) shows the elevation plots at azimuth = 40°.

shows the effects of tilting. When the aerial is tilted, the end of the parasitic element can become closer to the ground than that of the driven element. When considered as two separate aerials at different heights, the driven and parasitic elements will not have the same patterns. This reduces performance, but locating the parasitic element so that its end height equals that of the driven element can solve the problem. That is, increase the spacing to place the parasitic element end above that of the driven element. Models give this design 1 to 2dB gain advantage over more closely-spaced aerials, but construction is a greater mechanical challenge.

The driven element is fed at a current antinode, λ/4 from an end. The aerials can be made to exhibit a wide range of feed resistances - 20 to 300Ω or more (see **Tables 2, 3** and **4**). High resistances and wide offsets combine to produce low VSWR and useful gain over an unusually great bandwidth (Table 2). I've used λ/4 matching lines (using RG-62, a 93Ω line), 4:1 baluns and ladder lines to match the aerial successfully at high impedances. You can vary the aerial length (gain increases with length), height, offset, phasing and spacing as needed. This many variables would be difficult to work with if they were all critical adjustments but, fortunately, they are

Frequency (MHz)	VSWR (200Ω)	Impedance
14.0	1.54	293 + j48
14.1	1.25	248 + j13
14.2	1.16	172 + j0
14.3	1.75	127 + j54
14.4	2.61	107 + j113

Table 2: Impedance and VSWR versus frequency (Fig 5).

Current balance greatly affects F / B, with less effect on gain.

Phase angles change very slowly with aerial length.

Gain changes very little with changes of current and phasing.

Gain varies by a little over 1dB with a spacing increase from 0.01 to 0.04λ.

Spacing (λ)	Phase angle (°)	Relative current	Z of driven element	Gain (dBi)	Lobe angle (°)
0.01	-136	1.62	205 - j230	4.98	48
0.02	-141	1.29	128 - j138	5.54	48
0.03	-144	1.11	103 - j94	5.78	48
0.04	-149	0.97	80 - j59	6.1	48

Table 3: Element spacing versus phase angle, relative current, impedance, gain and lobe angle. Derived from *ELNEC*, free-space model, 14.2MHz, two λ/2 elements, offset λ/4.

Offset (λ)	Phase angle (°)	Relative current	Z of driven element	Gain (dBi)	Lobe angle (°)
0.1	-167	1.08	19 - j54	5.7	48
0.15	-157	1.18	48 - j101	5.67	48
0.2	-148	1.26	89 - j135	5.6	48
0.25	-141	1.29	128 - j138	5.57	48
0.3	-139	1.16	134 - j111	5.6	48
0.35	-138	0.963	123 - j70	5.58	48
0.4	-134	0.71	108 - j14	5.4	48
Pattern Reversal Begins					
0.5	-26	0.25	83 + j46	3.0	54
0.6	39	1.31	126 - j57	5.2	61
0.7	43	1.71	192 - j180	4.0	64

Table 4: Offset versus phase angle, relative current, impedance, gain and lobe angle. Derived from *ELNEC*, free-space model, 14.2MHz, two λ/2 elements, spaced 0.02λ. Notice how little the gain changes with different offsets.

not. Tables 1, 3, 4 and **5** show the tolerant design features of these aerials. From these tables, we can observe several trends.

Gain is nearly constant with offsets moving from 0.1 to 0.4λ.

Good F / B is easy to achieve, even though the aerial is designed for best gain or easy construction. Improved F / B ratios and

% short (λ)	Phase angle (°)	Relative current	Gain (dBi)	Lobe angle (°)
0	-140	1.30	5.54	48
1	-125	1.47	5.33	49
2	-107	1.53	5.02	51
3	-89	1.43	4.70	52
4	-75	1.23	4.44	53
5	-65	1.05	4.19	53

Table 5: Parasitic element length versus phase angle, relative current, gain and lobe angle. Derived from *ELNEC*, under free-space conditions with 14.2MHz, two λ/2 elements, spaced 0.02λ apart.

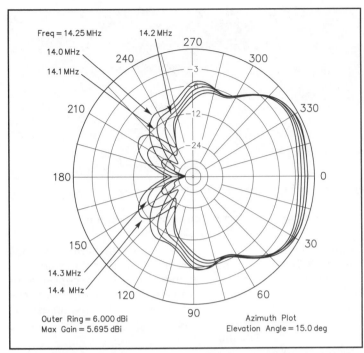

Freq = 14.25 MHz
14.2 MHz
14.0 MHz
14.1 MHz
14.3 MHz
14.4 MHz

Outer Ring = 6.000 dBi
Max Gain = 5.695 dBi

Azimuth Plot
Elevation Angle = 15.0 deg

Fig 5. Radiation pattern over a range from 14.0 to 14.4MHz. The pattern is that of a 3λ/2 aerial with 0.36λ offset, with the ends at λ/4 and 0.045λ. See Table 2 for the VSWR.

reverse-orientated patterns are possible from designs optimised at specific frequencies. Computer modelling is the

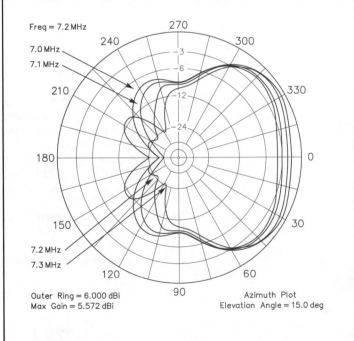

Freq = 7.2 MHz
7.0 MHz
7.1 MHz
7.2 MHz
7.3 MHz

Outer Ring = 6.000 dBi
Max Gain = 5.572 dBi

Azimuth Plot
Elevation Angle = 15.0 deg

Fig 6. Pattern plots over a frequency range from 7.0 to 7.3MHz. The aerial is 2λ/2 with λ/4 offset and 0.04λ spacing. The driven element is 1.02λ long. The director is 0.98λ long. See Fig 3 for the VSWR.

best way to optimise reverse patterns. **Figs 5** and **6** show some possible patterns and how the patterns vary with frequency. Table 2 and Figure 3 show predicted VSWR.

PRACTICAL AERIALS
Table 6 describes Super Slopers constructed at my station (refer to Fig 1 for nomenclature). The principal difference between the two 3λ/2, 20m aerials in Table 6 is the increased offset from 17½ft to 22ft. This changes the phasing, resulting in a slightly improved F / B ratio and slightly improved gain. The trade-off is a narrower pattern and a longer aerial. A 60ft mast supported the 3λ/2 and 2λ/2 20m versions. They were mounted back-to-back and tilted to fill the centre null. Another 3λ/2 20m unit was mounted from a 38ft mast. The 40m version sloped from 60ft down to 6ft. All aerials performed as predicted. Additional height at either end definitely increases low-angle radiation, but it reduces high-angle radiation. **Fig 7** shows how I assembled and spread the wires. The departure from straight lines (as depicted in Fig 1) has no practical effect on the aerial. Be sure to place the director over the driven element when erecting the aerial. A director placed at the side will skew the pattern, favouring the side of the director. Keep the Super Sloper support lines tight to minimise sagging. Severe sagging leads to improper phasing and

| Aerial Number | 1 | 2 | 3 | 4 | 5 | 6 |
Band	40m	20m	20m	20m	15m	10m
Length*	2	3	3	2	2	2
Driven (ft)	139.3	106.5	105.6	70	46	34.5
Director (ft)	134.3	104.0	102.2	68	45	32.8
Offset (ft)†‡	34.3	17.5	22	17.5	11.5	8.6
Spacing (ft)	6	1.5	1.5	1.5	1.0	1.0
Feed-point (ft)‡	34.3	17.5	17.25	17.5	11.5	8.6

* Length expressed as a multiple of $\lambda/2$.

† Offset is $\lambda/4$, except for aerial 3, where the offset is 0.31λ.

‡ Feed-point and offset are both measured from the high end of the driven element.

Table 6: Working aerial dimensions. Use a 4:1 step-down transformation to match 50Ω line.

degraded results. I put a support under my 40m Super Sloper at mid-span, but I just pull the 20m aerial support lines tight. The two elements have a tendency to twist and wrap together in the wind. You can prevent this by using two support ropes at the low end or by using spacers as used on transmission lines. Both methods work well. Super Sloper performance suffers from excessive ground losses when the low end is at ground level. I strive for an aerial slope (tilt angle) of 10° to 20° and a minimum height of 6ft. Higher is better.

A 200Ω feed-point impedance is easily transformed to 50Ω with a 4:1 balun. Ladder line and a tuner constitutes another option. Refer to the *ARRL Antenna Book* for other methods of transforming high feed impedances to values acceptable for modern transceivers. Do not feed the Super Sloper directly with coax, unless the coax is part of an impedance-matching section.

RESULTS AND CONCLUSIONS

I've built and used six Super Slopers very successfully. The F / B is often dramatic. A difference of six S-units is not uncommon when switching between two aerials built to favour opposite directions. This family of aerials has not yet been well researched and studied. Use an aerial modelling program before building designs that are substantially different (eg longer or made from tubing) from those described in Table 6.

NOTES

[1] *ELNEC*, and its successor, *EZNEC*, are computer aerial modelling programs available from Roy Lewallen, W7EL, PO Box 6658, Beaverton, OR 97007.

[2] Parasitic elements, offset more than $\lambda/2$ from the driven element, become reflectors.

[3] *NECWIRES 1.5* is a computer aerial modelling program available from Brian Beezley, K6STI, 3532 Linda Vista, San Marcos, CA 92069.

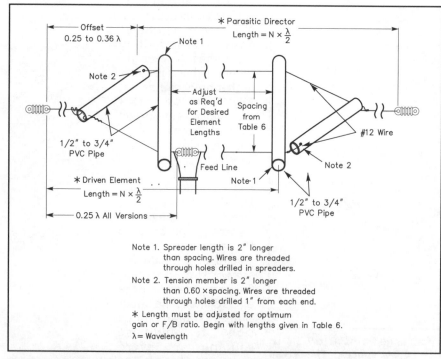

Note 1. Spreader length is 2" longer than spacing. Wires are threaded through holes drilled in spreaders.

Note 2. Tension member is 2" longer than 0.60 ×spacing. Wires are threaded through holes drilled 1" from each end.

* Length must be adjusted for optimum gain or F/B ratio. Begin with lengths given in Table 6.

λ = Wavelength

Fig 7. A method of constructing the long-wire parasitic aerial. Additional centre spacers reduce the tendency of the wires to twist in the wind.

THE SLOPER

by Arnie Coro, CO2KK

As solar cycle 23 neared or reached its peak, many of you surely were thinking about how to add new aerials for the 21 to 50MHz range in order to benefit from improved HF propagation. If you are on a tight budget, here are a few variations on the ever-popular sloper aerials which are easy to build and install, and which provide excellent performance with minimum cost.

THE ASD FOR 6m (AND OTHER BANDS, TOO)

The 'Asymmetric Sloping Dipole' (ASD) aerial evolved from a very effective 7MHz 'single-wire beam' designed by my good friend, CO2DC. His aerial consisted of a λ/4 wire, a centre insulator, and a 3λ/4 or 5λ/4 wire. This is essentially an asymmetric system, providing a very good match to 50Ω coaxial cable (don't forget the choke balun at the feed-point!) and a rather sharp main lobe in the direction of the longer arm of the aerial.

CO2DC's AD (asymmetric dipole) was really an ASD, or asymmetric sloping dipole, as the aerial was installed with a 30° slope angle, which certainly adds to its directivity, while also providing a lower take-off angle (TOA) than an all-horizontal system.

After testing a version of this aerial for the 15m band at my home QTH, I was so pleased with the results that the experimental system was taken down and replaced by a permanent one, which is again a λ/4 wire, the centre insulator and, at my downtown location, a 3λ/4 wire sloping gently toward Europe (see **Fig 1**).

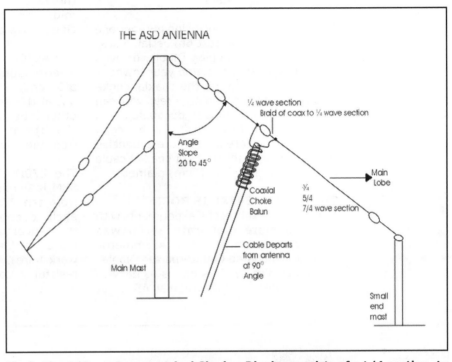

THE ASD ANTENNA

¼ wave section
Braid of coax to ¼ wave section

Angle Slope 20 to 45°

Coaxial Choke Balun

Cable Departs from antenna at 90° Angle

Main Lobe

¾
5/4
7/4 wave section

Main Mast

Small end mast

Fig 1: The ASD, or Asymmetrical Sloping Dipole, consists of a λ/4 section, to which the shield of the coax connects, and a longer section – 3λ/4, 5λ/4, or 7λ/4 for your band of choice. Your signal will be concentrated in the direction in which the larger segment is pointing.

I soon found out that the ASD concept was something to keep working on, because this aerial is a definite improvement over the standard half-wave or quarter-wave slopers!

TESTING ON 50 MHz

Using my 5-element, 3λ/4 wavelength boom Yagi as a reference, I decided to try an ASD aerial for 6m. Instead of making the long leg of the ASD just 3λ/4 long, though, this one was extended to 5λ/4, and sloping toward the north at a 30° angle.

Several summer Sporadic-*E* openings proved that the 6m ASD provided good signals at the very fringe area of the single-hop *E*-skip. Then, when working at my rooftop installation, I changed the azimuth of the 50MHz ASD to 300° in order to make room for another experimental aerial. This proved to be very fortunate, as one day in July, suddenly out of nowhere, what was obviously *F2* propagation brought several US 7th call area stations from Washington and Oregon for what proved to be a unique test. The ASD λ/4 to 5λ/4 aerial was switched in and out, comparing the signals with the 5-element Yagi, and the ASD produced very rewarding results.

As a result, here is conclusion number one – If you need a low-cost 6m aerial, install an Asymmetrical Sloping Dipole, or even two or maybe three around your tower or mast, and don't forget the coaxial choke baluns at the feed-point. (Yes, you can also use ferrite toroids to decouple aerial currents from flowing down the coax shield, but they are much more expensive than a simple eight turns of coaxial cable air-wound with a 6in (15cm) diameter.

THE ASTCD AERIAL IS BORN

After the very successful experiments with ASDs, a more elaborate aerial was developed. I named it the 'Asymmetric Sloping Terminated Counterpoised Dipole', or ASTCD (**Fig 2**). This one is as easy to build and install as the regular ASD, but

shows more directivity and what appears to be a cleaner horizontal radiation pattern (yet to be tested at the aerial range).

This version of the ASD uses the same λ/4 on one arm of the dipole, and either 3λ/4, 5λ/4, or even 7λ/4 on the other arm. However, I prefer to stay at the 5λ/4 arm length, because the aerial will otherwise show a very sharp main horizontal lobe in the radiation pattern, something that might not be a very good idea when chasing DX on 6m!

The ASTCD includes two more elements, a terminating non-inductive resistor and a 3- or 5-wire λ/4 counterpoise fanning out at the end of the aerial to which the other side of the resistor is connected (**Fig 3**). These radials slope toward ground from the support pole at a 45° angle.

The 270Ω terminating resistor for the 50MHz version of the ASTCD was made from ten 2W carbon resistors of 2700Ω each, connected in parallel (the ideal theoretical value for the resistor is 240Ω, but any value between 200 and 300Ω will work here). One side of the terminating resistor is connected to the aerial's long arm, and the other side goes to the group of λ/4-wave radials described above.

This ASTCD aerial is certainly a very lightweight system for portable use, and it can use a tree or a not-too-tall mast or other structure as the high-end support, while the lower end needs only a very short 3ft (1m) high mast. The whole aerial – wire, coax, terminating resistor and counterpoise – plus the small mast, can easily be carried inside a backpack! Also, it will weigh much less than a 3- or 4-element Yagi or quad.

Field installation of this aerial is a cinch! Just decide the main direction in which you

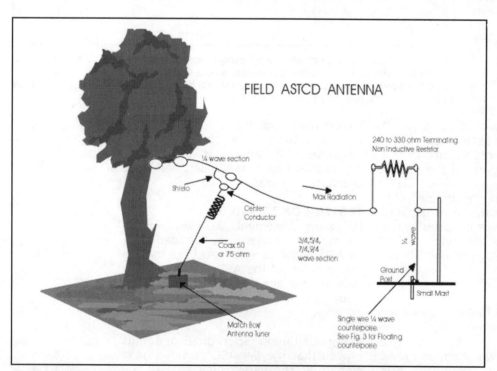

FIELD ASTCD ANTENNA

240 to 330 ohm Terminating Non Inductive Resistor

¼ wave section

Shield

Center Conductor

Max Radiation

Coax 50 or 75 ohm

3/4,5/4, 7/4,9/4 wave section

¼ wave

Ground Post

Small Mast

Match Box Antenna Tuner

Single wire ¼ wave counterpoise. See Fig. 3 for Floating counterpoise

Fig 2: The Asymmetric Sloping Terminated Counterpoised Dipole, or ASTCD, is a more elaborate version of the ASD, showing greater directivity in the direction in which the longer segment is pointing. Main differences are the addition of a terminating resistor and a counterpoise at the far end of the aerial.

want to try to work DX, hang the aerial with the long leg facing that direction, connect the coaxial cable to your aerial tuner (yes, it does help to use the tuner), and that's it! You can use the aerial without the tuner, as it will provide a very nice low VSWR all across the 50MHz band, but I do recommend using a simple π-network tuner.

My experiments with these aerials were on 6m, but the design will also work very well on any upper-HF band (see box for details).

WHAT ABOUT THE ASTCD AT HOME?

You can install not only one, but two or even three, ASTCDs at home, beaming in the most wanted directions, and provide for switching between them. This aerial seems to have not only a rather low TOA (take-off angle) in the direction at which it is pointing, but also a useful higher TOA, which explains why it works so well with *E*-skip signals.

If there is not enough space in one specific direction, install the shorter version λ/4 – 3λ/4 system. Best results will be obtained, though, with the λ/4 – 5λ/4 or the λ/4 –

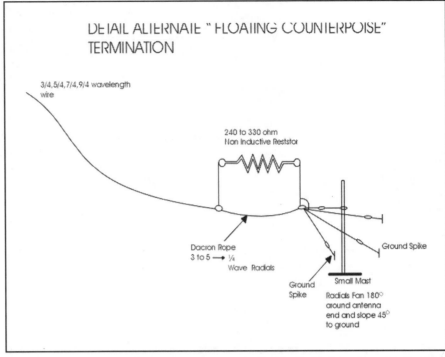

DETAIL ALTERNATE "FLOATING COUNTERPOISE" TERMINATION

3/4,5/4,7/4,9/4 wavelength wire

240 to 330 ohm Non Inductive Resistor

Dacron Rope 3 to 5 → ¼ Wave Radials

Ground Spike

Ground Spike

Small Mast

Radials Fan 180° around antenna end and slope 45° to ground

Fig 3: Detail of the 'floating counterpoise' alternative to the single-wire counterpoise shown at the bottom end of the aerial in Fig 2. This approach uses three to five λ/4 counterpoise wires arranged in a 180° 'fan' around the end of the aerial.

7λ/4 aerials with the terminating resistor and counterpoise.

Again, extending the aerial more than 7λ/4 wavelengths on the long arm of the dipole will make the horizontal pattern too sharp, something that may prove to be not a very good idea if you want to bring in DX from as many places as possible.

TIPS FOR INSTALLING THE ASD AND ASTCD AERIALS

- Keep the λ/4 element ('top' side of the aerial) at least 1m (3.28ft) away from the supporting structure.
- The coaxial cable should include a decoupling choke at the feed-point, either a coaxial choke balun (see main text), a ferrite bead decoupler, or a 1:1 balun.
- The coaxial cable should depart from the aerial at a 90° angle in order to reduce coupling from the radiating element.
- Select a tilt angle between 25 and 45°; experiments showed that a 30° tilt provided excellent directivity and a reasonable front-to-back ratio.
- Performance of both aerials will be very dependent on the surrounding objects, so try to have the long leg extending down into as clear an area as possible and pointing in the desired direction of radiation.
- Final tuning for minimum VSWR involves carefully pruning the length of the long side of the aerial. I found that once you set the short side to a resonant λ/4 at the centre operating frequency, final adjustments can be done by trimming the long sloping element.
- Whenever possible, use an aerial tuner, even if you achieve a 1.4 or 1.5 to 1 VSWR without the tuner!

THE 'SKYMISER' HF AERIAL

by John Ellerton, G3NCN

This aerial boasts little that is original, but it represents the results of a search for an adequate 1.8MHz aerial for housing-estate use, and is probably a solution likely to gain planning approval.

In my youth I lived in a village, in a house that possessed a 150ft garden and an unused field behind it. I never really thought how valuable the 270ft Windom aerial was that I was able to have. When I moved into the present QTH, some 30 years ago, I missed sorely the chance to have a good 1.8MHz aerial, having to be content with a trap vertical with poor radials.

Now that my family are grown and gone, I have taken up radio again and, faced with the same small site, have had to rethink the aerial solution. This is the result. Of course, aerials are never complete. There are always improvements to be tried, but this aerial is now at the first effective stage in its design life. It offers an effective space-saving solution for 1.8MHz - always my favourite band - and now one which I can often work with a possibility of success.

THE DESIGN
The aerial, with its basic layout shown in **Fig 1**, consists of a vertical section, fed at the top by a horizontal wire, the whole

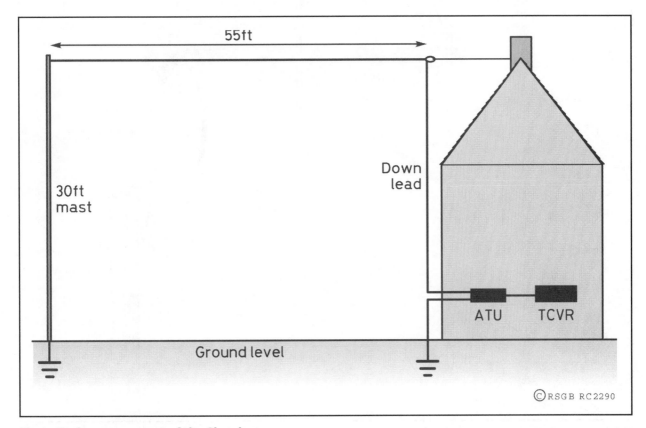

Fig 1. Basic arrangement of the Skymiser.

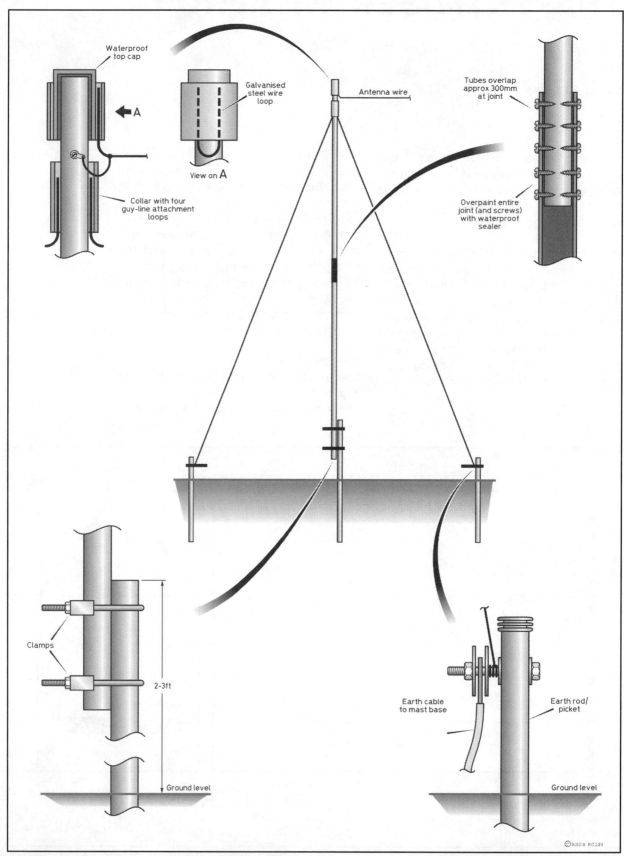

Fig 2. How the vertical section may be constructed (see text for description).

being tuned at the end by a conventional tuning arrangement. There is no complex high-*Q* matching unit, and no single-band solution. The aerial is simple to construct and will operate on all bands, but it is only a reasonably true vertical on 1.8MHz, possibly on 3.5MHz. I will leave it to the experts to calculate what the theoretical performance is! Though simple, you will not get away with anything less than hard work to put it up. This is because the secret of its successful operation will lie, not so much in the aerial, but rather in the earthing.

Development tuner for 1.8 and 3.5MHz, sitting on top of the MFJ tuner which is used on the other bands.

The aerial is electrically-continuous from the base of the mast to the shack. The horizontal wire is connected to the top of the mast directly (detail shown in **Fig 2**), ie not insulated. At the base of the mast and at the shack are independent earth systems.

At the base of the mast, the aerial is fastened by two TV aerial-type clamps to a 2in diameter stub mast about 5ft long, 3ft of which is driven into the ground.

The mast itself consists of two 15ft lengths of aluminium tube, the larger of which is 50mm diameter. The other length fits closely inside. The diameters are not critical, but the close fit of one tube inside the other is. The mast sections were obtained from a non-ferrous metal stockist. An overlap of about 300mm should be provided at the joint of the two sections, then the sections should be drilled and secured with self tapping screws (I used three rows of five screws, 120° apart).

At the top of the mast, a cap of fibreglass matting and epoxy resin is employed to keep out the rain. When this has hardened, a half-loop of galvanised coat hanger wire is formed and laid next to the cap. A collar of fibreglass matting is wound around the half loop and the cap, to secure it to the mast-head, then soaked in epoxy resin by stippling with a brush. The top section of the aerial will be fastened to this loop.

A second collar of fibreglass matting and resin is constructed just below the cap. Once it has cured, four half-loops of galvanised wire are placed on top of it and bound into place with a second layer of fibreglass matting, then soaked in epoxy resin (as was the cap). Guy lines will be fastened to these loops.

The earth rods (which double as pickets) are driven into the ground using a club hammer. The tubing may be expected to fold as it is driven into the ground. Drive in each rod with small, even blows, an even number of times around the top of the tube. Every few inches, remove the tube from the ground and remove any earth from inside the tube, then return it

One of the earth spikes, showing clearly how the tube can be made to collapse in a controlled fashion if it is driven into the ground carefully.

impedance is high - especially on 1.8MHz, where the length of the aerial approaches a quarter-wavelength, and also to some extent on 3.5MHz - so a special ATU was developed for the tuning task on those bands. For other bands, an MFJ tuner is used, in just the same way as it would be used for tuning any unbalanced long-wire aerial. The overall arrangement for tuning is shown in **Fig 3**.

When the MFJ ATU is used to tune the aerial, the output of the MFJ is connected directly to the aerial wire via S1, and the ATU is used with tuning elements selected. When connected for 1.8MHz, the aerial is connected to the top of the 'tank circuit', and the MFJ tuner (connected to the coil tap) is used without tuning elements. The VSWR meter of the ATU serves to indicate correct tuning in all cases.

The coil, L1, used for this tuner was an ex-transmitter tank tuning coil. Its diameter is 90mm, length 170mm, and it has 29 turns. The tap is set by a rotating 'finger' inside the coil which selects the appropriate turn for the tap. This is not wholly necessary, since the tapping point could be achieved by soldering a piece of wire onto the appropriate turn of a similar coil. The tuning capacitor, C1, is an ex-service wide-spaced twin-gang type (2 x 210pF). For 3.5MHz, it is used alone and, for 1.8MHz, it is in parallel with a high voltage 85pF fixed capacitor, C2. For 1.8MHz, the whole coil is used for tuning, and for 3.5MHz the top of the coil is at 22 turns from the earthy end.

EARTHING

At the shack end of the aerial, the transceiver system is earthed to three 4ft-long copper pipes, each driven into the ground adjacent to the house and connected together by 1in copper braid. A fourth earth pipe is added, which is connected to the transceiver directly, so as to preserve earth but avoid transmission of harmonics around the low-pass filter system.

At the aerial, the base of the mast is connected to a single 2in aluminium tubular post, driven about 3ft into the

to the ground and continue driving gently until the top of the tube is about 6in above the ground. Remove the rod one last time, and drill transverse holes through it at 6in intervals *below ground level* (the reason for this is explained later). Return the rods to the ground.

The guy lines - made from garden line - and earthing cables are fixed to the earth rods using stainless steel nuts, bolts and washers. All the fittings were purchased from Homebase.

This aerial is a true 'plumber's delight' construction. There are no complicated matching units at the base of the vertical and all controls are in the hands of the operator, so that changing frequency is as easy as tuning a long-wire aerial.

TUNING

Tuning is accomplished by an ATU in the shack. On some frequencies, the feed

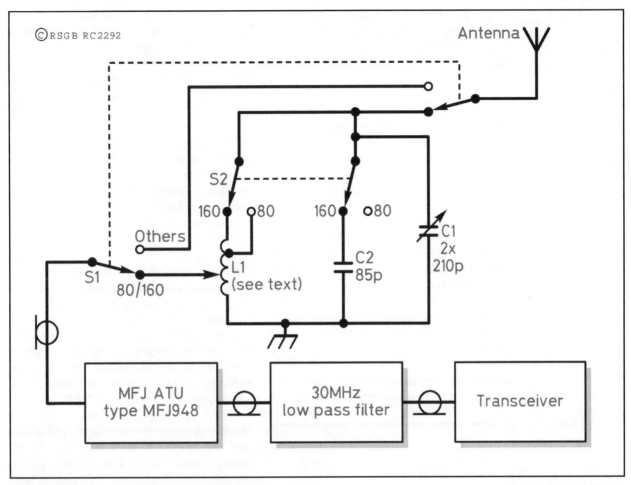

© RSGB RC2292

Fig 3. Tuning is accomplished on 1.8 and 3.5MHz using the home-made tuner. On other bands, the MFJ tuner suffices.

earth, which also serves as the main mast support. A further four 2in tubular posts, each 4ft long, are driven into the earth about 4ft away from the mast base and connected to the mast by thick copper cable (I used the strapped inner and outer of 50Ω coax for these connections). I later added a further five aluminium posts about 3ft long and about $^3/_4$in diameter. All posts are connected, star-fashion, to the mast base, using electricians' earth terminal straps to make the connections at the mast base itself. The connecting cables are laid in slit trenches, out of the reach of lawnmowers!

In installing the four 4ft, 2in-diameter tubular posts, each post was driven into the ground a few inches at a time, then extracted and the earth removed from the interior of the pipe. Repeating this every few inches until the pipe was almost completely buried, effectively drilled a 2in hole in the earth. Before finally inserting the post into the hole , the 2in pipe was drilled transversely with $^1/_4$in (6mm) diameter holes at regular intervals, below expected ground level. The purpose of these is that water, poured down the hollow interior of these earth pipes, would moisten the earth around them, thus keeping the earth resistance low even during dry summer conditions. (If the neighbours ask, the pipes are not expected to grow - even downwards - wonderful thought!)

HORIZONTAL SECTION/DOWNLEAD

The horizontal wire and downlead are made by twisting together 10 strands of 30SWG enamelled wire, which was fastened to a nail at one end, the other being clamped in a hand drill to effect the twisting action. The end connected to the mast top is mechanically tied to the mast, then the wire, terminated in a ring tag, is looped and the ring tag bolted to the masthead. This relieves strain on the electrical connection.

All connections of wire to the mast and between mast sections are painted with sealing paint of the kind used to make roofs waterproof. The horizontal aerial wire / downlead are multi-stranded, to reduce resistance due to RF skin effect.

CURRENT DISTRIBUTION

The diagrams of current distribution shown in **Fig 4** are visualised for 1.8, 3.5 and 7MHz. Practical tuning arrangements and behaviour tend to suggest that these hypotheses may be near to the truth! I am not an aerial expert, so would welcome further insights from those who know better.

On 1.8MHz, the aerial behaves as a top-fed vertical. Radiation tends to be omnidirectional, although currents in the horizontal section and feed-wire undoubtedly modify that.

Similar behaviour is expected on 3.5MHz, although modification of the omnidirectional characteristic will be greater, and some useful horizontally-polarised radiation helps in more local working (G and EU). Because of the length of the overall mast / wire combination being significantly less than $\lambda/2$, the feed-point impedance is high, and needs the special tuning arrangement, similarly to 1.8MHz.

On 7MHz, the vertical feed-wire and the mast team up to emulate two verticals out of phase, which my operating results suggest is true. The aerial gives good results east / west, in the plane of the mast and downlead. Some north / south radiation is also expected from the top section, but I believe this is higher-angle and therefore not so good for DX.

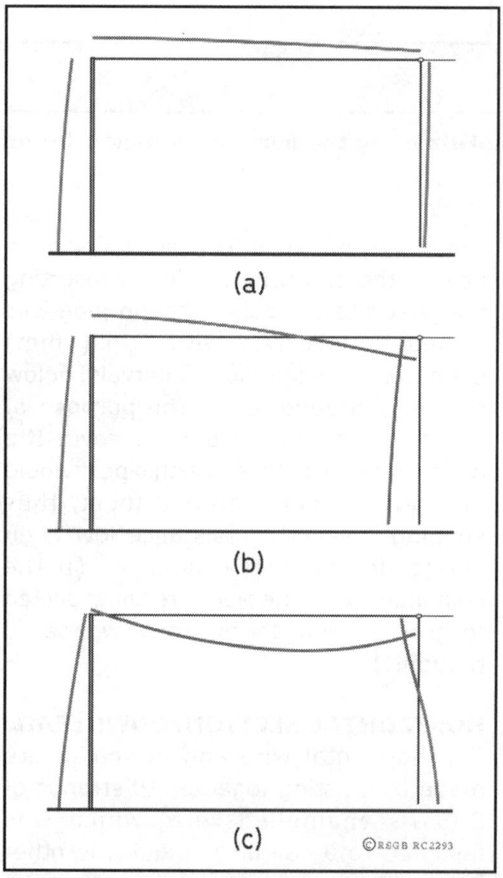

Fig 4. Imagined current distribution for (a) 1.8MHz, (b) 3.5MHz, and (c) 7MHz.

Modifying the length of the top to be 66ft and the masts to be 33ft long can be expected to enhance the phased vertical behaviour on 7MHz, and increase the gain along the plane of the mast / downlead. On 3.5MHz, the feed impedance should become lower and the MFJ tuner will more likely be used for tuning. On 1.8MHz, the special tuning unit will be necessary more than ever, because the feed impedance is expected to be raised as the length becomes closer to $\lambda/4$.

PRACTICAL RESULTS

The aerial was used for two years without taking serious consideration of the earthing system. It behaved tolerably well for G-working, but was not a competitive aerial by any stretch of the imagination. However, until I retired and made the time to develop the aerial, nothing could be done. The aerial was still the best solution for me, since the profile was low. A single mast with a thin horizontal wire makes very little impression on the neighbours! Certainly it is far more acceptable to the estate-dweller than a 50ft mast with a 3-element beam on top! Its consumption of sky space is really mean, hence the name.

The aerial had, moreover, the virtue that it was easy to tune on several bands using the MFJ tuner, and was a wonderful 'plumbers delight' aerial in that it needed no mast insulator, no base matching unit to control remotely, and nothing to waterproof. In fact, the wetter the better.

The gift of an old TV mast from a neighbour was the signal for manufacture of the earth system, and this produced a startling improvement in ground-wave signal strength as experienced by local stations. Obviously, the aerial was worthy of further development. Further 'earthworks' have been undertaken and, at present, the author is experimenting with $\lambda/4$ radials connected to the mast base which, after the initial significant leap, make progressively smaller improvements.

During the latter half of 1998 I was active on 1.8, 3.5 and 7MHz, using 100W. So far, I have worked plenty of USA stations on all three bands, Russians (both European and Asiatic), and one or two more exotic stations.

CONCLUSIONS

This aerial does not represent the highest gain, most DX-efficient aerial, but has proven itself as a very creditable estate solution. With its low profile, it is a relatively non-confrontational aerial when in close proximity to a number of neighbours, especially if the mast can be sited close to trees. It is easy to engineer, requires little adjustment, and performs well. It did not winkle out 9M0C from the huge pile-up and so far has not raised the VP8 station currently operating at the time of writing, but it does allow the estate dweller to hope for DX, local and EU operation on a number of bands.

Performance on higher frequencies has not yet been established, due to lack of operating time - life includes other things as well, even when one is retired, especially if one's XYL is retired too!

THE UA3IAR SWITCHABLE QUAD FOR 20m

by Jim Mackison, VK5MB

This versatile single-band aerial was designed and built by UA3IAR in Kalinin, USSR, and was described in the Russian magazine *Radio* in June, 1976. It also appeared in 'Technical Topics' in the RSGB journal *RadCom* in 1978.

Basically, the UA3IAR aerial is a two-element Quad array supported from a single pole. This is a Quad-type aerial that is fixed, requires no framework of self-supporting elements, and yet can be remotely switched so that the main lobe falls in any one of four quadrants. Since the unidirectional pattern is about 90° wide (between the -3dB points) this means that the array provides coverage through 360° with no turning delay.

The array is, in effect. a two-element Quad with a fed-reflector. The array is formed from four half-loops, which can be selected so that, at any time, two half-loops form the radiator and the other two the reflector. Four-position switching provides the four basic configurations for unidirectional beams. In each position, two half-loops form the driven element, while the other two form the driven reflector with its phasing section of transmission line.

Fig 1 shows the aerial for comparison with a conventional two element Quad. The upper vertices of the UA3IAR Quad are joined together, while the lower vertices form feed points. Guy wires pull out the middle portions of the loop. All wires, in fact, are held in place by guying rather than by a framework, and all wires are electrically connected together at the top of the array. The switching technique used

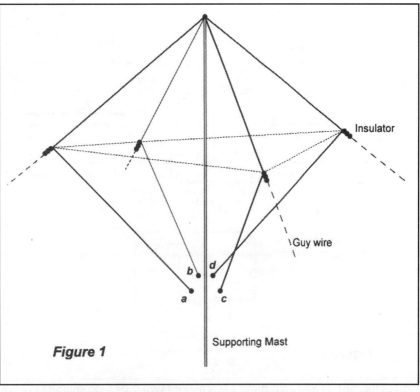

Figure 1

Fig 1: The UA3IAR switchable Quad aerial for 20m, which was developed from a conventional Quad. The four half-loops a, b, c and d, are electrically joined at the top. Pairs of half-loops are used to form the full-wave loops which function either as radiators or, with the additional phasing extensions, as driven reflectors.

by UA3IAR is shown in **Fig 2**. To form a unidirectional radiation pattern, it is necessary to provide a suitable phase difference between the currents flowing in the two loops. This phase difference is slightly more than 180°. The exact value of phase shift depends upon the effective spacing between the loops. with an initial phase difference of 180° being obtained by suitable connection to the appropriate windings of the ferrite core transformer, T1. Extra phasing elements are connected into the loop, forming the reflector elements, with all switching provided by relays, RLA and RLB. The switching sequence depends upon the position of the selector switch.

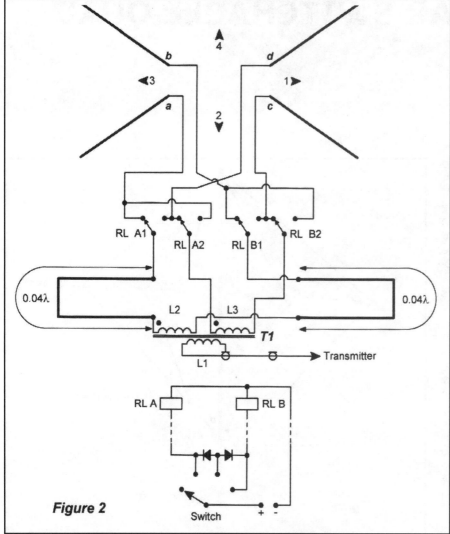

three other switch positions. Four vacuum relays connected in pairs are used by UA3IAR.

Contact rating of the relays is not important, as no aerial switching takes place with power applied to the aerial. Transformer, T1, is wound on a large toroid core. L1 has 10 turns, L2 and L3 have eight turns each. The aerial is fed with 75Ω coaxial line. A 30ft mast is used.

For 20m, the length of each half-loop of wire is 10.95m. The relays RLA and RLB are 24VDC, but any suitable voltage is acceptable. Four core cable was used from the aerial switching box to the shack. The relay power supply and control switch are installed in a metal box located in the shack.

I have used this aerial successfully for about 15 years.

Fig 2: The control and switching system. The two 0.04λ extensions are used to provide a 0.08λ phasing section to connect the appropriate loop into a reflector. T1 is a large ferrite core. Dots indicate the winding polarities. Wind L1 spaced around the complete core, and wind each of L2 and L3 on half the core. In the absence of relay energising voltage, the beam is set in direction 1.

In switch position 1, as drawn, both relays are un-energised and winding L2 of transformer, T1, is connected to half-loops a and b through the coaxial line phasing elements. In this fashion, two complete loops (ab and cd) are formed with ab acting as a reflector. In this example, the beam direction is that indicated by arrow 1. Arrows 2, 3 and 4 correspond to beam directions of the

The switch box and phasing

TRAP DIPOLES – INEXPENSIVE MULTIBAND AERIALS

by Dean Frazier, NH6XK

Most of us are 'taught' that traps are lossy and should be avoided. It is true that a trap made from very close-wound, thin wire will experience unacceptable losses but, if the turns are wide-spaced, and if more substantial wire is used, losses can be kept to a minimum; the advantages of multiband operation are obvious.

Trap dipoles are not all that difficult to build and make work, and their construction cost is minimal. You can work the world on them.

THE TRAP DIPOLE

A trap, consisting of a coil of inductance L in parallel with a capacitor C, and both in series with a radiator of varying RF energy, does several things. The trap has a natural resonant frequency, f_o, governed by the value of L and C, at which frequency the trap presents a high impedance. This will become significant later. Above f_o, the traps acts as a capacitor, while below it the trap acts as an inductor. 'Capacitive loading' as it is called, electrically shortens the aerial, while 'inductive loading' electrically lengthens the aerial. An electrically shortened aerial is physically longer than it would be without the electrical shortening; an electrically lengthened one is physically shorter.

These three phenomena, a trap's resonant frequency and high impedance at that frequency, its ability to electrically shorten (Xc) an aerial, and its ability to lengthen electrically (X_L) an aerial, allow us to make an aerial operate on more than one band, as an aerial's natural resonant frequency is a function of its electrical length.

So you're convinced a properly made trap dipole (or trap-any-aerial, since most are variations on dipoles) may have some merit. What's the fuss all about? Why not just buy one ready-made, or make one from someone else's design? Why design and build one yourself? For me the latter is more fun; when you sit down and

generate a design, and then build it, and discover that it works. What follows is my method for accomplishing just that... building a trap dipole to work on specific bands. But first, a bit of designing is in order.

DESIGN

Suppose you require a trap dipole which will operate on 10 to 80m. If the aerial was an electrical quarter-wave on 80m, all the other main bands would be possible, as they are multiples of such quarter waves, and the WARC bands should be achievable with a ATU. Now, to be a quarter-wave on 80m forces the aerial to be a half-wave electrically on 40m. This becomes our starting point in design. See the box for band and fractional wavelength values.

The design itself is straightforward (**Fig 1**). Half-wave on 40m is about 19.8m. Half this, for each leg of the dipole, out to the traps, is 9.9m. Call this length 'A'. We make the traps such that they are resonant at 7.2MHz, thus offering a high impedance to a 40m (7.2MHz) signal, effectively divorcing from the aerial sections 'B' (the remaining length of wire on each leg of the aerial), with the result that, from coil-to-coil, we have a half-wave 40m dipole.

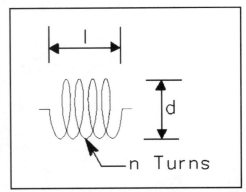

Fig 1. Trap coil dimensions, for use in the equations.

Next, we choose a value of capacitance, C, for trap resonance at 7.2MHz. Experience has shown that 100pF works well at this frequency. Of course, we must use a capacitor (one in each coil) which will handle our power requirements.

5000VDC transmitting capacitors are recommended.

Then, recalling that

$$f_0 = \frac{1}{2\pi\sqrt{LC}},$$

we solve for the inductance, L, required for resonance:

$$L = \frac{1}{4\pi^2 f^2 C} = \frac{1}{4\pi^2 (7.2)^2 (100)} = 4.9\mu\text{H},$$

(using f in MHz and C in pF).

We thus need to design two identical coils of 4.9μH each, one for each leg of the aerial. A coil of 12 or 14SWG wire wound to the correct length, of the correct number of turns, on 65mm PVC tubing, serves our purpose. The capacitor can be housed in the tube.

But how long should our coil be? How many turns of wire? Again, we resort to formulæ. A fairly good approximation for inductance, L (in μH), as a function of an air-wound coil's diameter, d (in mm), length, l (mm), and number of turns of wire, n, is as follows [1]:

$$L = \frac{d^2 n^2}{457d + 1016l},$$

Stated another way:

$$n = \sqrt{\frac{L(457d + 1016l)}{d^2}},$$

(see Fig 1).   If we make l=54mm, knowing d=65mm, then:

$$n = \sqrt{\frac{4.9(457 \times 65 + 1016 \times 54)}{65^2}} = 10 \text{ turns}.$$

This turns out to be not quite five turns per 25mm of coil (see **Fig 2**). How much wire do we use up in a coil? Well, each turn uses $65\pi/1000$m of wire, so 10 turns use

$$\frac{65\pi}{1000} \times 10 = 2.04\text{m}.$$

Now all we need to do is calculate the remaining leg length, B. To do so is easy if we realize that the distance from the feed-point to the end of the aerial needs to be an electrical quarter-wavelength on (in this example) 80m, and we've already used up wire in the coil and on the inner leg, A.

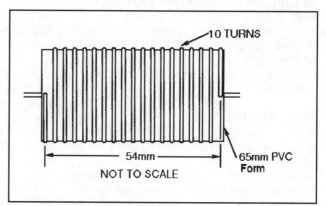

Fig 2. Winding details.

This is how our final trap dipole design looks (see **Fig 3**).

After this rather long design dissertation, relax. For other combinations of bands of operation I've done the calculations for you. See **Table 1** for the various design parameters you need to build your own trap dipole.

CONSTRUCTION DETAILS

Wind the required number of turns to the required length on 65mm OD PVC tubing, and fix the wire in place. Holes drilled in the ends of the tube through which the wire is passed serve as strain relief. The capacitor is soldered from coil end to coil end, and is housed inside the tube. The PVC tube ends may be capped for water tightness, and electrical tape can be wrapped around the outside of the coil and wire. Alternatively, the entire trap may be housed in a lightweight plastic container. Much construction ingenuity and creativity is possible here.

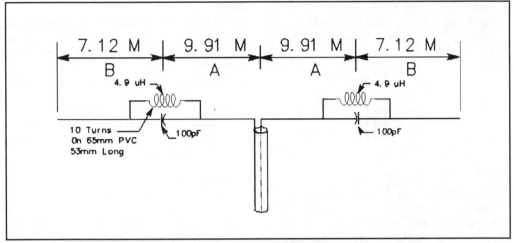

Fig 3. Final dimensions and component values (see Table 1).

| Band (m) | Leg lengths (m) | | Trap data | |
	A	B	Coil	Capacitor
80, 40, 30, 20, 17, 15, 12, 10	9.9	7.12	10t 65mm PVC 54mm long	100pF, 5kVDC mica
40, 30, 20, 17, 15, 12, 10	5.02	3.50	7t 65mm PVC 51mm long	50pF 5kVDC mica
30, 20, 17 15,12, 10	3.94	2.12	5t 65mm PVC 38mm long	50pF 5kVDC mica
20, 17, 15, 12, 10	3.35	0.86	4t 65mm PVC 29mm long	50pF 5kVDC mica
17, 15, 12, 10	2.85	0.44	4t 50mm 29mm long	50pF 5kVDC mica

Table 1: **Winding details.**

TUNING AND TRIMMING

Ideally, one builds a trap and then stretches or compresses the coil windings either to raise or lower (respectively) the trap's resonant frequency, checking with a grid dip oscillator, noise bridge, or frequency counter. Failing these devices, one can get a fair measure of how close to the design resonant frequency is the trap (with leg 'A' in place) by applying low power and noting the VSWR at the aerial feed point (or at the transceiver, provided the coax feed-line is a multiple of a half wave on the design frequency), and making a plot of VSWR as a function of frequency to determine where the SWR curve 'bottoms out'. Most hams use this latter method.

So what do you do if you find that your almost-finished aerial (we have not added lengths 'B' yet) shows lowest VSWR at (say) 7.0MHz when we desired 7.2MHz? Shortening of legs 'A' equally on each side of the feed point, is required. Detuning agents (wood, metal) in the field of the aerial are causing it to resonate too low in frequency.

Once you get the aerial (from the feed-point out to the traps) resonant on (in my model) 40m at or near the desired frequency, add lengths 'B' to each leg and test the entire aerial for lowest VSWR on 80m (3.75MHz). You'll note little change, if any, to your 40m VSWR 'low point' (recall that the traps, being resonant at 7.2MHz, offer a high impedance to a 7.2MHz signal).

Do all of this trimming either with the aerial in its ultimate location, or at least in a clear space away from detuning agents (buildings, trees, metal fences, etc)

Band (m)	Wave fraction
80	$\lambda/4$
40	$\lambda/2$
30	$3\lambda/4$
20	λ
17	$5\lambda/4$
15	$3\lambda/2$
12	$7\lambda/4$
10	2λ

Notice that to get 80m, we design for a half-wave on 40m, which results in a quarter-wave on 80m, so we will have multiples of the lowest frequency $\lambda/4$, to accommodate all the other bands, in steps of $\lambda/4$ of the lowest frequency (80m), as this is how the HF bands are related.

and for best all-round operation, the final feed point height should be as high as you can manage. Unless you achieve a half-wave on a band, you won't experience the text book figure-of-eight radiation pattern, but such does not mean you won't be able to operate with the feed-point not quite so high. It just means, among other things, that your radiation pattern will be more omnidirectional.

Experiment with tuning straight through from radio to aerial and/or via tuner. On some bands you'll be able to operate straight through with low VSWR; others will require the tuner's help to match impedances. I suggest that you use the tuner all the time, however; although you induce a minor signal loss this way, you also clean up spurious harmonics to some extent, resulting in a cleaner, sharper audio, and less TVI/RFI problems.

IMPEDANCE

Using the data of Table 1, the trap dipole radiation resistance can be as high as 100Ω and as low as 25Ω depending on the aerial feed-point height at your particular QTH, which represents an VSWR range of 2:1 to 1:1. The tuners in modern radios can easily handle VSWR mismatches up to 3:1. Because of this, I have found the use of 50Ω coax for the feed-line to be satisfactory.

SUMMARY

So there you have it. Although the example given was for 80 - 10m, the methodology applies to other band ranges in exactly the same manner. You make a dipole and a trap for a specific band. Then you add wire for the next band lower in frequency. On the higher band the trap 'cuts off' the outer wire. On the lower band the signal doesn't 'see' the trap. You're back to a dipole for that band. That's really about all there is to it. Some shortening of the 'B' sections will be required, because of the shortening effect induced by the traps, but the Table 1 data will give you a good starting point.

So now you're saying "Phooey... I can buy one of these things for peanuts. ..so why go to all this trouble?". Sure, you can purchase an 'off-the-shelf' model and it will most likely work from the moment you hook up your feed-line. But doing this, you won't be able to say your aerial is homebrew!

REFERENCE

1. *ARRL Handbook*, 77th ed, p6.22, (ARRL), 2000.

THE G3RXO 'UNITENNA'

by R D Brown, G3RXO

While touring New Zealand some years ago, I needed a portable all-band HF aerial and conceived the following design concept (see **Fig 1**), which produced surprisingly good results. Back in the UK, I did have time to construct and test it and it worked surprisingly well. It is extremely cheap, extremely light, and works continuously over an extremely broad bandwidth. It is non-resonant, vertically polarised and out-performs a ground plane throughout a 3:1 frequency range. Accepting a loss of some 3dB from a ground plane, its usable frequency range is some 5:1. It has very low angles of radiation throughout the range, requires no radials, and is not susceptible to static.

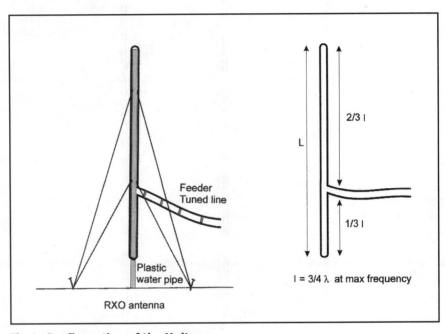

Fig 1: Configuration of the Unitenna.

My thinking was along the following lines.

(1)   Consider a vertical dipole, its current distribution and resultant polar diagram.

(2)   Consider it as a folded dipole.

(3)   Consider its current distribution (**Fig 2**) and polar diagram if it is fed off-centre. The dissimilar currents in the two elements of the dipole are within one evanescent induction field and are therefore cumulative with regard to radiation, which can give rise to an overall current distribution and polar diagram which change very little with change of frequency.

(4)   By feeding at approximately one-third of the way along the dipole, the current distribution and polar diagram vary approximately from that of a vertical dipole to that of a vertical quarter-wave over a frequency range of some 3:1; for example, from 7MHz to 21MHz.

(5)   Above the aerial's maximum usable frequency, the polar diagram becomes split and of high angle.

(6)   As the applied frequency is reduced below its normal range, the polar diagram remains much as for a vertical quarter-wave, but with diminishing efficiency, although still useful over a frequency range of some 5:1.

(7)   Since the aerial is a closed loop, it is less susceptible to static.

(8)   It requires no radials and therefore incurs no ground losses.

(9)   It is fed with a tuned line, which should be perpendicular to the aerial.

(10)   Variation of the feed point to about 25% from the aerial's end results in slightly better current distribution, but reduced bandwidth.

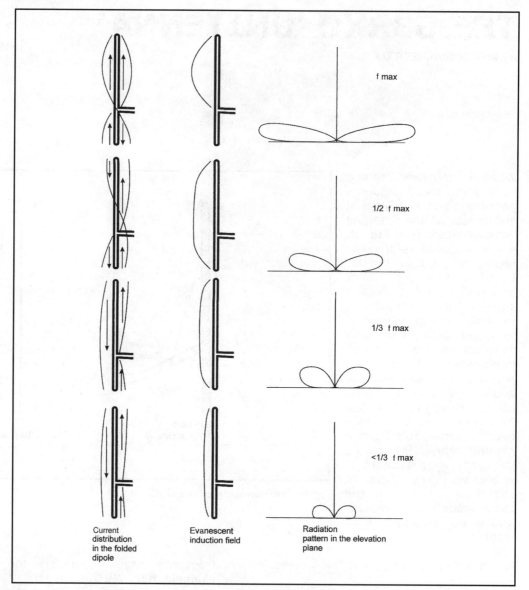

Fig 2: Polar diagrams for various distributions of current.

The optimum point is around 30 - 35% from the end.

(11) It is cheap to produce, lightweight, portable, unobtrusive and has virtually no power limits.

The original aerial was made of regular single-core conductor taped down each side of lengths of plastic waste pipe and guyed with bricklayer's line. For example, practical dimensions are a 9.2m dipole,

fed 3m from base and about 1m above ground; coverage 7MHz to 21MHz continuously with full efficiency. Pro-rata for other frequency ranges.

I found the aerial to be surprisingly quiet with respect to background noise and very effective at low angles and long range. I hope that others will give this design a try and would be most interested to learn of their results with it.

WIDEBAND 80m DIPOLE

by Rudy Severns, N6LF

The 500kHz width of the 80m band makes it by far the widest HF amateur band on a percentage basis - 13% of the centre frequency. Over the years, a legion of articles has described aerials that purported to provide a VSWR of less than 2:1 over the whole band. Some did, some didn't. With my two transceivers - a Drake TR7 and Yaesu FT757GX - even a 2:1 VSWR wasn't low enough because the rigs automatically began to reduce output power before a 2:1 VSWR was reached. I suspect this is not an uncommon occurrence with other rigs (not equipped with built-in automatic aerial tuners) as well.

What's really needed is an aerial that provides a VSWR below 1.6 or 1.7 over the entire band. It'd be really convenient to jump from one end of the band to the other without having to think about adjusting the aerial tuner or rig, or buying an automatic aerial tuner. Such a requirement makes aerial design tough!

The following is a description of an aerial that meets the need. This one has been built - and it works well with no noticeable VSWR degradation caused by rain, snow, wind or other elements. Surprisingly, it's a simple wire aerial that's only as long as a standard dipole.

EARLIER AERIALS

My idea has its roots in two well-known aerials - the open-sleeve dipole [1 – 3] and the folded dipole [4]. With an open-sleeve dipole, additional conductors are added in close proximity to - but not connected to - a common single-wire dipole, as shown in **Fig 1**. In addition to the fundamental resonance of the simple dipole, the added conductors create new resonances. This effect can be used to multi-band or broad-band an aerial - and it's an idea that's been around since WWII.

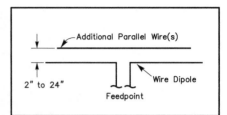

Fig 1: Open-sleeve dipole.

A folded dipole's bandwidth is greater than a single-wire dipole made of the same wire size. Although the bandwidth attainable with a folded dipole is better, by itself it's still not good enough for our needs. **Fig 2** shows the typical VSWR plot for a folded dipole, using 12in element spacing, #14 wire and centred on 3.750MHz. This aerial's 2:1 VSWR bandwidth is

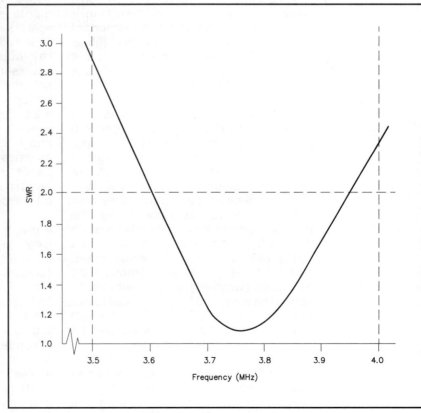

Fig 2: Typical VSWR for a folded dipole resonant at 3.75MHz.

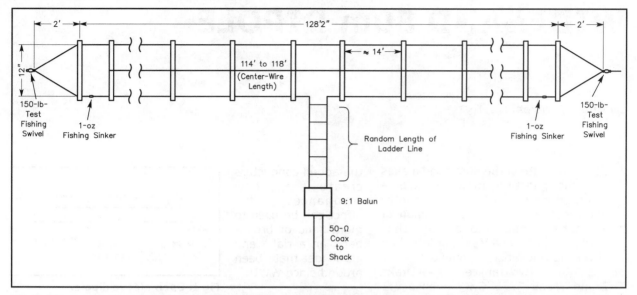

Fig 3: The open-sleeve folded dipole – simple and inexpensive. The aerial is fed with a random length of 450Ω open-wire transmission line through a 9:1 balun.

approximately 375kHz. You can improve things a bit by using greater element spacing, but then the weight and length of the spacers gets to be inconvenient and you still won't have sufficient bandwidth.

AERIAL HEIGHT

One common problem with any 80m aerial is installing it high enough to do some good. Because the current maximum is at the centre of the dipole, it's important to keep that part of the aerial as high as possible. For most installations, 70ft is pretty high, but at 80m, 70ft is only one quarter of a wavelength.

A dipole's radiation angle is largely determined by the height of its centre. If the aerial is strung between two supports, there's bound to be some sag, height is lost and the radiation angle raised. Weight of any sort - baluns, long lengths of coax, matching networks, etc, particularly near the aerial's centre - contribute to sag. The resultant high-angle radiation is great for local QSOs, but bad news for DXing. If I can't provide support for the aerial centre, I prefer to use lightweight transmitting twin-lead (weighing in at 2.4lb/100ft, versus the 9.4lb/100 ft of RG-8 coax), with the balun at ground level. The 450Ω ladder-line is quite efficient, relatively light and costs much less than coax.

The feed-point impedance of a folded dipole is about 300Ω. Although 300Ω ladder-line is available, making the transition from 300Ω to 50Ω requires a

6:1 balun. Such baluns can be bought or made, but 4:1 or 9:1 baluns are much more common.

A BROAD-BAND 80m AERIAL

The aerial I came up with is shown in **Fig 3**. It's simply an open-sleeve version of the folded dipole. The resonator wire added midway between the two folded dipole elements is supported by the spacers already used for the folded dipole. That's all there is to it; a single wire down the middle of a folded dipole! One interesting result of adding the wire is that not only is the aerial very broad-band but, by juggling the spacing and wire lengths a bit, Z_r is very close to 450Ω, which fits in nicely with available transmission lines and a 9:1 balun. The transmission line operates with a very low VSWR and can be of virtually any length. Several advertisers offer 450Ω open-wire transmission line.

A graph of the measured VSWR for two lengths of the centre wire (L_c) is shown in **Fig 4**. The measurements were made with considerable care, using Bird wattmeters. For L_c = 118ft, the highest VSWR is 1.5, and is less than that over most of the band. For L_c = 114ft, the worst-case VSWR is 1.8, but the overall 2:1 bandwidth is extended to 800kHz. Experimenting further, I shortened L_c to 112ft, which pushed the 2:1 bandwidth up to nearly 1MHz (3.3 to 4.25MHz). For most hams, that may not be of great importance, but it's something to keep in mind. Fig 3 shows the number and separation of the wire spacers. It's important to keep the spacers as light (and inexpensive!) as possible. The two spacers on each end have to be fairly stiff, so I used sections cut from solid fibre-glass electric-fence wands [5]. The rest of the spreaders are made from half sections of $^{1}/_{2}$in CPVC plastic pipe. They're about half the weight of the fibre-glass wand spreaders. I could have used full sections of the CPVC pipe for the end spreaders but, for the same weight, they would have had more wind loading.

SUMMARY

Modelling this aerial, which is essentially a transmission line, doesn't work very well on *MININEC*-based programs [6]. NEC programs such as *NECWIRES* [7] are needed, and even then, you have to use 50 to 100 segments per $\lambda/2$ for the final design. Using *NECWIRES*, the total computed loss was only 0.07dB (1.6%) for #14 wire and 0.09dB (2%) for #16. Combined with the very low loss of the open-wire transmission line, if a good three-core, 9:1 Guanella balun [8] is used, the overall efficiency will be quite good.

At best, these aerials will be close to the ground in terms of wavelengths. The ground effects are important and will affect the impedances and final dimensions. This aerial was modelled at a height of 70ft over poor ground (ε_r= 13, σ = 2mS), which corresponds (more or less) to my location and support height. I only had to adjust the centre wire a bit to get the predicted performance. At another location or aerial height, the final performance and dimensions may be different.

A folded dipole loves to rotate when being hoisted and it twists when the wind blows, which really upsets the VSWR if the parallel wires short together. In Fig 3, I've included a couple of details that help reduce this problem. The ends of the dipole are not symmetrical. To aid in avoiding aerial twist, 1oz fishing sinkers are added to the bottom wire on each end. I also use two heavy-duty (150lb capacity) fishing-line swivels at the aerial support points.

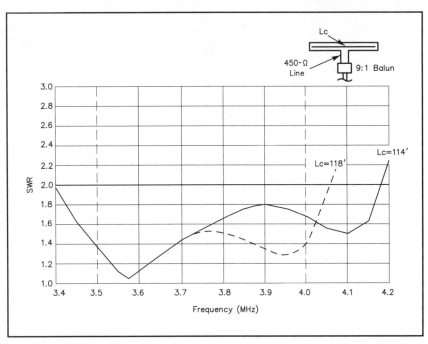

Fig 4: VSWR curve of the open-sleeve dipole of Fig 3, showing curves for different lengths of the centre wire, L$_c$.

NOTES

[1]   R Cox, WB0DGF, 'The Open-Sleeve Antenna: Development of the Open-Sleeve Dipole and Open-Sleeve Monopole for HF and VHF Amateur Applications', *CQ*, Aug 1983, pp13-19.

[2]   G Breed, K9AY, 'Multi-Frequency Antenna Technique Uses Closely Coupled Resonators', *RF Design*, Nov 1994, pp78-85.

[3]   B Orr, W6SAI, 'Radio Fundamentals - the Open Sleeve Dipole', *CQ*, Feb 1995, pp94-98.

[4]   R D Straw, N6BV, Ed, *The ARRL Antenna Book* (ARRL, 17th ed, 1994), p2-32.

[5]   These wands, which measure $^{3}/_{8}$in diameter, are 4 feet long, are usually available from farming supply stores and Sears.

[6]   *ELNEC* is available from Roy Lewallen, W7EL, PO Box 6658, Beaverton, OR 97007. *AO 6.1* is available from Brian Beezley, K6STI, 3532 Linda Vista Dr, San Marcos, CA 92069.

[7]   *NECWIRES* is available from Brian Beezley, K6STI; see Note 6.

[8]   J Sevick, W2FMI, *Transmission Line Transformers* (ARRL, 2nd ed, 1990), p9-28.

THE W3RW 6m AND 10m LONG WIRE

by Bob Witmer, W3RW

My favourite wire aerial - in terms of overall ruggedness, simplicity and pattern coverage-is a 4λ long wire. In the spring of 1999, with the sunspot cycle improving, I decided I needed an aerial that would also provide some gain over a dipole on 10m. With this goal in mind, I investigated how to make a long-wire aerial that works well on 6 and 10m. Here's what I found.

WHY USE A LONG-WIRE AERIAL?

Wire aerials are among the easiest to install and use (and arguably lowest in cost), but most hams don't think of using long-wire aerials on VHF. Long-wire aerials can be used on VHF - particularly on 6m - as easily as on the HF bands. The following paragraphs

The aerial in action.

describe typical long-wire gain and pattern characteristics; feed-point characteristics are discussed later.

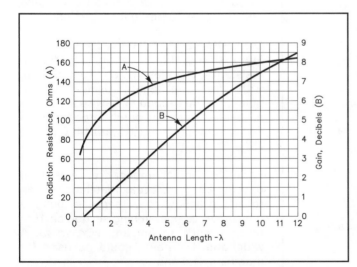

Fig 1. The variation in radiation resistance and power in the major lobe of harmonic (long-wire) aerials. Curve A shows the change in radiation resistance with aerial length, as measured at a current loop, while B shows the power gain in the lobes of maximum radiation for long-wire aerials as a ratio to the maximum of a λ/2 aerial.

GAIN

Aerials more than a couple of wavelengths long at the operating frequency exhibit gain over a dipole. The maximum lobe of an aerial 4λ long has an estimated gain over a dipole of approximately 3dB (3dBd); see **Fig 1**. The estimated gain for other multiple-wavelength wire aerials varies. A 3λ aerial should have a gain of slightly more than 2dBd; a 5λ aerial exhibits a gain of about 4dBd.

PATTERNS

With the gain increase comes a change in the aerial's radiation pattern. Along the axis of the wire, there is a narrowing and increase in the amplitude of

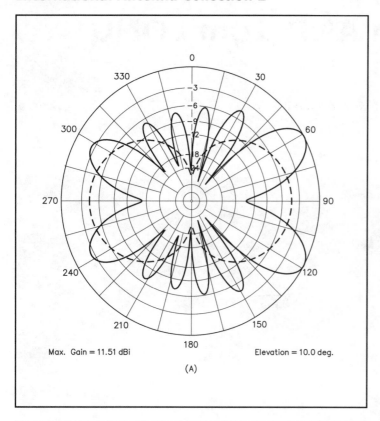

(A)

Max. Gain = 11.51 dBi   Elevation = 10.0 deg.

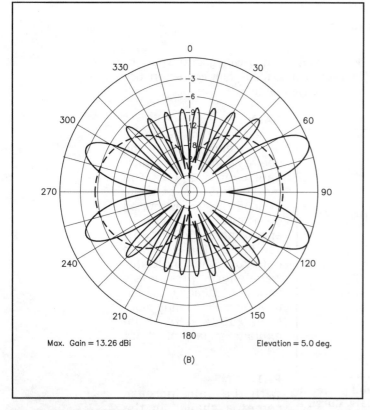

(B)

Max. Gain = 13.26 dBi   Elevation = 5.0 deg.

Fig 2. Predicted horizontal radiation patterns of a long-wire aerial as a function of length. (A) Pattern of a 50ft-high, 3λ long wire (solid lines) compared to that of a dipole (dashed). (B) Pattern of a 50ft-high 5λ long-wire aerial (solid lines) compared to that of a dipole (dashed). (N6BV)

the gain lobes compared to those of a typical dipole aerial's broadside pattern. Also, there's an increase in the number of lobes (and nulls) that provides somewhat omnidirectional coverage. **Fig 2** shows some theoretical pattern comparisons.

DUAL-BAND LONG-WIRE DESIGN CONSTRAINTS
By changing which trees I used to support my wire aerial, I had room (just over 105ft) to put up an aerial longer than the original 77ft, 4λ aerial. After playing with the aerial-length formulas, I found that a 3λ, 10m-long wire or a 5λ, 6m-long wire would fit. Both aerials provide the gain I was looking for - but I didn't have the room to put up both!

EUREKA! THE DUAL-BAND LONG-WIRE AERIAL
Like the 4λ, 6m-long-wire aerial, I wanted a configuration with its feed-point at a current loop (λ/4 from one end of the aerial) to present a low-impedance to the feed-line. This approach essentially separates the aerial into a 'long' section and a λ/4 section. After examining the individual 3λ and 5λ aerial dimensions using 28.35MHz and 50.15MHz as frequencies of operation, it became clear that these aerials have one thing in common: the long sections are almost equal in length. With that in mind, I came up with a dual-band long-wire aerial design (see **Fig 3**) that uses ladder-line as part of the λ/4 sections for each band and shares a common long section.

DUAL-BAND MATCHING ISSUES
Fig 1 shows the variation of radiation resistance, as measured at a current loop, with wire aerial length. Using this as a guide, the dual-band long-wire aerial has a theoretical feed-point impedance of about 125Ω on 10m (3λ) and 140Ω on 6m (5λ).

Either feed-point impedance lends itself to using a λ/4, 75Ω coax matching section to match a 50Ω coax feed-line, but the typical λ/4 coax matching section on 10m doesn't work on 6m and *vice versa*. A wideband 4:1 balun could be used for matching, but the
resulting impedance transfer would probably not be as close to 50Ω as the λ/4 matching technique provides. Also, most 4:1 baluns are relatively heavy, adding to aerial sag.

Wideband 4:1 baluns are also expensive compared to the cost of 20 to 30ft of coax. So, I decided to evaluate other approaches.

EUREKA AGAIN! THE DUAL-BAND COAX MATCHING SECTION

I thought of the dual-band matching solution when I decided to experiment by adding a number of λ/2 coax sections after the 6m and 10m λ/4 sections. Comparisons showed that there is a combination of λ/4 and λ/2 transmission-line sections that results in total coax lengths for each band that are almost the same. (See **Fig 4** and the box 'Characteristics of Half-Wavelength Transmission Lines'.)

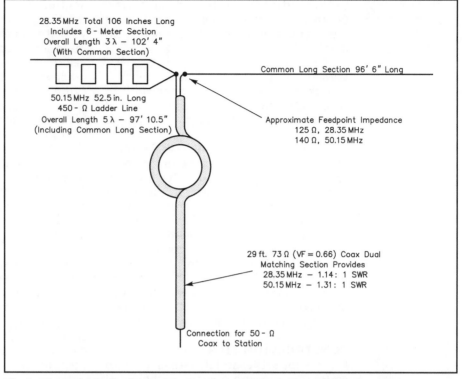

28.35 MHz Total 106 Inches Long Includes 6 - Meter Section Overall Length 3 λ − 102' 4" (With Common Section)

50.15 MHz 52.5 in. Long 450 - Ω Ladder Line Overall Length 5 λ − 97' 10.5" (Including Common Long Section)

Common Long Section 96' 6" Long

Approximate Feedpoint Impedance 125 Ω, 28.35 MHz 140 Ω, 50.15 MHz

29 ft. 73 Ω (VF = 0.66) Coax Dual Matching Section Provides 28.35 MHz − 1.14: 1 SWR 50.15 MHz − 1.31: 1 SWR

Connection for 50 - Ω Coax to Station

Fig 3. The W3RW dual-band long-wire aerial. At 28.35MHz, the total aerial length is 102ft 4in (3λ). At 50.15MHz, the overall aerial length is 5λ (97ft 10.5in).

The total lengths of the two coax sections are close enough that the combination match works for the frequency pair of 28.35 and 50.15 MHz, although frequencies of 50 and 29.9 MHz provide an optimum calculated dual match. With the combination of the dual-band matching section and the dual-band long wire, an overall good match to 50Ω line is obtained over the low-frequency ends of 6 and 10m.

ON-THE-AIR PERFORMANCE: DOES IT WORK?

The system appears to work well - just like individual 6m and 10m long wires! With the long-wire aerial's maximum-strength lobes favouring the north / south directions, I use a two-element 6m quad in the attic to provide extra gain to the west.

Although there are directions in which the quad is significantly better than the dual-band long wire, I've found that the long wire can hear everything the quad can

hear, including some signals the quad doesn't.

My first QSO with the aerial came just after I finished making some adjustments. With my IC-706 connected directly to the end of the coax matching section, I answered a station in upstate New York calling CQ on 50.125MHz. He came right back to me and we exchanged good signal reports (he was off the slightly weaker major lobe's end of the aerial). After that, I switched

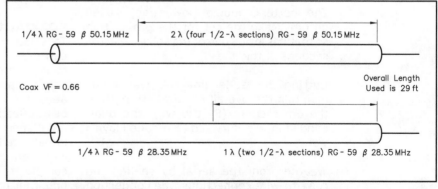

1/4 λ RG - 59 β 50.15 MHz   2 λ (four 1/2 - λ sections) RG - 59 β 50.15 MHz

Coax VF = 0.66

Overall Length Used is 29 ft

1/4 λ RG - 59 β 28.35 MHz   1 λ (two 1/2 - λ sections) RG - 59 β 28.35 MHz

Fig 4. The W3RW dual-band matching section. Lengths shown here are for coax with a velocity factor of 0.66. The upper cable leg consists of a 50.15MHz λ/4 section of RG-59 coax in series with a 50.15MHz 2λ section (four λ/4 lines in series) of RG-59 coax. The lower leg is a 28.35MHz λ/4 of RG-59 coax in series with a 28.35MHz 1λ section (two λ/2 lines in series) of RG-59.

to 10m and proceeded to work quite a few South and Central American stations in the mainline of the aerial's stronger gain lobes.

With the help of a small aerial tuner, I stretched the aerial's 10m bandwidth to cover the repeater segment and proceeded to work several additional stations.

As I write this, the September VHF contest and hurricane Floyd's visit occurred about two months ago. I didn't actively participate in the contest, but I did use it to check the aerial's 6m performance. With a transmitter RF output of 100W, I found I could work everything I heard, including several sporadic-E contacts late one Sunday, but I did have to use a 400W amplifier to make an auroral contact. Ten-metre performance has been great! I've had no trouble working most DX I can hear from all over, with just 100W output.

CONSTRUCTION TIPS

Fig 3 shows the aerial details (not to scale). Cut the wire sections of the aerial a little long and wrap the far ends of the extra wire lengths back onto the main wire. This way, if you need to lengthen the aerial, you just unwrap the extra wire; you don't have to worry about adding more wire. If the aerial is too long, simply wrap more wire back onto the main run to reduce the aerial's overall length.

I started out with a little more than 5ft of 450Ω 16SWG stranded copper-clad ladder line for the $\lambda/4$ aerial section, allowing for connection to the centre insulator and the 10m wire extension.

As shown in Fig 3, one conductor of the 450Ω line (the upper one) is used on 10m. The shorter conductor (lower one) is used on 6m. Make the cut for the 6m section so that it is inside one of the solid-dielectric sections of the line.

Cutting the ladder-line this way helps maintain the overall physical strength of the 6m section. (By the way, the dual-band long wire survived Hurricane Floyd's visit!)

Weatherproof the aerial by sealing the coax-to-wire connections, the connection between the matching-section coax and the 50Ω feed-line, and the connections at the ends of the matching section. Use a low-loss 50Ω cable between the matching

section and your shack. To cut the matching line properly, you must know the velocity factor of the 75Ω coax! The matching section I use is made of 0.66 velocity factor RG-59 coax, but cables with other velocity factors can be used as well. (When selecting the matching-section coax, remember that the centre conductor in foam-dielectric coax has a tendency to migrate, potentially resulting in a short to the shield if the coax provides some structural support or is coiled.) I took the precaution of verifying the coax velocity factor by cutting an approximate $\lambda/4$ section and checking its length and frequency characteristics using a dip meter.

Larger-diameter 75Ω coax (such as RG-11) can be used if you want lower loss, but the cable is heavier than RG-59, and will likely increase the aerial sag. Interestingly, the data tables for coaxial cable show that the loss of many RG-59 coax types is similar to, or slightly lower than, RG-8X coax types at 50 MHz.

ADJUSTMENT

To tune the aerial, first adjust the lengths of the $\lambda/4$ sections, then adjust the long-wire sections to minimize the VSWR on both bands. Then check the $\lambda/4$-section lengths again. It takes no more than a couple of iterations to achieve the lowest VSWR on both bands. The exact length of the dual-band coax matching section doesn't appear to be critical. I cut the matching section a little longer than 29ft (using 0.66 velocity-factor coax) to provide the extra length needed for the connections to the wire and ladder-line sections and for the end coax connector. The resulting match was close enough to not require adjustment.

COAXIAL CHOKE BALUN

To isolate the feed-line from the radiating currents of the aerial, I use a choke balun consisting of 4ft of the matching-section coax wrapped in four turns just below the aerial feed-point. This approach may not be as effective as using a traditional balun, but it seems to work and, considering the unbalanced aerial configuration, it may work almost as well. I have had no complaints about RF in the shack or house on either band [1].

SUMMARY

The W3RW 6m and 10m long-wire aerial is a resonant multi-wavelength aerial that provides gain over a dipole on 6 and 10m and integrates a unique coax-cable matching section to provide a close match to 50Ω on both bands. This is a predominantly horizontally-polarised aerial optimised for the SSB portions of the 6- and 10m bands. Considering its simplicity and low cost, you ought to give it a try!

REFERENCE
1. *ARRL Handbook*, Table 19.4, p19.16, ARRL 2000.

FURTHER READING
The ARRL Antenna Book (15th ed, ARRL 1988)
'A Multi-Band Long-Wire Antenna', Edward M Noll, W3FQJ, *Ham Radio*, pp28-31, Nov 1969.
Wire Antenna Classics, ARRL, 1999.
Practical Wire Antennas, John D Heys, G3BDQ (ed), RSGB, 1989.

CHARACTERISTICS OF HALF-WAVELENGTH TRANSMISSION LINES
A key factor in the dual-band matching solution is the $\lambda/2$ characteristic of transmission lines. Any impedance presented at one end of a $\lambda/2$ length of coax - with coax of any impedance (that's the important part) - that same impedance is seen at the opposite end of the cable. For example, if you connect a $\lambda/2$ (or any multiple of $\lambda/2$) of 75Ω coax to a 50Ω load, a 50Ω impedance is seen at the other end - even though the characteristic impedance of the coax in-between is 75Ω. (All wavelength references are to electrical lengths of coax; this takes into account the velocity factor of the cable.)

THE SKELETON-SLEEVE-FED MONOPOLE

by Dan Richardson, K6MHE

The Skeleton-Sleeve-Fed Monopole (SSFM) is really a J-pole aerial with improved performance characteristics. This aerial has an excellent omnidirectional pattern, exhibits a good match to 50Ω coax, and can be constructed in about an hour at a low cost and from easily obtainable materials.

THE PROBLEM OF A STANDARD J-POLE AERIAL

The J-pole is an easy aerial to construct and, if certain precautions are followed, it provides good performance. However, the J-pole does not produce a true omnidirectional pattern due to radiation from the λ/4 stub (matching) section (see 'The J-pole Revisited', by K6MHE, *CQ*, March 1998).

J-poles usually are built using one of the two popular configurations shown in **Fig 1** - the shorted-base technique fed by open-wire feed lines, or the open-stub-fed aerial fed by coax. However, whichever arrangement (open or shorted base) is used, the J-pole's skewed

The Skeleton-Sleeve-Fed Monopole (SSFM) mounted to a vertical pole using the Radio Shack mounting bracket.

omnidirectional pattern remains essentially the same.

THE SOLUTION

The directional pattern can be improved by modifying the λ/4 matching section. This technique entails replacement of the λ/4 element with a cylinder surrounding the radiator to form the λ/4 coaxial section shown in **Fig 2**. Although the aerial can no longer truly be called a J-pole, because it does not resemble the letter 'J', it operates on the same theory as the J-pole, but with a true omnidirectional pattern.

One problem in using this technique is the difficulty of constructing and mechanically-supporting the outer sleeve segment. This problem can be overcome by replacing the solid outer sleeve with four vertical stubs. The result is the Skeleton-Sleeve-Fed Monopole depicted in **Fig 3**. The aerial's excellent omnidirectional performance can be seen in the computer-

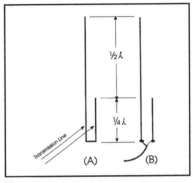

Fig 1: Two possible J-pole configurations: (A) shorted base and (B) open base.

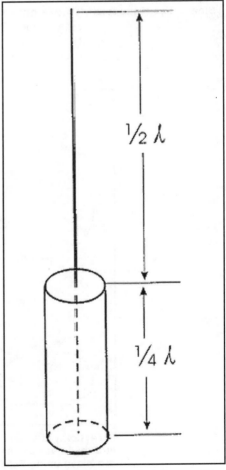

Fig 2: A coaxial-sleeve-fed monopole.

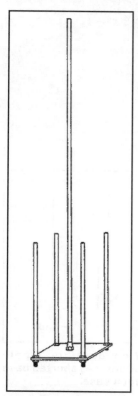

Fig 3: The Skeleton-Sleeve-Fed Monopole.

generated plots shown in **Fig 4**.

CONSTRUCTION

Fig 5 shows the aerial assembly information and materials list. The layout and dimensions for the base mounting plate (which was made from a scrap piece of $1/_8$in thick aluminium panel stock) are given in **Fig 6**. The total cost of the required materials was less than $30. The aluminium rod and stainless-steel hardware were acquired at my local home-supply store. The centre element support and mounting bracket assembly is an inexpensive mobile aerial-mounting bracket obtained at Radio Shack (catalog #21-937B).

With the exception of the hole diameters, the base-plate dimensions (Fig 6) are not critical. However, be sure to drill the five holes in the base plate perfectly vertical and maintain equal distances between the centre-element mounting hole and each of the four stub-element mounting holes to retain good balance. Carefully cut threads into one end of each of the aluminium rods as shown in Fig 5.

Keep the thread cutting die perpendicular to the rod when cutting the threads, to ensure that all of the elements are perpendicular after the aerial is assembled.

The $59^1/_4$in length given for the driven element in the materials list is correct. Attaching the aerial mounting bracket to this element adds the $1/_2$in required to yield the proper length ($59^3/_4$in) of the radiating element.

ADJUSTMENT

If the aerial is built to the specifications shown in Figs 5 and 6, it should be resonant at approximately 146MHz and should provide a good match to 50Ω coax. The aerial measured less than 1.2:1 VSWR at resonance (146MHz) and not greater than 1.5:1 at the band edges. Calculated and measured VSWR curves for the SSFM are shown in **Fig 7**.

The long $1^3/_4$in thread length on the λ/4 stub elements should provide enough range to adjust the aerial to resonance within the 2m band. In addition, the length of the 3λ/4 radiator element may also require adjustment. Remember, when building self-resonant aerials, making aerial elements slightly longer and then

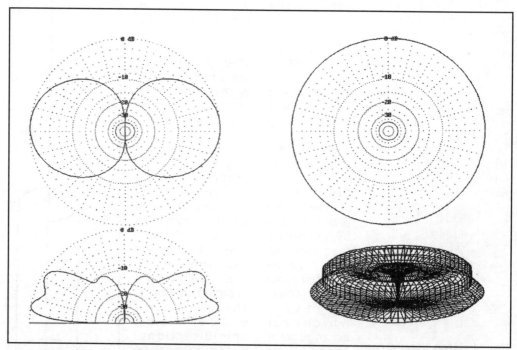

Fig 4: Computer-generated plots for the SSFM. The upper two plots are free-space patterns, and the lower plots (elevation and 3-D) are above average ground. Computer plots were produced using *EZNEC* aerial software (by Roy Lewallen, W7EL, PO Box 6658, Beaverton, OR 97007).

trimming them for the desired frequency is always good practice.

INSTALLATION NOTES

The effect of common-mode current on the transmission line can be very detrimental to any aerial's operation, especially at VHF / UHF. At these frequencies, the transmission line usually is several wavelengths long, and the radiation resulting from the common-mode current on the transmission line, when combined with that of the aerial, produces an increase in the signal being launched at higher take-off angles. Unless you are interested primarily in talking to airplanes, a common-mode choke should be employed for better performance of any aerial fed with a coaxial transmission line. The SSFM is no exception. The use of a common-mode choke on the transmission line is just good engineering practice. It can't hurt and probably will only help.

You can make your own choke by coiling up a few turns of the coax, or better yet, by installing ferrite beads (W2DU-type balun) at the aerial end of the transmission line. Complete details on making common mode chokes can be found in the *ARRL Antenna Book*.

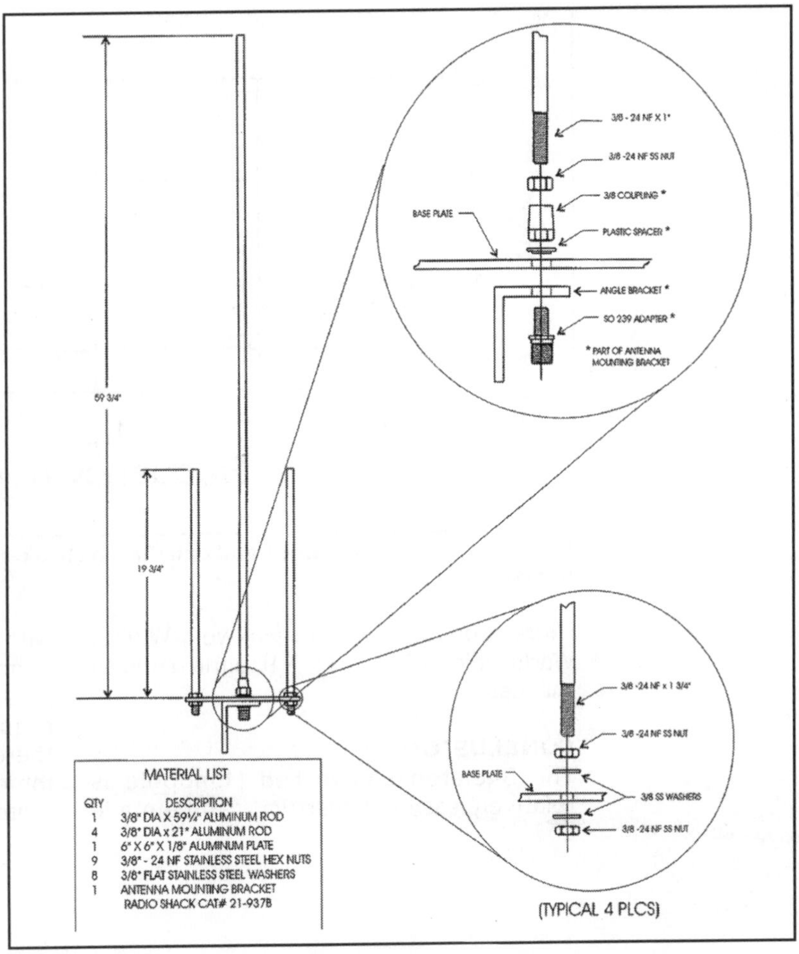

A WORD OF CAUTION

Not all VHF connectors are created equal! When I first constructed this aerial, I used a cheap CB mobile aerial adapter, obtained at a flea market, for the mounting of the centre $3\lambda/4$ element. When measuring the VSWR of the SSFM utilising this adapter, I obtained readings of almost 1:1 at resonance and less than 1.2:1 across the entire 2m band. That seemed too good to be true - and it was!

On further investigation, I found that the bargain aerial mounting assembly was no bargain at all. The unit had been constructed in such a manner that it had high losses at VHF, which in turn lowered the *Q* of the aerial, giving lower (and incorrect) VSWR values. Although the VSWR values appeared great, the aerial was not operating as efficiently as it should have been. It has been said, "Too low a VSWR can kill you."

Fig 5: SSFM assembly drawing and materials list (see text).

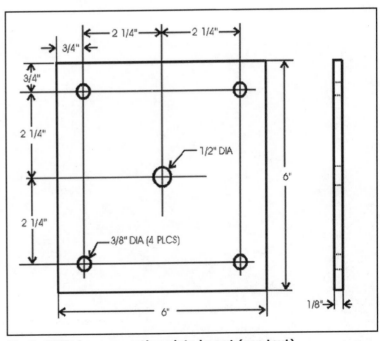

Fig 6: SSFM base mounting plate layout (see text).

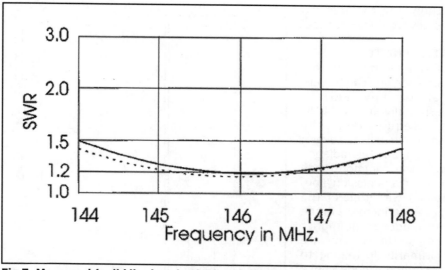

Fig 7: Measured (solid line) and calculated (broken line) VSWR values for the SSFM.

[*Reflections II*, M Walter Maxwell, W2DU, Worldradio, 2001 – *Ed*.] It almost did in this case!

CONCLUSION

The Skeleton-Sleeve-Fed Monopole is relatively easy to construct, can be made with simple tools at low cost, and provides improved performance over a standard J-pole. Like the J-pole, the SSFM does not require any additional ground system, thereby making it an excellent candidate for operation on boats or on fibreglass motor homes.

AN 80- AND 40-METRE LOADED DIPOLE

by Vince Lear, G3TKN / ZL1VL

This antenna uses loading coils in place of more conventional traps to obtain two-band operation. The idea of using loading coils in this way was described by W J Lattin, W4JRW, over 40 years ago [1]. It offers the advantage of simplicity over trap construction, and also results in considerable shortening of the antenna, which now takes up less space than the popular G5RV with its 31.09m (102ft) top, and the standard 33.53m (110ft) trap dipole.

In the 40/80m loaded dipole (**Fig 1**), the coils are sufficiently large that they show a high impedance on 40m, and provide inductive loading on 80m. Lattin found that values between 80µH to 120µH gave good results when used in this way, the larger values of inductance requiring less wire on the outer sections for 80m resonance.

However, Lattin acknowledged that no exact formulæ have been found to determine the relationship between coil size, wire lengths, and the two frequencies for dual-band resonance. Therefore, the published design may be regarded as a starting point for experimentation.

It should be appreciated that, when an antenna is inductively loaded,

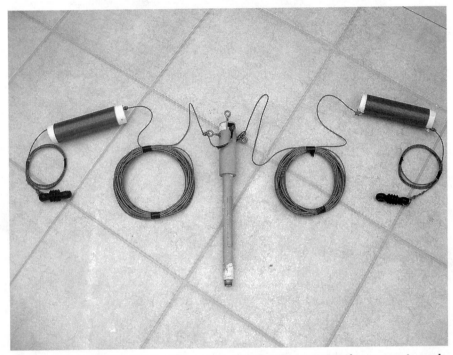

The 40/80m loaded dipole uses a commercial Ferromagnetics current-mode balun at its feed-point [5]. The aerial is made from flexible grey plastic-covered 14-strand copper wire.

several things happen. The most noticeable is the reduction in bandwidth of the system. The greater the loading, the smaller the bandwidth.

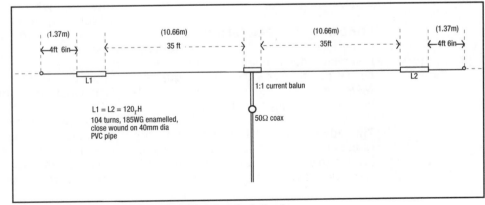

L1 = L2 = 120µH
104 turns, 185WG enamelled,
close wound on 40mm dia
PVC pipe

(1.37m) ←4ft 6in→
(10.66m) ← 35 ft →
(10.66m) ← 35ft →
(1.37m) ←4ft 6in→

L1

L2

1:1 current balun

50Ω coax

Fig 1: Dimensions of the 40 / 80m loaded dipole.

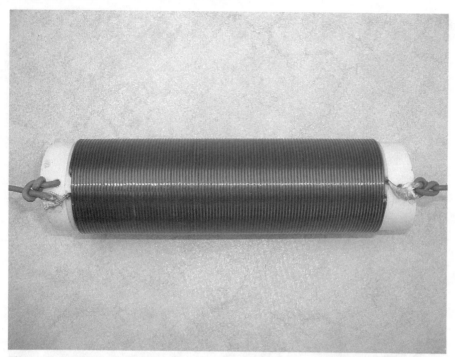

The coil used in the 40/80m dipole is made from standard 40mm (1.6in) diameter PVC pipe. It is 17.8cm (7in) long, with a winding length of 14cm (5.5 in). Holes are drilled at each end to secure the aerial wire.

The disadvantage is that it results in a narrower operating bandwidth when the aerial is used on 80m.

A good match is obtained to a 50Ω feeder on both 40m and 80m, although the bandwidth on 80m is restricted to about 60kHz between the 2:1 SWR points. No such problem occurs on 40m, where an SWR of about 1.5:1 was achieved across most of the band.

CONSTRUCTION

In my version of the 40/80m antenna I constructed the 120µH coils by close-winding 104 turns of 1.25mm (18SWG) enamelled copper wire onto a 17.8cm (7in) length of white PVC pipe of 40mm (1.6in) diameter. The winding length was 14cm (5.5in). Note that the total length of wire needed to construct these coils is a little more than that available from a standard 250g reel of wire. I used a 1kg reel of wire [3].

An alternative, although this has not been tried, could be to divide the wire from a 250g reel into two equal lengths and use these to wind as many turns as possible onto the two formers, making sure that they have the same number of turns. With care, it should be possible to achieve about 92 close-wound turns which will yield around 106µH. The dimensions of the antenna will be affected, but those given for the 120µH version should make a good starting point for experimentation. As always, when experimenting with antennas, make them longer than expected and then trim down for resonance.

The PVC piping is obtainable from most DIY outlets in 1.8m (6ft) lengths.

The antenna wire was fixed to each end of the loading coil via holes drilled in the PVC pipe. The ends of the coil were anchored through small holes in the coil, and soldered to the aerial wire.

The efficiency of the antenna also decreases. However, this decrease in efficiency is dependent on where in the aerial the loading coils are placed and, more importantly, on the construction of the loading coils. In a loaded wire aerial, the size and weight of the loading coils have to be important considerations, so to some extent there will always be some compromise between efficiency and what is practical.

As the loading is increased and the aerial becomes shorter, the feed-point impedance decreases. With a very heavily-loaded antenna, it may not be possible to feed it with 50Ω coax, and some extra matching circuitry may need to be employed.

LOADING COIL PLACEMENT

Using loading coils to achieve two-band resonance does mean that one has no choice but to place the coils a quarter-wavelength out either side of the feed-point on the higher frequency.

The advantage is that, on 80m, the radiation resistance is kept at a higher level in this configuration than if the coils were placed close-in to the feed-point.

A short section of the PVC piping was checked out in a microwave oven to examine for any heating effect. None was found, so it was therefore assumed that the material was quite suitable for use in this application.

Care should be exercised in the use of some PVC piping which may be quite lossy if it is carbon-filled.

The whole coil assembly was given two coats of marine yacht varnish. The operation of the aerial was not effected during periods of heavy rain, so the weather proofing provided by the varnish appeared quite adequate.

The aerial handled 400W from a linear amplifier without any problems, although this was only done when the SWR was no greater than 1.5:1.

The photos show the coil construction and the aerial components, together with a commercial Ferromagnetics current-mode balun [5].

Losses are greater in a voltage-mode balun if used off resonance where reactive components are present. A current-mode balun can easily be constructed by winding 5 to 8 turns of RG58 coax (5mm diameter) around a pair of stacked ferrite rings. For more information on baluns, see [2].

ADJUSTMENT
The 40m section needed to be 10.66m (35ft) per leg as opposed to 10.05m (33ft) for resonance. This was the same length as found by W4JRW.

If an aerial has end capacity-loading (as would be the case for a top-loaded vertical with a large capacity hat of wires fanning out from its top), its length can be reduced due to the end capacity. However, in the case of the 40m section in the 40/80m loaded dipole, inductive loading is seen at the end, and hence the opposite occurs with a resulting increase required for resonance at 7MHz. This effect should not be confused with

inductive loading in series with an aerial rather than at its end. In the former case, the aerial will be electrically lengthened, and hence a shorter length of wire will be required for resonance.

The trimming of the end sections is very critical. I found that 1.27m (4ft 2in) gave resonance on 3774kHz with a resulting 1:1 SWR, the 2:1 SWR points occurring at 3805kHz and 3742kHz. The aerial should, of course, be trimmed for one's favourite part of the band.

The use of the auto ATU in my transceiver allowed for some limited excursion outside of the 2:1 SWR points on 80m. However, it should be appreciated that this in no way reduces mismatched line loss on the coaxial feeder.

As the coils also offer a high impedance on 15m, the inner section can be used as a 'near' $3\lambda/2$ dipole on that band. The actual resonance in this mode was found to be 20.2MHz but, using the auto ATU, the transceiver was able to deliver full power across all of the 15m band.

160m OPERATION
The aerial may be used on 160m instead of 80m by extending the wires on the outside of the loading coils from around 1.22m (4ft) to 7.62m (25ft). This gave a 1:1 SWR on 1840kHz. The bandwidth between the 2:1 SWR points is in the region of 35kHz on 160m. The aerial will now function on 40 and 160m.

A 20/40m LOADED DIPOLE
A very successful 20/40m version was constructed and tested using the same principles as used for 40 and 80m (**Fig 2**). This had an overall length of 11.89m (39ft) and used coils of 47µH.

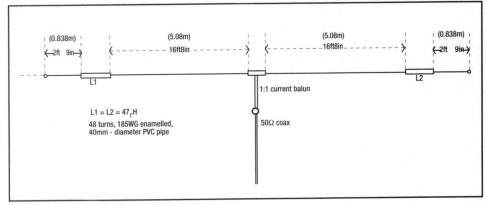

Fig 2: The 20 / 40m version.

The coils were again made of 1.25mm (18SWG) enamelled copper wire, close-wound with 48 turns on standard 40mm (1.6in) diameter PVC pipe. Coil formers of 10cm (4in) length were used. The aerial had 5.08m (16ft 8 in) inner sections with 0.83m (2ft 9in) outer ends.

The SWR on 20m was less than 1.5:1 across most of the band, and the aerial showed a 1:1 SWR on 7072kHz with a 2:1 SWR bandwidth of 96kHz.

Typical dipole performance resulted on 20m, with good all-round reports on 7MHz.

EXTENDED OPERATION USING OPEN-WIRE FEED

If the standard 40/80m design is fed with open-wire line (or 450Ω ladder-line) coupled into the transceiver via a balanced ATU, the aerial could be operated efficiently on both 17m and 20m.

The inner section will operate as two half-waves in phase on 20m, and as a double extended Zepp on 17m with theoretical broadside gain figures of 1.6dBd and 3dBd, respectively [4].
On 21MHz and above, a multi-lobe pattern will result.

CONCLUSION

Using loading coils in place of traps, to get two-band operation, has the advantages of ease of construction and considerable reduction in antenna length. However, the main disadvantage is reduced bandwidth on the lower band.

The 40/80m design also offers useful operation on 15m. With the addition of a strapped 20m dipole at the feed-point, a reasonably compact four-band coaxial-fed

antenna of just 24.08m (79ft) could be constructed.

Alternatively, the aerial could be fed with open-wire line to produce an inductively-loaded doublet.

The same principles outlined above could also be applied to multi-banding vertical or inverted-L systems.

Although the original intention of this article was to describe a compact and reasonably-efficient aerial for 40m and 80m, I have mentioned some other possible design variations that may encourage others to experiment further and develop a system suitable to their particular needs.

REFERENCES

[1]   'Multiband Antenna Using Loading Coils', W J Lattin, W4JRW, *QST* April 1961

[2]   *Backyard Antennas*, Peter Dodd, G3LDO, available from the RSGB Shop

[3]   Available from Scientific Wire Company, 18 Raven Rd, South Woodford, London E18 1HW. Tel: 020 8505 0002, website www.wires.co.uk

[4]   *ARRL Antenna Handbook*, 19th ed, available from the RSGB Shop

[5]   Ferromagnetics, PO Box 577, Mold, Flintshire CH7 1AH. Website www.ferromagnetics.co.uk

DEDICATION

This article is dedicated to my long-time friend and neighbour, Ron Ford, G3NKO / C56RF, who was killed in the Gambia, West Africa, in September 2002 (see *RadCom*, Dec 2002, p10).

INVITED ARTICLE

YOUR TUNER
DOES TUNE YOUR AERIAL

by Kurt N Sterba

For those who have not yet had the pleasure of picking up a copy of the American ham magazine *WorldRadio*, let me explain that Kurt Nostradamus Sterba is its regular 'Aerials' columnist. He writes in a 'no-punches-pulled' manner, and takes great glee in finding hyperbole in aerial manufacturers' advertisements. He also declares open season on magazine writers and editors who let slip the slightest error, either through ignorance or hangover. He is frequently taken to task by those who are unaware of his awesome power of rebuttal – he is always right!

Before you continue, here are a few descriptions of the 'masked crusader' for aerial rights, published by kind permission of *WorldRadio*. They will make you smile, and put you in the right frame of mind for Kurt's invited article. Don't be misled by the style – the facts are there and you can test them for yourself.
George Brown, Editor

Kurt N Sterba is an alias [really?]. He insists on such because he does not want to run into the people on the air who call him 'asinine' and 'stupid' in letters. This mature gentleman, urbane and erudite, has but one answer for such people: "I'm made of rubber and you're made of glue. Whatever you say bounces off me and sticks on you".

Kurt N Sterba is obviously a nom de plume. Kurt said his true identity had to be protected as he works with a lot of hams. He doesn't want them coming up to him and saying, "I know more about antennas than you do". This may be true, but he comes cheap.

Some criticise this columnist for writing under an alias. He replies, "'tis better to write the truth under a disguise than (as others do) write hooey under their real names".

Kurt N Sterba goes by that alias specifically so he can speak his mind, sometimes about people he likes, and still remain friends.

KNS pens covertly to avoid confrontation with those who put up antennas with directivity but no gain.

The secret Kurt N Sterba is really your friend. Unlike the big and famous manufacturer, he will never tell you that a 17ft antenna is a half-wave on 20.

Kurt N Sterba goes by his pen name to avoid in-person confrontations with those who have never figured out what one R stands for, let alone the other two.

Compassionate Kurt, a kind and gentle soul, says his feelings are not hurt by letters calling him an ignorant know-nothing. He is letting his critics step into the web. Answers are going out individually, not in print and identified, so they don't lose their technical jobs. They'll just have to sit at the dinner table and explain to their wives why they are crying.

Kurt, who counselled Billy Batson and taught him to say "Shazam", sits in a damp cave searching for the truth. He is perplexed by short antennas that are claimed to be half-wave and longer antennas that are touted as quarter-wave.

WorldRadio's mystery man 'Kurt N Sterba' writes articles, the likes of which would appear in other ham magazines, if they had a sense of responsibility toward their readers.

Now read on...

Krusty Olde Kurt is always astounded at the amount of misinformation he sees in amateur radio periodicals, aerial catalogues, and on the Internet. The worst offenders are some of the aerial manufacturers who tend to exaggerate claims of aerial gain. Then there are the new aerial firms that show up with astounding new concepts. Miniature, wideband, and efficient aerials that work on newly-discovered principles. Kurt has unmasked a number of these to great protestation from the 'inventors'. But not one of them has ever produced the one thing required to silence the Masked Avenger – certified field strength measurements.

A third, and more persistent problem, is found in periodicals and on the Internet – incorrect technical explanations of everyday problems. Some of them are so old they become folklore: "High VSWR causes radiation from your feed-line"; "VSWR must be kept below 2:1 to prevent excessive loss in the feeder"; and the one Kurt will discuss here – "Your tuner fools your transmitter into thinking that your aerial is in tune". Kurt is horrified to see statements like this appear over and over and over in major technical periodicals.

Kurt will now explain in detail exactly how your aerial tuner *does* tune your aerial to resonance. [British readers will appreciate the description that an aerial tuner 'does what it says on the tin' – Ed.] We are talking about the usual station setup shown in **Fig 1**. Here, the transmitter output goes to the aerial tuner through cable A into which the VSWR meter is inserted. The tuner output goes to cable B that goes out to the aerial.

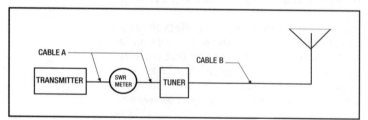

Fig 1: The commonest station setup.

Before getting into the explanation, Kurt wants to bring up a significant fact that is often not recognised but is essential to understanding the problem. We'll call it 'Krusty Kurt's Theorem': if the aerial is not an exact match to the transmission line, the power going through the cable toward the aerial is always greater than the transmitter power.

At first this sounds as if it violates the Law of Conservation of Energy. But it does not. The reason for this will become clear shortly. Also, be advised that, later on, Kurt will describe a simple experiment you can perform in your own station that proves the point.

HISTORY

A series of articles in *QST* during the late 1970s by Walt Maxwell, W2DU, was the first to explain how your tuner tunes your aerial. He uses the mechanism of wave reflections to show how it happens. He talks a lot about the Conjugate Match. This occurs at a junction of two networks (such as a transmission line and an aerial) when the resistances of the two are made equal and the reactances are made equal but opposite in sign. The reactances cancel, leaving a resistive match. In this example we can say that the transmission line 'tunes the aerial' because its reactance has disappeared.

The Conjugate-Match Theorem specifies that, 'if a group of four-terminal networks containing only pure reactances (or lossless lines) are arranged in tandem to connect a generator to its load and, at any junction, there is a conjugate match of impedances, there will be a conjugate match of impedances at every other junction in the system'. This means that, referring to the setup of Fig 1, if we adjust the tuner so that it matches cable A (that is, the VSWR meter reads 1:1) then there is a conjugate match between the tuner and cable B and between cable B and the aerial. The aerial is tuned.

To carry this even further, W2DU gives an example where cable B is made up of several cables in series. One of them is 300Ω cable, one 450Ω cable and another 600Ω cable. If the tuner matches cable A then all three 'B' cables are matched along with the aerial which is tuned to resonance.

This all sounds quite reasonable and it does work, but there is a little fly in the ointment. In Fig 1, when our tuner has tuned the system so we have 1:1 VSWR on cable A and the conjugate match thus produced has tuned the aerial to resonance we find, to our surprise and horror, that the VSWR in cable B is not 1:1. Depending on the aerial, it may be 2:1 or 3:1 or some other value.

Why is this? The VSWR on line B depends on the ratio of the aerial impedance to the characteristic impedance of the transmission line. The conjugate match does not change this ratio and so the VSWR does not change. Kurt will give a more complete explanation later on.

VSWR is caused by wave reflection, and W2DU goes on to explain wave actions and reflections. Of course we measure voltage and current in the line, but we should not forget that the voltages and currents are caused by waves travelling down the line. These contain the RF power and move it down the line as they go. The waves have frequency and wavelength.

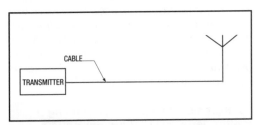

Fig 2: Direct connection of transmitter to aerial.

W2DU first asks us to look at the situation shown in **Fig 2**. The transmitter is connected directly to the transmission line and it connects directly to the aerial. If the aerial is a perfect match to the transmission line, all the transmitter power goes into the aerial. (We are using lossless transmission lines in our examples to keep things simple. We'll add losses later.) If the transmitter puts out 100W then 100W goes down the line and into the aerial.

Now suppose that the aerial does not match the line. What happens? The mismatch prevents the aerial from absorbing all the power. Some of the power is reflected and another wave, containing the reflected power, travels back to the transmitter. For example, if VSWR=2, and with 100W forward power, the aerial will absorb only 89 watts. Eleven watts will be reflected.

When this reflected wave reaches the transmitter what happens? It is *not* absorbed by the transmitter. Instead it is totally reflected *again* and adds to the forward power. Now we have 100W forward power in the transmission line, 11W reflected power moving backwards and 89W going into the aerial. And what

is our 100W transmitter doing now? It does not see its proper load and it has reduced its power to 89W. The 11W reflected power is totally reflected and adds to the 89W from the transmitter to give 100W forward power.

Kurt wants you to note that:
(1)   The forward power is greater than the transmitter power, and
(2)   All of the transmitter power, all 89W, is absorbed by the aerial.

W2DU points out that, "All power delivered to a lossless line is absorbed in the load, regardless of the degree of mismatch. A non-resonant aerial absorbs the delivered power with 100% efficiency".

The power reflected from the mismatched load is called 'reflection loss'. There are instruments that measure this as 'return loss'. But the power is *not* lost. W2DU has just explained that it is not.

Next, W2DU asks us to look at the case where we put an aerial tuner right at the aerial. See **Fig 3**. When the tuner is properly adjusted, it gives a conjugate match to the aerial. Also it looks like 50Ω on the transmission-line side. Thus, there is 1:1 VSWR on the line and no reflection 'loss', so the whole 100W goes into the aerial.

If we move the tuner back to the transmitter, as in Fig 1, what happens? With our non-resonant aerial connected, the transmitter end of cable B no longer looks like 50Ω. It will have a different resistance and a reactance. Their values depend on the aerial impedance and the length of the transmission line.

We adjust our tuner to give a conjugate match, that is, the same resistance that

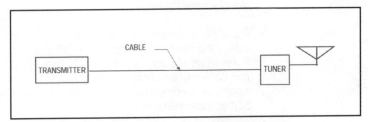

Fig 3: Using an ATU at the aerial end of the feeder.

appears on cable B and a reactance equal to but opposite in sign. When we do this, line A sees an exact match at the tuner input. And the aerial? It sees a conjugate match. Since the transmitter sees its desired impedance it puts out the full 100W. This travels down the line to the aerial. The aerial is tuned, but the tuning is done by the transmission line. The transmission line still sees just the aerial in its untuned state. The forward wave sees this mismatch and there is a reflection as before. If it is a 2:1 mismatch, 11W is reflected back toward the transmitter.

When this wave gets to the tuner output what happens? It is *totally reflected*. This is called reflection 'gain' and cancels the reflection 'loss'. It adds to the forward power which now becomes 111W. So, again, we have more forward power than the transmitter provides. 111W goes forward down line B. When it gets to the aerial, the aerial absorbs 100W and 11W is reflected. Note that, again, the *full* transmitter power goes into the aerial.

W2DU has shown us that, with a lossless transmission line, we get 100% efficiency whether we tune the aerial or not and whether we use a tuner or not. So why do we use a tuner? So the transmitter sees a proper load so it can put out full power. Without a tuner it can see wildly differing load impedances and just won't perform properly.

But when we *do* use a tuner, it can be located either at the transmitter or at the aerial with no difference in results. However, in the real world there are problems with either approach. With the tuner at the aerial it is out in the rain and too far away to adjust by hand. You have to have an automatic tuner that is expensive and usually limited in power handling. With the tuner at the transmitter, cable B has a VSWR when the aerial is not resonant. This gives increased cable loss but, in most cases, not enough to worry about.

W2DU's original articles have been collected and augmented in the book *Reflections II* published by WorldRadio [1]. You can get the complete story in his own words by reading this book. Kurt, and your Editor, recommend it.

KURT'S EXPLANATION

The wave reflection explanation gives an understanding of the way our tuner tunes our aerial. But there are those who do not believe all aspects of it. For those people,

Kurt is going to show in a different way just how it works. He will take advantage of a tool that did not exist when W2DU wrote his articles: the transmission line computer programme. With this, we can easily determine the impedance that occurs at one end of a transmission line when we put a known load on the other end. All we have to do is put our load numbers into the programme and tell it what cable we are using, its length and the frequency of operation.

Kurt loves these programmes. They are easier to use than the Smith chart and you don't have to learn much of anything to use them – you just plug in your numbers. With them you easily can check Kurt's explanation for accuracy. Kurt will use the *Transmission Line for Windows* programme that comes with the *ARRL Antenna Book*. There is a similar programme, *TLDetails*, available free at www.qsl.net/ac6la/tldetails.html

For Kurt's explanation we are going to use a 40m aerial at 7250kHz which is *not* its resonant frequency and where it has 75Ω resistance and an inductive reactance of 66Ω. It is connected to our tuner by a 40ft length of special RG-8A cable. This is 50Ω cable (actual resistance 52.2Ω and velocity factor 0.66, the same as RG-8A), but is special by having no loss at all and a purely resistive characteristic impedance. With this lossless cable, all the arithmetic works out perfectly. After proving the point, we'll enter the real world with ordinary RG-8A cable and see what difference there is.

For the computer programme, the aerial is the 'load'. It is 75 + j66Ω in vector nomenclature. We put that into the computer and it tells us that, at the input end (at the tuner), the cable looks like 35.02 + j45.84Ω. That is 35.02Ω resistive and 45.84Ω inductive.

Now we tune our tuner to get a conjugate match. That means that the tuner supplies a capacitive 45.84Ω to cancel the inductance presented by the cable. Also, it has to be set to be a resistance transformer with 50Ω at cable A and 35.02Ω on the cable B side. So the cable now sees 35.02 −j45.84Ω. This now is our 'load'. The computer programme then tells us that, at the other end of the cable, it looks like 75 −j66Ω. The 75Ω resistive matches the aerial resistance and the 66Ω capacitive reactance exactly cancels the aerial's inductance. The aerial is tuned! The conjugate match theorem really is correct.

Unfortunately, we cannot buy lossless cable. Instead, Kurt uses RG-8A in his station. It has losses at this frequency of 0.49dB per 100ft. Also, it has a capacitive reactance of 0.42Ω as part of its characteristic impedance. Let's see what happens when we use it instead of the perfect cable.

We connect cable B to the same aerial with its $75 + j66\Omega$ impedance. But now the computer programme tells us that the impedance at the tuner end of the cable is a bit different from before: 37.67Ω resistance and 44.14Ω inductive reactance. So we set the tuner to provide $37.67 - j44.14\Omega$ to give a conjugate match. The cable sees this as its 'load' and, at the other end, at the aerial, we see 75.1Ω resistive and 57.4Ω capacitive. The resistive part is a very close match but the capacitive reactance is too small. The aerial is not quite in tune.

That's what happens when there are losses in the cable. The larger the losses, the further off is the tuning. Welcome to the real world! That's not the only difference. With the lossless cable we had a VSWR of 3 at the aerial and at the tuner. Now we have a VSWR of 2.93 at the aerial and 2.77 at the tuner. Why is that? As the power from the transmitter travels to the aerial, some of it is lost as heat in the cable. At the aerial, the same percentage of power is reflected as before but, since the forward power is lower at this end of the cable, the reflected power is lower also. Then, as the reflected wave travels back to the tuner more of it is lost. But, at the tuner, we have the full transmitter power. With full transmitter power and a smaller reflected power, we have a lower VSWR. The greater the cable loss, the lower the VSWR at the transmitter end and the poorer the match at the aerial.

Not to worry! The aerial still absorbs all of the transmitter power minus the cable loss. As W2DU showed before, even an untuned aerial will absorb the full available power.

MULTIPLE CABLES
It is interesting to examine W2DU's statement that you can use several different impedance cables to connect your tuner to the aerial and still get the exact same results as with just one cable type. To keep things from getting too complicated, Kurt will use just two cables. One will be 50Ω coaxial cable and the other 450Ω open wire line with a velocity factor of 0.91. Each will be 20ft long, so we have the same total length as in the previous example. See **Fig 4**. Both will be lossless, so that the numbers come out perfectly. We'll also use the same aerial at the same frequency as before.

Now we have 450Ω line with the aerial as load at 75Ω resistive and 66Ω inductive. And what do we see at the other end of this line? A much different impedance: $2728 + j288\Omega$. That is the load for the 50Ω line which is going to have a VSWR of 55! At the other end of the 50Ω line the tuner sees $1.25 - j31\Omega$. So, of course, we set our tuner for $1.25 + j31$. Now, going back towards the aerial, at the other end of the 50Ω line, the computer programme says we have $2739 - j282\Omega$. We expected

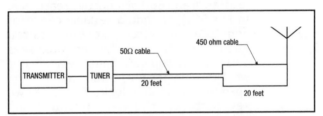

Fig 4: Mixing your drinks – using different feeders between ATU and aerial.

to get the same as we had before, but you can see that we're off a little. Why? Kurt ascribes that to rounding errors in the computer calculation. We'll use that figure anyway as the load for the 450Ω line. This gives us, at the aerial, $74.78 - j66.25\Omega$. Rounding to the nearest whole number, we have $75 - j66\Omega$, exactly the needed value to tune the aerial. So W2DU was right, we *can* use two different, or three or four different, transmission lines and still tune the aerial just fine. Of course, in practice, there can be problems. Remember the 55:1 VSWR we found in the 50Ω line. In the real world you have to look your design over carefully to make sure there is no 'sleeper' error.

LINE SWR
Kurt would like to explore more carefully the reason for the VSWR on the transmission line, even when the tuner has

tuned the aerial. This has worried a number of his readers.

Look at **Fig 5(a)**. This is an ordinary fixed inductor with resistance in its winding. We want to tune it to a specific frequency. To do this we add a variable capacitor as in **Fig 5(b)**. We adjust the capacitor until the combination of inductor and capacitor resonates at the desired frequency. We have tuned the 'circuit', that is, the combination of the components, to our desired frequency. Note that, in Fig 5(b), the capacitor looks at the inductor. The inductor and its resistance do not change at all during the tuning process. After tuning they look exactly the same as they did before.

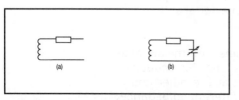

Fig 5: (a) A coil with its internal resistance; (b) The same coil being resonated with a capacitor.

Now look at **Fig 6(a)**. Here we have a non-resonant aerial. This one has 50Ω resistance and 66Ω of inductive reactance. In **Fig 6(b)**, we add a variable capacitor and tune the circuit to our desired frequency. Note that the capacitor sees 50Ω resistive and 66Ω inductive no matter what the tuning. But, after tuning, if we open the circuit and 'look in' at X - X, we see just 50Ω resistive because the inductive reactance of the aerial and the capacitive reactance of the capacitor cancel. We're in tune. If we connect a 50Ω line to X - X, as in **Fig 6(c)**, we'll have 1:1 VSWR, no aerial tuner needed.

But now let's take away the capacitor as in **Fig 6(d)**. We connect our 50Ω line

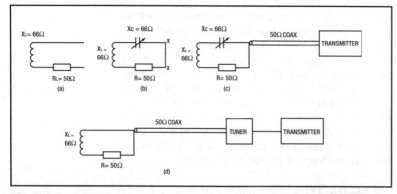

Fig 6: (a) The coil alone, representing the non-resonant aerial; (b) The aerial being resonated with a capacitor. Break the circuit at X – X, where the impedance is 50Ω resistive; (c) Insert 50Ω feeder at this point from the transmitter; (d) Remove the capacitor and use an ATU at the transmitter.

directly to the aerial. At the transmitter, we use a tuner and adjust it to give our conjugate match. This match will make the transmission line, aerial end, look like 50Ω resistive with 66Ω capacitive reactance, exactly right to tune the circuit to resonance. That is, the transmission line will show exactly the same capacitance as the capacitor did in Fig 6(b) and Fig 6(c). The transmission line now *is* the capacitor. And the aerial is tuned just as it was with the variable capacitor. But note *very very* carefully that the transmission line always sees the aerial, and that the aerial resistance and inductance do not change. They are the same before and after we adjust our tuner. The transmission line sees 50Ω resistive and 66Ω inductive both before and after tuning.

The VSWR on the transmission line depends on the load it sees. Since that does not change, the VSWR does not change *even though our tuner has tuned the aerial.* That's why the transmission line VSWR does not change when we use our tuner to tune our aerial.

KURT'S EXPERIMENT

We've seen how wave theory tells us that reflections cause power to move back toward the transmitter and then to add to the forward power to give more forward power than the transmitter puts out. There are those readers who think that theory is all well and good, but they would prefer to see it with their own eyes.

So Krusty Olde Kurt has devised a simple experiment that shows that this reflected power really does move around as described. We make use of the common VSWR meter that is found in all amateur stations. These meters measure forward and reflected power and, from these measurements, determine and display VSWR. Most of them display forward power as well as VSWR. If you connect them backwards they measure the power going the other way.

Kurt's experiment uses equipment that can be found in most amateur stations. We need a transmitter, a dummy load, and two power meters. Also, we need two 4:1 RF transformers. These are easy to build, and Kurt will give full instructions for this. The setup is shown in **Fig 7**. Cable C drives the 50Ω dummy load

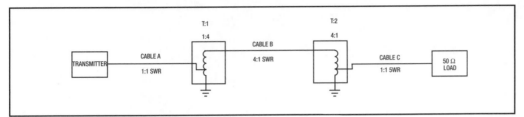

Fig 7: Kurt's experiment.

so it has 1:1 VSWR. The 4:1 transformer, T2, raises the impedance to 200Ω as the load for cable B. So this cable has 4:1 VSWR. The 1:4 transformer, T1, drops the impedance back to 50Ω as the load for cable A, so it has 1:1 VSWR.

So what happens when we apply transmitter power to this arrangement? Let's assume 50W out of the transmitter. The cables need be only a couple of feet long so there are practically no losses. The entire 50W will go through the system and be absorbed by the dummy load. Cables A and C have 1:1 VSWR so they will have

That's the theory. Now let's perform the experiment. Construct two 4:1 transformers as shown in **Fig 8**. Connect the equipment as shown in **Fig 9**. It shows three SWR/Power meters – one in each line. If you have only two put them in positions M1 and M3. When you apply transmitter power, you should see the same amount of power in each meter. Maybe a bit less in position 3 if there is some loss in the transformers. Kurt suggests using the 40 or 80m band, because transformer loss will be less than at higher frequencies.

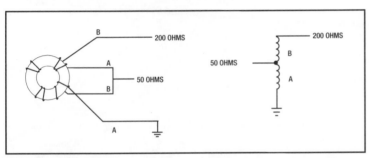

Fig 8: Winding details for the two 4:1 transformers. Use a ferrite core rated for use between 2 – 10MHz. Kurt used a F114-61 core, which is 1.1in OD and has a permeability of 125. Use two wire colours to make it easier. Hold the two wires side by side and wind eight bifilar turns, connecting them as shown.

50W forward power and no reflected power. But cable B has 4:1 VSWR. The 50W will proceed forward but, at the 200Ω load, 30W will be reflected. This will show as reflected power in the cable. And it will be re-reflected at the 200Ω load presented by the other transformer and will add to the forward power to give 80W forward power.

Now move meter M3 to position M2. Apply power again and adjust the transmitter to give the same power as before in meter M1. Then check meter M2. If you have 50W in M1 you will see 80W forward in M2 and 30W reflected.

CONCLUSION
Kurt hopes and prays that this experiment will convince all who try it that reflection theory tells the true story. Power really is reflected and adds to forward power without being lost anywhere except in normal cable loss. And he hopes that all who are convinced will help spread the word. Help stamp out ignorance. Kurt does his best but can't do it all alone. Please help!

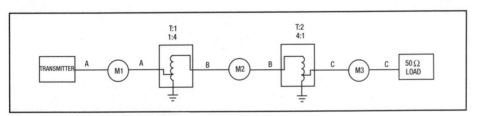

Fig 9: The experimental setup.

THE TWO-ELEMENT PENTAGON FOR 40m

By Bruce Fleming, KI7VR (ex-G3NDG)

Quads are fine antennas and, on the higher frequencies, are easy and cheap to build. The problem with quads for 40 and 80m is *size* - they are physically huge, but I have found that by making two design changes and one compromise, a 40m 'loop' antenna can be built without too much heavy engineering.

The compromise is in regard to rotation: *don't try to turn it!* The fixed 'loop' is much simpler to build. Obviously a non–rotating, two-element 'loop' should be aligned for the most important DX direction, but it can also be readily switched 180° by changing the parasitic element from a reflector to a director.

The first design change needed to simplify a big fixed Quad is to hang the loops from one corner – this method needs only a single spreader per loop, which in my case, is a vertical bamboo pole. I will refer to a Quad loop hanging from one corner (**Fig 1(a)**) as a 'Diamond Quad'. TI5KD has constructed a single-element Diamond Quad for 80m on a 110ft (35m) tower. The diagonal corner-to-corner distance of this single-loop Quad is 95ft (30.7m) for resonance at 3.525MHz, hence the need for a high tower! The loop corners are pulled out with nylon cord attached near ground level to open up the loop. The resulting loop antenna beams north into the USA/Europe and also beams south to South America. The same tower carries a two-element 40m Diamond Quad which beams north. The signals from these Quads are very impressive, but major engineering is involved. After coming home from operating at TI5KD's shack in Costa Rica, I badly wanted a two-element 40m Quad, but I had neither the cash nor the stomach for heavy engineering. So I sought a way to reduce the height requirement of the Diamond

The two-element Pentagon for 40m at KI7VR. The wires have been re-touched to make them visible.

Quad while retaining the single-spreader construction.

PENTAGON DEVELOPMENT
In free space, the ideal loop antenna comprises a circular conductor with a

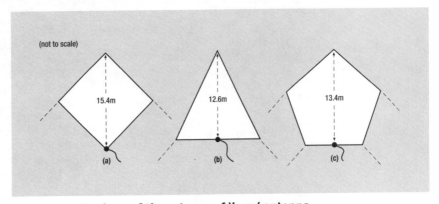

Fig 1: A comparison of three types of 'loop' antenna.

circumference equal to one wavelength [1], or multiples thereof. Circular loops are indeed used on the VHF bands, but on the HF bands, a circular shape is hard to achieve and loop antennas have tended to become triangular (Delta Loops), or square (Quads).

The conventional square Quad needs support at two high points per loop – normally achieved with long spreader poles mounted at 45° to the horizontal using a special bracket on the boom (lots of torque where the spreader pole attaches to the bracket) – this is difficult to engineer for 40m and 80m. The fixed Diamond Quad is simpler and more robust, with its single vertical spreader per loop – but there is a drawback - the Diamond Quad needs 1.4 times more vertical height than the square Quad. The Delta Loop (**Fig 1(b)**), with its flat base, needs less height than the Diamond Quad; however this 'less open' type of loop may not be as efficient as the square loops. John Devoldere, ON4UN, calls the Delta Loop a "Poor man's Quad" [2].

This article describes a Pentagon Loop, which is more 'open' and requires less height than a Diamond Quad, but still hangs from one corner.

The 40m Diamond Quad (Fig 1(a)) has sides 10.87m long and a total circumference of 43.5m. When suspended form a corner, it occupies a vertical height of 15.4m. The corresponding Delta Loop (Fig 1(b)) has sides 14.5m long and a height of 12.6m. The Pentagon Loop (**Fig 1(c)**) has sides 8.7m long and a height of 13.4m. The Pentagon requires only 87% of the vertical height needed by the Diamond Quad shown in (a).

The Pentagon Loop requires but a single vertical support at the apex. The two upper corners are pulled out with nylon cords to open up the loop.

The bottom is made flat, as with a Delta loop, to minimise the vertical height requirement. It is apparent that the Pentagon Loop is more 'open' than either a triangular or square loop and thus might be expected to radiate and receive somewhat better. A Pentagon has a 10% greater capture area than a square antenna made with the same wire. Tensioning the cords at the lower corners raises the bottom wire a few feet. I am not sure whether the bottom ropes are really necessary – without them, the wire droops in a catenary curve - although the wire hangs closer to the ground, the loop opens up even more.

MY INSTALLATION FOR 40m

An old 30ft crank-up tower was given to me by a friend: I constructed the tower base on the edge of my property where the ground drops sharply to the south. I used a 10ft stub mast made of steel fence railing (1.375in diameter) – cheap, but maybe too flimsy (we'll see). To the stub mast (8ft above tower top), I attached a 20ft boom made of two bits of the same fence railing, the ends of the boom being pulled up to a short centre support pole using Dacron cord, thus preventing sag and strengthening the assembly, a technique used in the past with aircraft wings. Each end of the boom carries a vertical piece of 3in OD aluminum tube (18in long) into which a varnished bamboo

---

DIMENSIONS OF THE 40m PENTAGON

Driven element design resonance:	7050kHz
Side lengths:	five equal sides of 8.7m
Total length:	43.5m
Reflector length:	103.5% of driven element - four sides of 8.7m, bottom side: 10.2m
Total length:	45.0m

Note 1: the resonance shifts a bit with soil moisture content; I needed to shorten the loops as the soil dried out during summer.

Note 2: if the parasitic element is to be a *director*, its length needs to be 97% of the driven element, ie 42.2m. I used four sides of 8.7m and a bottom side of 7.4m.

pole (homegrown, 20ft long) [3] is bolted. The height at the top of the bamboo is 58ft. The antenna wire (copper-clad steel, multi-strand 14-gauge) is attached to the top of each bamboo pole. A small loop is soldered into each wire at the four remaining corners and Dacron cord attached to each corner point.

How you pull out those top corners depends on your property. If you have lots of space (eg a field) then you can extend the Dacron cords far out until they approach ground level and then attach them to ground stakes. On my half-acre lot, I had to climb nearby trees and put my Dacron cords through smooth plastic rings fixed to convenient upper branches.

After final adjustment of the cords, the bottom wire hangs 19ft above the ground. I had calculated 17.5ft, so I guess it means I haven't quite got my tree branches in the right spots and I don't have perfect pentagons, but I will leave the trees where they are for now. By loosening the ropes, it is possible to drop the bottoms of the loops low enough so that, using stepladders, the coax connection can be modified, or the length of the parasitic element changed.

MATCHING

The two-element Pentagon described above has an input impedance of about 100Ω when fed in the centre of the lower side (see [4] for a discussion about feeding loops at other points). For matching, I used a quarter-wave transformer of 23ft of RG-6/U coax (75Ω) attached at the bottom centre of the driven loop. This connects to R-G58/U (50Ω) running to the shack. The VSWR at the shack is 1.2:1 at resonance and I have run 500W on CW into this setup with no problems. RG-8/U would be better than RG-58/U, but I do things on the cheap!

COST

My total cost was $214 – of which $75 was for concrete mix; steel tube for boom and stub, $21; three heavy-gauge aluminium boom-to-mast coupling plates, $56; Dacron cord and antenna wire, $62. The tower, bamboo and coax were already available.

PERFORMANCE

You may wonder about an antenna that is so close to the ground on 40m. Well, I have a secret - the ground at my QTH falls away steeply to the south, so steeply that I am practically living on a cliff edge. With the antenna pointed at ZL, the boom has an effective height at the boom of 175ft. With 400W into the antenna on 7002kHz, the reports from ZL and VK are that "it sounds like a local" when the band was open (summer 2003). Received signals are up by about two S-points over a dipole and the noise is the same or lower. This antenna gives me good 'ears'. Long-path results to Europe have been excellent with the antenna pointed at New Zealand - eg 599 from OH4RH in October 2003.

Not everyone has a QTH like mine, but the Pentagon Loop is a way to get a low band 'quad' in the air for a reasonable price with a rather small tower. If you can manage to place said tower on a hill or a cliff - so much the better!

REFERENCES

[1] *Low Band DXing*, by J Devoldere, ON4UN, ARRL 1999, p10-1.
[2] *Ibid*, p10-5.
[3] MFJ Enterprises Inc produces a 33ft fibreglass telescoping mast (MFJ-1910) which, in lieu of bamboo, would probably do the trick. Available in the UK from Waters & Stanton PLC.
[4] *Low Band DXing*, by J Devoldere, ON4UN, ARRL 1999, p10-4.

THE TRIPOLE

by Phil Ferrell, K7PF

On a recent visit to my house, Dick Bingham, W7WKR, tossed a thumb at my tower. "Why don't you put a few radials on that and drive the radials?" he asked. I was getting ready to put up a 75m vertical, and his suggestion fell on attentive ears.

My tower is a 30-year-old Tri-Ex MW65 (four-section, tilt-over–crankup) which fully extends to 65ft. The tower-top rotator holds a 10ft section of 2.25in thick-wall T4 aluminium pipe. Various HF and VHF aerials have been up there over the years, but it currently hosts a pair of 13-element VHF Yagis. Attached at the top of the pipe is a Diamond X-510 dual-band vertical colinear, which is 17ft long. The tip of that is 92ft above ground. The tower is guyed at the 20ft level, and one of the guy cables acts as a messenger, carrying all transmission lines and rotator control wires to the house. Neglecting the top loading due to the VHF Yagis, that leaves 72ft above the elevated ground plane at 20ft, a little more than a quarter-wave on 80m.

With help from Jack West, W7LD, and Mike Michaeledes, W7ADR, four insulated 62ft radials were placed at 90° intervals and attached to the tower at the 20ft level. The four radials were connected together using a ring made of #12 copper wire attached to each radial with a copper split-nut. The centre conductor of the 50Ω coaxial feed-line was connected to the radial ring, and the coax shield was grounded to the tower. Details are shown in **Fig 1**.

At this point, I had an excellent vertical aerial with a VSWR of less than 2:1 over an incredible 400kHz bandwidth (3.7 to

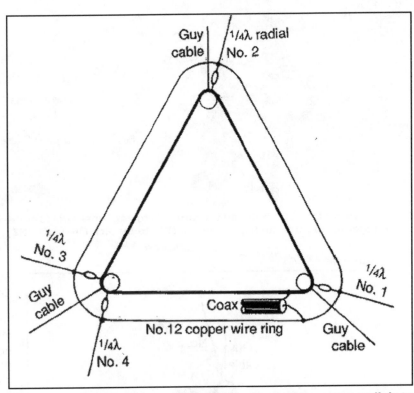

Fig 1: Arrangement and connection of the four quarter-wave radials to create the elevated ground-plane vertical. Note that the centre conductor of the coax goes to the copper ring connecting the radials, and that the shield is grounded to the tower.

4.1 MHz). With the elevated ground radials in place, the resulting vertical aerial showed 32–34Ω resistance and 0–20Ω reactance over the 75m band. Keep in mind, though, that the radials were the driven elements of this 'vertical'; that turned out to be a very important distinction.

I became very curious as to why I'd never heard of this crafty road to a nifty vertical. I queried vertical aerial expert Rudy Severns, N6LF(1), via e-mail, and he assured me that mine was a well-known configuration. He included a reference to a *QST* article [2], which describes my aerial as an 'elevated ground-plane' vertical.

Close-up view of the 20ft point on the author's tower, where his four driven radials come together to form the tripole aerial. (Photo by Dick Miles, K7RNZ)

RADIALS OR DIPOLES?

I gradually noticed that local signals were weaker on the vertical than on a short horizontal wire. The new vertical gave superior performance for long-range, presumably low-angle, signals and on local vertically-polarised signals. Next, I noticed the similarity between the four quarter-wave elevated radials and a pair of low horizontal dipoles at right angles. Thus arose the idea for the tripole aerial.

It got so that when I looked at my tower, I saw two half-wave dipoles instead of four ground radials. There had to be a way to have it all. A little back-of-the-envelope doodling gave the answer.

It takes three DPDT relays to reach all three aerial configurations (two horizontal dipoles and the elevated ground-plane vertical). One relay changes from the vertical aerial to an internal balanced feed, and the other relays route the balanced feed to one of the opposed pair of radials, which becomes a horizontal half-wave dipole (see **Fig 2**). The unused pair of radials remains connected together at the centre, but are at right angles to the energised dipole so that little RF current is induced on the unused dipole.

Fig 3 shows the wiring of the DPDT relay contacts. It also shows a simple aerial selector switch and how to connect the relay coils to achieve aerial switching. I used 12V relays with 160Ω coils and contacts rated at 15A. I also used a separate control line for the relays. At the cost of a couple of RF chokes and coupling capacitors, you could use the RF transmission line to carry the control voltage. If you do that, be careful not to have a 'sneak circuit' short out

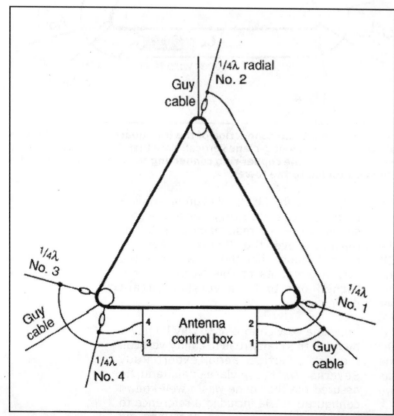

Fig 2: Same arrangement of radials, but with the copper ring replaced by a switch box and separate feed-lines to each radial. This permits operation of any two sets of near-parallel radials as a half-wave dipole.

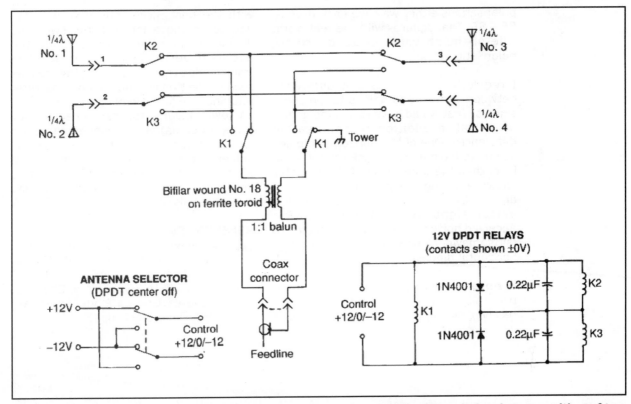

Fig 3: Detail of the tower-mounted control-box circuitry. The 12V DC relay switches between either of two sets of radials and the elevated ground-plane vertical.

the 12V source. That's really embarrassing.

I epoxied the three relays into a 2in x 2in x 5in plastic project box. An SO-239 female coax connector and a two-pin Molex provided RF and control connections. I used four box-mounted pin jacks as connectors to the radials. They exactly fit the #12 copper wire leading to each radial, attached there with a split-nut. Each piece of #12 wire was burnished at each end and coated with Dow-Corning silicone grease (DC4). If female pin jacks are unavailable, female banana jacks can be substituted, requiring a male banana connector on each of the #12 radial connector wires. The control wire and coaxial feed-line connectors were likewise weather-protected with DC4. All internal RF wiring uses short pieces of #18 nylon (Formvar®) coated copper wire.

Just a word about the 1:1 balun: The major consideration is that the toroid core fits inside the box. I used two foot-long pieces of #18 Formvar®-covered copper wire close-spaced to approximate a 50Ω parallel line. This short piece of transmission line was bifilar-wound around a 1in diameter toroidal core (from

WA7OK's well-supplied junk box). Nine turns covered the inside of the core. You could use either RG-58 or RG-174 rather than the #18 copper wire for a 50Ω line on the toroid. RG-174 would limit the transmitter power, and with RG-58 the resulting balun might not fit in the control box.

As you may gather, the balun is not very critical. Once upon a time, you could go to the local ham store and have a choice from a wide variety of ferrite cores. At least I remember when you could do that. Radio Shack does not stock ferrite cores. Pity.

TRIPOLE ON THE AIR
The tripole works amazingly well. I use a DPDT centre-off switch as a 'rotator'. The centre-off position gives me the 'elevated radial' vertical, and each 'on' position of the switch activates one horizontal dipole.

Jack West, W7LD, lives about 13 airline miles from me. He has a large aerial collection, including a vertical dipole and a horizontal two half-waves in phase, both for 75m. Using either vertical-to-vertical or horizontal-to-horizontal polarisation, we are S9 to each other. Crossing our polarisations either way, we each drop to S5 – S6. That squares with the real-world rule-of-thumb value of 20 dB cross-polarisation loss.

I regularly see a six S-unit difference between vertical and horizontal on some signals. That would have to include angle-of-arrival in addition to polarisation differences. One of the horizontal dipoles seems to have a lower background noise level than the other. Even if the S-meter shows a stronger signal on the 'noisier' dipole, the 'quieter' dipole can give a better signal-to-noise ratio (SNR). Received noise from the vertical seems to fall somewhere between that of the two horizontal dipoles.

A note on transmitting*:* You want to transmit on the aerial with the strongest received signal, but receive using the one with the best SNR. Thus you may find yourself doing a lot of aerial switching during a marginal contact. Switching between vertical and horizontal on transmit does measurably change the load seen by the transmitter, but no transmitter retuning is required in my case. Depending on tower height, top-hat capacity (guy wires or aerials), and available real estate for the radials, your tripole could be implemented on 160 or 40m instead of 75m. It adds an intriguing element to operating – What will happen when you switch aerials?

REFERENCES
[1]   R Severns, N6LF, 'Verticals, Ground Systems and Some History', *QST,* July 2000, pp38 – 45.

[2]   T Russell, N4KG, 'Simple, Effective, Elevated Ground-Plane Antennas', *QST,* June 1994, pp45 – 46.

THE SUPER-C AERIAL – A CRITICAL APPRAISAL

by Prof Dr-Ing Gerd Janzen, DF6SJ

For reasons of space, the author's thoughts on the 20m band have been left out. The full article can be found under www.cqdl.de/rubrik/technik

In [1], Manfred Salzwedel, OH/DK4ZC, reported about the 'Super-C Aerial', a shortened radiator for HF. DF6SJ set himself the task of understanding the aerial geometry [2] with the *EZNEC* simulation program on the computer.

The Super-C aerial, published on the Internet, is intended for 20-10m. Its VSWR = 2 bandwidth is given as >1.4MHz in the 10m band and as 250kHz in the 20m band. The manufacturer gives earth losses of near zero for a mounting height directly above ground. The efficiency is given as >90%. However, the meaning of the term 'efficiency' is not defined. The manufacturer expressly excludes ground effects on the radiation and proper functioning. Neither does he give the gain, the most important and most interesting figure for an aerial. Concrete details of the radiation angle and the radiation pattern, respectively, are also missing.

This is surprising: has the manufacturer of this aerial [2] never heard of the 'fat' aerial [6, p167 – 74] or the aerial 'subjected to capacitive load' [6, p219 – 68]? Both versions lead to more wide-band radiators and can, especially in the case of capacitive loads, often be substantially shorter than λ/4 or λ/2. In most cases, compensation coils at the feed-point are not needed either.

A LOT OF 'OLD HATS'

If one looks at the Super-C aerial without the manufacturer's advertising copy, this radiator can be put into the categories of 'very short', 'fat' and 'subjected to capacitive load'. And these are all 'old hats' - capacitive ones, in this case!

For the simulation of an aerial in *EZNEC*, it is necessary to enter the aerial wires into a table ('Wires'). The simulation of a radiator of geometric complexity such as the Super-C requires a lot of experience and knowledge, to avoid being stuck with time-consuming input of hundreds of pieces of wires. The first problem to be solved is the selection of a suitably tight-meshed grid.

Practical layout of a Super-C aerial by Manfred Salzwedel, OH/DK4ZC.

Fig 1 shows the basis of the simulation, consisting of an arrangement of 1313 wires with 1317 segments. The

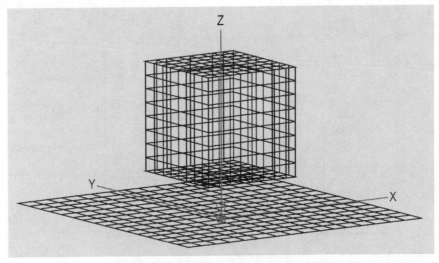

Fig 1: View of the Super-C aerial, simulated with *EZNEC-Pro*, consisting of 1313 wires and 1317 segments. The overall height of the aerial is 91cm. The ground net measures 1.83m x 1.83m. The feed-point (circle) is directly above the zero coordinate.

disadvantage is that the computing time rises with the number of segments squared! And thus, a calculation for a frequency takes almost five minutes on a 350MHz computer.

The diameter of all net wires is defined as 2mm. The short vertical radiator between the ground net and the bottom end of the wire basket is depicted as a 40mm aluminium tube. Below, the simulation uses the 10m corner band as an example.

DIFFERENT GROUNDS

Initially, the aerial is – as described in the Internet brochure – mounted near the ground. In our simulation calculations, this will be at a height of 5cm above a normal horticultural ground (normal ground = NG).

EZNEC permits the input of grounds of very different electrical qualities [7]. An even lower mounting height, eg directly on the ground can, however, cause mathematical problems.

28.5MHz gives an aerial input resistance $ZA = 4.9\Omega - j26\Omega$ which, therefore, comprises a real portion of 4.9Ω and a negative (ie capacitive) reactance of -26Ω. Ideally, the real portion is the 'radiation' resistance of the aerial, which ought to be as high as possible – the quantity which sends out our transmission power and which represents a 'loss' resistance for the transmitter, but is useful to us. The capacitive, reactive, part shows that the aerial is too short for 28.5MHz.

This input resistance thus requires a minor inductive compensation which, due to the finite coil quality, introduces losses into the aerial circuit. If the compensation has been effected by a series-connected coil with the inductive resistance of $+26\Omega$, the real portion of 4.9Ω still has to be matched to 50Ω. This requires only two components which, for example, can be dimensioned according to [6, p146] and (importantly!) measured at the operating frequency according to [8].

LOW-LOSS MATCHING NETWORK

The losses in this matching network, which introduce further coil losses, are normally low and will be neglected here. It is narrow-band, thus only works well at the design frequency (here – 28.5 MHz). A wideband matching circuit would consist of a wideband transformer (transmission-line transformer) or toroidal-core transformer [6, p127].

The efficiency, which arises due to the compensation coil losses, is easy to calculate. For an assumed coil quality QL = 100 and the required compensation reactance $+26\Omega$, the loss resistance of the coil Rcoil = $26\Omega/100 = 0.26\Omega$. This value of 0.26Ω competes with the effective resistance of 4.9Ω of the aerial and thus gives an efficiency $\varsigma = 4.9\Omega/(4.9\Omega + 0.26\Omega) = 95\%$.

This value is the compensation coil efficiency, which can also be called up by *EZNEC* in the menu item 'Load Data'. Here, the program shows a coil loss of 5W - assuming 100W of HF power supplied. *EZNEC* also calculates the relative coil losses (5W / 100W = 5%) and the efficiency thus defined (95%).

This figure sounds outstanding. Unfortunately, it is not the whole truth; the real portion of the aerial input resistance of 4.9Ω contains, in addition to the radiation proportion mentioned, yet further losses stemming from the lossy aerial wires and, in particular, the non-ideal ground nearby.

Fig 2: Ripple curves over the frequency for all Super-C aerials examined in the 10m band with mounting heights of 0.05m (continuous lines) and 4m (dotted lines) over different grounds.

How can these harmful losses be separated from the useful quantity 'radiation resistance'? This would be very difficult in a practical experiment. In a simulation, one can attempt to mount the aerial on an ideal base, ie an infinitely-expanded metal plate of infinitely high conductivity, instead of over lossy earth.

OUTWITTING GROUND LOSSES

How, in practice, can we avoid ground losses? We mount the aerial a bit further away from the ground, possibly 4 m above the normal horticultural ground – something which could be a bit of a technical and optical problem with the Super-C aerial. For this setup, *EZNEC* calculates ZA = (1.5 -j32)Ω. The compensation of this reactive portion introduces 32Ω/100 = 0.32Ω to the circuit. The aerial, mounted at a height of 4m over an ideal metal plate, has ZA = (1.44 -j32)Ω. With compensation, there is an input resistance of the aerial standing on ideal ground of ZA = 1.76Ω.

Telling evidence of the absurdity of an overall efficiency calculated according to the above pattern is provided by the simulation results of the Super-C aerial mounted at a height of 4m over normal ground and over an ideal underground, respectively. Over normal ground, there is an input resistance ZA = 0.47Ω -j111Ω. Mounted at a height of 4m over an ideal metal plate, there is ZA = 0.51Ω -j 111Ω.

It is surprising to find that the real portion of the aerial standing on ideal ground has even increased by 0.04Ω (!). A simple explanation of this would mean that, over the ideal underground, higher losses than over lossy earth will occur. This cannot be, and thus proves that the considerations regarding overall efficiency, applied in discussing the 10m band aerial, are absurd.

LOOKING AT THE BANDWIDTH

For a correct bandwidth calculation, the aerial must always be provided with the necessary compensation; otherwise, it would be hopelessly mismatched. For wide-band tests, it must be entered in *EZNEC* as inductance, L, and not as reactance, XL. Thus, from this inductance, L, the program can then calculate the correct reactances XL = ωL = 2πfL

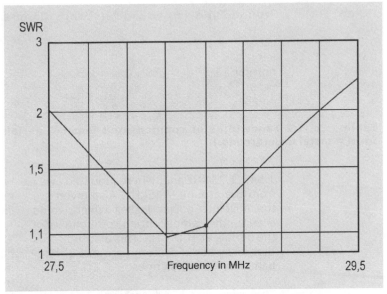

Fig 3: Ripple s = SWR as a function of the frequency in the 10m band for a Super-C aerial, which is mounted 0.05m above normal ground. The aerial is compensated for 28.5MHz and the bandwidth adjusted to 50Ω.

appearing for the particular default spot frequencies, *f*.

Six different configurations (**Fig 2**) illustrate the connection between SWR and mounting height (0.05m, 4m) over certain grounds (ideal, normal, urban). The ripple values and frequencies calculated in *EZNEC* were adopted as a 'component' in the *MathCad* mathematical program. Thus, for comparison purposes, all plots could be drawn together in a single diagram.

Fig 3 again shows the detailed SWR curve for a Super-C aerial, which is mounted 0.05m over a normal ground. One recognises compensation and matching to 50Ω at 28.5MHz, which leads to the SWR minimum there.

HEIGHT AFFECTS BANDWIDTH

It can be seen at first glance that all Super-C aerials at 5cm height above ground are relatively wide-band, and that all aerials erected at 4m operate in a narrow-band mode. This result is plausible, since aerials represent an open oscillating circuit which becomes more wide-band through increased attenuation (increased ohmic losses through ground proximity).

Table 1 summarises the bandwidths between the ripple values s = SWR = 2. For the Super-C aerials mounted directly over real grounds, they are

Height (m)	Ground Type	Bandwidth (MHz)	Compensation Loss (W)
0.05	normal	1.73	5.0
0.05	urban	1.54	5.9
0.05	ideal	1.25	6.7
4	normal	0.54	17.8
4	urban	0.55	17.5
4	ideal	0.52	18.2

Table 1: s = 2 bandwidths of compensated Super-C aerials in the 10m band. Ideal = metal underground.).

GAIN AND RADIATION ANGLE

Two important characteristics of an aerial is its gain and radiation angle; these values determine how the signal reaches the receiver, and at what signal strength external signals can be read at one's own station.

1.54...1.73MHz and, where mounted away from the ground, 545kHz. Also given are the absolute power losses which would occur in the compensation components of the aerials at 100W HF. This also indicates that lossy aerial systems are more wideband than low-loss ones.

The calculated bandwidth values for the 10m band match quite closely, for mounting close to the ground (ie lossy mounting), with the details in the brochure for the Super-C aerial.

The measurement of aerial gains is a particular problem (or even impossible) in the short-wave range, since ambient influences can hardly be excluded. Moreover, the access to the space in front of the aerial is generally impossible. Large commercial aerial systems are even surveyed with helicopters!

These difficulties with the experimental determination of the gain give free reign to apparently crazy details. Therefore, details given by aerial manufacturers and also by radio amateurs should be treated with caution. The simulation, however, prepares new paths. In this instance too, however, gains are only ever calculated as precisely as the user is able to enter data of the aerial and the environment, especially regarding the underground.

In addition, *EZNEC* prints out pretty 2-D or 3-D radiation patterns, from which one can read what gain in which direction and at what principal radiation angle can be expected.

Fig 4 shows the radiation patterns of two aerials mounted at different heights - 0.05m and 4m over normal ground. 1.07dBi for 15° principal radiation angle results for the heightened setup and -1,38dBi at 30° radiation angle for the setup close to the ground.

If the aerials are mounted over urban ground at the given heights, then *EZNEC* calculates the two radiation patterns in **Fig 5**. Comparing the pictures, note that the 0dB outer circles always have different dBi values assigned.

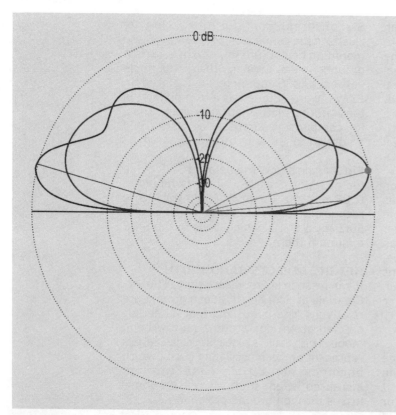

Fig 4: Elevation radiation patterns of a simulated Super-C aerial at 4m and 0.05m height over normal ground at 28.5MHz. The aerial 4m high radiates 1.07dBi at the principal radiation angle of 15°, the aerial close to the ground radiates 1.38dBi at 30°. (The outer circle is equivalent to 1.07dBi).

8dBi AS A MAXIMUM

The evaluation of these and further radiation patterns not shown here gives the Super-C aerial the highest (theoretical) gain of almost 8dBi at 28.5MHz for the highest mounting (h = 4m) over infinitely-expanded, ideally-conducting ground. If it was mounted only 5cm high over the same ideal underground, the gain would already drop to 5.2dBi.

If an ideally-conducting wire (instead of the aluminium net) was now used, the gain would again rise a little to 5.22dBi. Compare with this the two first rows of numbers in **Table 2** with ideal wire and aluminium wire, respectively. Over the ideal metal ground, the radiation maximum is always reached at 0°.

If the aerial is mounted closely over a real normal ground, a gain of only around -1.38dBi at a radiation angle of 30° can be expected. The gain can be somewhat increased, and the radiation angle reduced, if the aerial including its ground net is raised. This gives a value of 1.07dBi, thus 2.45dB more – equivalent to about half an S-point – for an radiation angle of 15° and the mounting height h = 4m.

Much worse than horticultural ground is an urban ground with one-fifth of the HF conductivity. The gain, when mounted close to the ground, only is -2.35dBi at a radiation angle of 32°. Each increase in distance, especially for an HF-defective base, clearly improves this unfavourable data. At 4m height over urban ground, the gain is already 3.73dB (more than half an S-point) more than at 5cm mounting height. The radiation angle reduces from 32° to 18°, and clearly improves the DX operation.

Table 2 shows a list of gain values and principal radiation directions of Super-C aerials, once made from no-loss ideal wire, then from real aluminium material, mounted at different heights over an infinitely

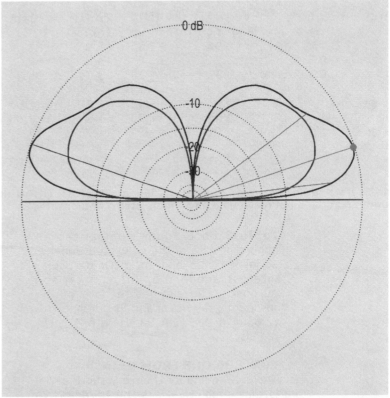

Fig 5: Elevation radiation patterns at 4m and 0.05m height over urban ground at 28.5MHz. For h = 4m, the gain is 1.38dBi at the principal radiation angle of 18°, the aerial close to the ground radiates -2.35dBi at 32°. (The outer circle is equivalent to 1.38dBi).

extended metal plate (no ground losses), a horticultural ground (HF normal ground) and urban ground (HF-defective).

The gain values of uncompensated aerials are often given. This, however, is unrealistic, as the compensation always required in practice (as needs to be achieved with a coil) drastically lowers the gain. The uncompensated values are not given here.

Underground	Material	Height (m)	28.5MHz comp Gain (dBi)	ϕ (°)
ideal	ideal wire	0.05	5.22	0
	Al wire	0.05	5.2	0
	Al wire	4	7.97	0
normal	Al wire	0.05	-1.38	30
	Al wire	4	1.07	15
urban	Al wire	0.05	-2.35	32
	Al wire	4	1.38	18

Table 2: Gain values and principal radiation directions of simulated Super-C aerials for ideal and real undergrounds, ideal and real aerial wire and for different mounting heights h = 0.05m and h = 4m at 28.5MHz.

Aerial	Height/g (m)		Vertical length (m)	ZA (Ω) uncomp	ZA (Ω) comp	Gain	φ	B/W	Comp loss	Losses (relative)
Super-C	0.05	NG	0.91	4.9 -j26	5.2	-1.38	30°	1.73	5.0 W	0.22 dB
Super-C	0.05	UG	0.91	4.3 -j27	4.6	-2.35	32°	1.54	5.9 W	0.27 dB
Super-C	0.05	ideal	0.91	3.5 -j25	3.74	5.2	0°	1.25	6.7 W	0.3 dB
Super-C	4	NG	0.91	1.5 -j32	1.8	1.07	15°	0.54	17.8 W	0.85 dB
Super-C	4	UG	0.91	1.5 -j32	1.8	1.38	18°	0.55	17.5 W	0.84 dB
Super-C	4	ideal	0.91	1.4 -j32	1.76	7.97	0°	0.52	18.2 W	0.87 dB
λ/4	4	NG	2.61	22.2	22.2	0.79	14°	1.00	0	0

Table 3: Data of compensated Super-C aerials at 28.5MHz. (NG = normal/horticultural ground, UG = urban ground; ZA aerial input resistance uncompensated/compensated).

Table 3 once again summarises all important data of the simulated Super-C aerial for 10m operation. Of particular interest should be, for comparison purposes, the simulation data of the resonant λ/4 vertical aerials of full length (2.61m in the 10m band) with 4 x λ/4 radials.

CONCLUSIONS FROM GAIN

The bottom line for the 'very short' aerial is that - mainly – it is the HF-defective but, unfortunately, not unrealistic underground which lets the short Super-C aerial become a problematic radiator. The simulations show that the laws of Physics also apply to this aerial. A different and somehow 'special' physical behaviour could not be found.

The results obtained do not contradict what data there are on Super-C aerials published on the Internet. The other (non-published or inaccurately-defined) aerial data such as 'efficiency', gain and radiation angle can thus also be transferred from the simulation to the real aerial.

Ultimately, it would be tempting to test if simpler geometric structures of short or very short vertical radiators could not compete, as regards radiation angle and gain values, with the Super-C aerial so enthusiastically praised by the manufacturer.

[These investigations follow in the next article in the book – Ed.]

LITERATURE AND SUPPLY SOURCES
[1]   Manfred Salzwedel, OH/DK4ZC, 'Super-C-Antenne als Nachbau im Praxistest', CQ DL 10/02, pp737-41.
[2]   GAP Antenna Products, www.gapantenna.com/superc.htm
[3]   Roy Lewallen, W7EL, PO Box 6658, Beaverton, OR, 97007, USA; http://eznec.com
[4]   Gerd Janzen, DF6SJ, 'EZNEC 3.0 - Antennensimulation unter Windows', Funkamateur 10/00, 11/00, 12/00.
[5]   Gerd Janzen, DF6SJ, 'Antennensimulation mit EZNEC', a talk during the 4th Specialist Seminar on Short Waves (Kurzwellen-Fachtagung) of the DARC, March 2001, Munich.
[6]   Gerd Janzen, Kurze Antennen, Franckh-Verlag, Stuttgart, 1986, reference: author.
[7]   Gerd Janzen, Monopolantennen und Vertikalantennen, Kempten, 1999, reference: author.
[8]   Gerd Janzen, HF-Messungen mit einem Aktiven Stehwellen-Messgerät, Kempten, 1996, reference: author.

Here, results from EZNEC are sometimes given to two decimal places. This high accuracy, however, is mostly unrealistic, since the' inner part' of NEC-2, the basic mathematical computation routine of EZNEC, contains rounding errors and further inaccuracies.

The gain values are given in dBi. The 'i' means isotropic, since the radiation of these aerials is compared with a non-existent, ideal omnidirectional radiator (spherical radiator) with a gain of 0dBi. 3dBi thus means that this radiator radiates 3dB better (twice more power) in the given direction than the isotropic radiator. Compared with a dipole, which already has 2.15dBi compared with a spherical radiator, this means -6.9dBi = (-6.9-2.15)dBd = -9.05dBd.

HF RADIATION BY SIMPLE MEANS

By Prof Dr-Ing Gerd Janzen, DF6SJ

Is the material and cubical effort of the Super-C aerial justified? Calculations with *EZNEC* show that a simple vertical aerial with roof capacity leads to similar results.

In the previous article [published as the foregoing article in this book – *Ed.*], a commercially-manufactured vertical aerial [1] was examined with *EZNEC*. The technical-mechanical effort for implementing this 'Super-C' design is quite high, because a three-dimensional cubical structure is mounted on the end of a short radiator [2]. Wind resistance and tilting moment have an unpleasant effect. Add to this that a wire net more than 3m² in size must be mounted under this aerial which, even if mounted slightly higher above the ground, involves stability problems.

The question is whether a much simpler 'classic', but also much shorter aerial geometry gives similar aerial data in simulation and practice.

COMPARISON OF AERIAL DATA

A comparison with the aerial data of a 'full size' vertical with the length $\lambda/4$ is always appropriate, to keep ideas of the quality of an aerial in respect of gain and radiation angle realistic.

Therefore, the following investigations first concern themselves with the classic vertical aerial with radials, then with the much shortened aerial subjected to a capacitive load at the top end. Here, as in [1], the investigations are limited to the 10m band.

The aim is a much simpler aerial design for a very short radiator operating from the 20 – 10m band similar to the Super-C aerial. Commercial aluminium tubes 10 – 20 mm in diameter, available at all DIY stores, as well as 10mm aluminium angle sections with lengths of 1m and 2m, are used.

VERTICAL WITH FOUR RADIALS

To obtain comparative data of a non-shortened aerial, first a full-size ground plane [7] for 28.5MHz is designed and simulated with *EZNEC* [3].

The wavelength is λ = 300m/28.5 = 10.53m. From this follows, for the four horizontally projecting radials, a length of $\lambda/4$ = 2.63m.

A vertical wire of the same length is entered in the 'Wires' menu of *EZNEC*. The aerial is mounted at a height of h = 4m over a normal horticultural ground (= normal ground [7]) and consists of 2mm copper wire.

Since the simulation of the input resistance of this vertical still gives a slightly reduced inductive value with the quarter wavelength calculated, the length of the vertical part will be reduced. This is done until the base resistance takes an approximately pure real value, the reactance portion thus being negligible.

Resonance is achieved for 28.5MHz with a radiator length of 2.61m. Thus, the 'full-size' vertical already is completely simulated. The input resistance is ZA = 22.23Ω - j0.5Ω, and the gain is 0.79dBi for the optimum radiation angle ϕ = 14°. This certainly is not a bad aerial! The SWR = 2 bandwidth results from recording the SWRs over the frequency range when adjusting the real portion of 22.23Ω to 50Ω at around 1MHz.

GROUND LOSSES HAVE AN EFFECT

If, instead of 4m, this vertical aerial is built only 0.05m over normal ground (= NG), there will be a surprise. Due to the ground losses, the input resistance rises to 34.2Ω, and the aerial gain drops to -0.14dBi. The DX operation, too, with the steep 27° angle, becomes clearly more difficult than at 14°. This aerial no longer is very advantageous! The only positive side effect, caused by the increased ground

Ht (m)	Gnd	Len (m)	Radiator (vert, mm)	ZA (Ω)	Gain (dBi)	φ (°)	B/W (MHz)
0.05	NG	2.59	2 Cu	34.2	-0.14	27	1.55
0.05	NG	2.50	20 Alu	33.6	-0.06	27	1.55
0.05	UG	2.57	2 Cu	31.7	-0.86	29	1.41
0.05	UG	2.53	20 Alu	31.3	-0.81	29	2.10
4	NG	2.61	2 Cu	22.2	0.79	14	1.00
4	NG	2.59	20 Alu	21.8	0.98	14	1.40
4	UG	2.61	2 Cu	22.6	1.44	17	1.02
4	UG	2.59	20 Alu	22.1	1.63	17	1.52

Table 1: λ/4 radiator with 4 x λ/4 radials for 28.5MHz at different heights over normal ground (NG) and urban ground (UG).

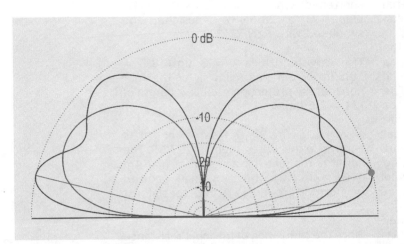

Fig 1: Radiation pattern of a 10m-band aerial, λ/4 in size, at 28.5MHz. (Radials 4 x λ/4, vertical part made from 20mm aluminium tube.) Over normal ground (h = 4m), there is a gain of 0.98dBi at 14° radiation angle (ID point in the diagram); directly over urban ground (h = 0.05m), there is a gain of -0.81dBi at 29°.

losses, is the rise of the SWR = 2 bandwidth from 1.0MHz to 1.55MHz.

If the λ/4 monopole, 4m in height, was constructed from 20mm aluminium tube instead of 2mm copper wire, there would be hardly any changes: new resonance length of the vertical part 2.59m, input resistance ZA = 21.8Ω, gain 0.98dBi for the radiation angle of 14°.

An overview can be obtained quickly from **Table 1** and **Fig 1**: aerials over urban (UG) or normal ground have much steeper and thus inferior DX principal radiation angles of 27 – 29° than aerials mounted 4m above ground with 14 – 17° radiation angle.

ROOF C MADE OF ALUMINIUM ANGLES
Now for the heavily-shortened vertical aerials. A metal grid – as is attached under the Super-C aerial – is deliberately not used. Radials 6 x 2m long, made of 10mm aluminium tubes, are used instead. While the 2m pieces are not resonant, they can be used optimally and without waste. For reasons of stability, a thicker 20mm aluminium tube will be the radiator rod. Initially, this will also be 2m long and carry, at the upper end, a hexagonal 'hat' made from light, but torsionally-rigid, aluminium angle sections 10mm x 10mm x 1mm.

This hat consists of six spokes 1m in length, departing from a central point. In turn, the free ends are connected with 6 x 1m lengths of the named aluminium angle section. This produces a stable frame of six adjoining equilateral triangles with a side length of 1m (**Fig 2**).

During the practical setup, ensure that the anodised angle sections are scraped at the screw connection points and made mutually conductive.

The input of this geometry into the 'Wires' menu of *EZNEC* can be very difficult since, to define the outer end points of the six spokes, trigonometric functions have to be used again and again. Much smarter is the automatic radial generation contained in *EZNEC 3.0*, which we use here for generating the hexagonal roof capacitance.

For this, only a prototype structure made of the wires 2 and 3 is defined, the automatic radial generator ('Wires' menu -> 'Other' -> 'Create Radials') is called up and, in the menu, the creation of six radials is selected - and everything is ready.

75Ω BASE RESISTANCE
The simulation of the geometry described with the 2m-long vertical part for 28.5MHz at a mounting height h = 4m over normal ground gives, for this vertical aerial

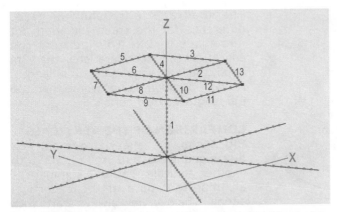

Fig 2: *EZNEC* model of the vertical aerial subjected to capacitive load, 1m in length, with six radials 2m in length. The points on the wires identify the segments which *EZNEC* requires for the calculation of the aerial data. At the base of the vertical part, the feed-point (circle) and the compensation point (square) can be seen.

subjected to a capacitive end load, a base resistance ZA = 75.33Ω +j399.5Ω.

The reactive portion of the complex input resistance is heavily positive, thus inductive - the radiator is (electrically) much too long for the 10m band and demands capacitive compensation. The capacitive reactance of the series capacitor necessary at the base is jXc = -j399.5Ω. A capacitor with the capacity Ccomp = 1/(Xc x 2π x 28.5MHz) = 14pF fulfils this.

Capacitors are generally seen as no-loss components. To create really true conditions, we do not want to make such as stipulation, but assume a realistic capacitor quality Qc = 1000. This then introduces a loss resistance Rvcond = 399.5Ω/1000 = 0.4Ω to the aerial circuit. These values are entered in the *EZNEC* 'Loads' menu. Following recalculation, the result now gives the input resistance ZA = 75.73Ω +j0.644Ω.

The reactive portion +j0.644Ω, now negligible, shows that the compensation through the 14pF capacitor acts correctly at 28.5MHz. The aerial data is: gain 1.01dBi for 14°. In 'Load Data' of *EZNEC*, one can see how great the absolute losses in the capacitor are – eg for 100W HF power, just 0.53W or 0.023dB.

The bandwidth of this shortened vertical aerial can be read from the SWR plot. **Fig 3** shows two ripple

plots of SWR over the frequency of 27 – 30MHz. The lower of the two plots results for the aerial optimally-compensated at 28.5MHz for direct connection to a 75Ω system. This suggests itself here since the aerial, at 28.5MHz, has almost exactly 75Ω input resistance. The same plot also applies if a wide-band adjustment of 75Ω to 50Ω was made, for example with a 1.5:1 wideband transformer.

The bandwidth between the two s=2 frequencies is about 1.43 MHz. If the aerial is directly connected to a 50Ω system, the upper of the two SWR plots applies. One can see the mismatch of s = 75Ω/50Ω = 1.5 at 28.5MHz. In this case, however, there is a reduced s=2 bandwidth of about 0.94MHz.

REDUCED FROM 2m TO 1m
How does the data of the vertical aerial change – when subjected to capacitive load – if the perpendicular vertical rod is shortened from 2m to 1m? The 6 x 2m

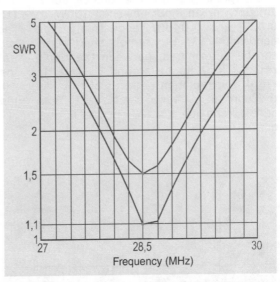

Fig 3: Ripple curves over the frequency range in the 10m band for a vertical radiator 2m long with capacitive hat. The two curves differ in their matching. The plot going down to the ripple value s = 1.1 applies to a wide-band matching to 75Ω, the other applies – without matching – to direct connection to a 50Ω cable (h = 4m over normal ground).

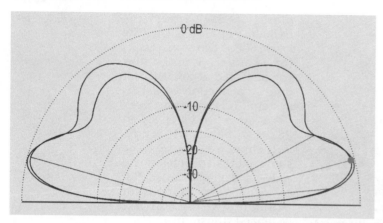

Fig 4: Radiation patterns of the full-sized 10m band λ/4 radiator and of the vertical radiator shortened to 1m in vertical length with capacitive hat. Gain and principal radiation angle of the short hat aerial (= ID point) only differ insignificantly (0.77dBi/15° against 0.98dBi/14°). The steep radiation of the λ/4 radiator is greater. Data common to both aerials: 28.5MHz, h = 4m over normal ground.

The diagrams only show a clear difference for the steep radiation not important to DX. This permits the conclusion that, for operation in the 10m band, the 'hat' aerial only 1m in length, for DX operation, is not worse than the full-length vertical aerials.

COMPARISON OF THE VERTICALS

Fig 5 shows the aerial geometries, discussed here and in [1], next to another, to scale. **Table 2** summarises all important data of these vertical aerials. The overview always starts with the 'normal' resonant, ie an unshortened λ/4 ground plane with four horizontally-stretched λ/4 radials, followed by the heavily-shortened monopole aerials calculated here with the vertical lengths 2m and 1m with a large capacitive hat at the end of the radiator rod. For a direct comparison, then follow the Super-C aerials simulated in [1] with the large wire net cube and the base net.

radials and the hexagonal roof capacity are maintained.

For a 1m-long uncompensated vertical, at 28.5MHz, $Z_A = 8.614\Omega + j81.52\Omega$. The compensation capacity is $C_{comp} = 1/(81.52\Omega \times 2 \times \pi \times 28.5MHz) = 68.5pF$, its loss resistance $81.52\Omega/1000 = 0.08\Omega$. Thus, the aerial has an input resistance of $Z_A = 8.7\Omega$ and a gain of 0.77dBi at 15° radiation.

The losses in the compensation capacitor amount, for an input power of 100W, to 0.92W and 0.04dB, respectively. The bandwidth of this extremely short aerial can be determined, between the ripple points s = 2, to be around 735kHz. In **Fig 4**, the radiation patterns of this and the 'normal' λ/4 aerial can be seen. Both aerials stand at h = 4m height over normal ground.

All aerials stand at heights of h = 4m and h = 0.05m over normal horticultural ground (NG) or over HF-defective urban ground (UG). Also given is the base resistance of the as-yet uncompensated aerials, as well as the pure effective resistance of the inductively- or capacitively-compensated aerials.

There then follows the aerial gain in dBi (thus in comparison to the isotropic radiator) and the associated optimum radiation angle, ϕ, then the s=2 bandwidth as well as the absolute compensation losses for an assumed input power of 100W and the relative compensation losses in dB.

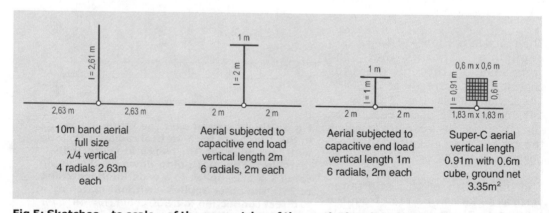

Fig 5: Sketches – to scale – of the geometries of the vertical aerials compared to one another.

Aerial Ht (m)	Gnd	Vert len (m)	Za (Ω) uncomp	Za (Ω) comp	Gain (dBi)	φ (°)	B/W (MHz)	Comp loss	Loss (rel)
λ/4 radiator of full length, 4 radials									
0.05	NG	2.50	33.6	33.6	-0.06	27	1.55	0	0
4	NG	2.59	21.8	21.8	0.98	14	1.40	0	0
0.05	UG	2.53	31.3	31.3	-0.81	29	2.10	0	0
4	UG	2.59	22.1	22.1	1.63	17	1.52	0	0
Vertical radiator with capacitive hat and 6 x 2 radials									
0.05	NG	2	161+j438	161	-0.58	27	3.00	0.25	0.01
4	NG	2	75.3+j400	75.7	1.01	14	1.43	0.53	0.02
0.05	UG	2	144+j424	144	-1.48	30	3.00	0.28	0.01
4	UG	2	76.9+j400	76.9	1.58	17	1.44	0.52	0.02
0.05	NG	1	20.4+j99	20.5	-1.12	30	1.70	0.49	0.02
4	NB	1	8.6+j82	8.7	0.77	15	0.74	0.92	0.04
0.05	UB	1	18.8+j94	18.9	-2.18	32	1.59	0.50	0.02
4	UG	1	8.8+j82	8.9	1.16	18	0.73	0.90	0.04
Super-C aerial [1,2]									
0.05	NG	0.91	4.9-j26	5.2	-1.38	30	1.73	5.0	0.22
4	NG	0.91	1.5-j32	1.8	1.07	15	0.54	17.8	0.85
0.05	UG	0.91	4.3-j27	4.6	-2.35	32	1.54	5.9	0.27
4	UG	0.91	1.5-j32	1.8	1.38	18	0.55	17.5	0.84

Table 2: Input resistances, radiation data and power losses of compensated as well as uncompensated vertical aerials at 28.5MHz.

A QUESTION OF THE BEST AERIAL

At first glance, the sheer number of figures is quite confusing. However, even if the columns of figures have been studied for a while and 'good / bad' tendencies have been found, a fundamental question remains: What *is* a good aerial?

One could define that it should be possible for a good aerial to be connected to a coaxial cable without extensive matching. This, however, would automatically exclude the bulk of aerials, above all the short ones. Will the bandwidth then be important? Yes, but a great bandwidth often is a sign of a lossy aerial.

It is probably undisputable that a high aerial gain and a flat radiation angle make a good (DX) aerial. While, for 'local' HF communication, a steep radiation angle is better, the following discussion is to emphasise good DX aerials.

What is more important: a high gain or a flat radiation angle, if both cannot be achieved simultaneously? This is a question which is difficult to answer. However, let us make a simple, almost primitive model, omitting the curvature of the earth.

A FEW JUMPS FOR DX

The F-layer of the ionosphere lies at a height of around 300km. If, under the angle of elevation φ, we radiate in the direction of this highest ionospheric layer, the beam hits this at a (horizontal) distance of around L = 300km / (tan φ).

Example 1: φ = 20° -> L = 824km.
Example 2: φ = 45° -> L = 300km.

This simple assumption only applies if the radiation angle, φ, is not too great. If the curvature of the earth is included in the consideration, the beam will not reach as far.

If we want to circumnavigate half the globe, 20,000 km / (300km/(tan φ)) reflections will be required. For φ = 20° this will be 20,000km / 824km = 24 reflections; for φ = 45°, this will be 20,000km / 300km = 67 reflections. About half of these concern the ionosphere, with the other half concerning the earth's surface.

Each reflection is imperfect and brings about an attenuation for the wave trajectory in the sea. The jump distance is slightly shorter, taking the curvature of the earth into account. Therefore, under both radiation angles, more reflections than 24 or 67 are needed, but the main train of thought does not change.

However, a further increase in attenuation is added. Because of the zig-zag trajectory of the wave beam between ionosphere and earth, a greater distance than the 'straight' one has to be overcome. For radiation angles, ϕ, which are not too small, this is, on the way to the sea, with the above data, approximately 20,000 km / (cos ϕ), thus for ϕ = 20°, we derive about 21,300km but, for ϕ = 45°, already it is 28 300 km. Calculated simply, this greater distance already gives 2.5dB more attenuation; this is equivalent to around half an S-point.

Let us summarise: a steep radiation angle thus causes both a higher overall reflection attenuation and a greater free-space attenuation (path attenuation) than a flat radiation angle.

A QUESTION OF GAIN

Table 2 summarises the data of all vertical aerials for the 10m band, simulated here with *EZNEC*. Which are the aerials with high gain?

The aerial with the highest gain (1.58dBi) in Table 2 is the 2m-long monopole subjected to capacitive load, which is attached 4m over an urban ground (HF-defective). This 2m monopole does not radiate significantly worse (1.01dBi) over normal ground (better for HF). At first glance this is surprising, and the problem of what is good and what is bad already becomes very apparent.

Over normal ground, the radiation angle is 14° but, over urban ground, it is 17°. Which aerial now is the better one? Most likely the one with the flatter radiation angle because, on its way to the sea, it manages with clearly fewer ionospheric and earth reflections than the one radiating 3° steeper.

Let us again approximate: the number of reflections for ϕ = 14° is about 16 but, for ϕ = 17°, it is already 20. A single further reflection certainly causes a higher attenuation than the difference (1.58 - 1.01)dBi = 0.57dB between the two gain values. According to this primitive calculation, if DX is required, even an only slightly flatter radiation angle is worth much more than a higher gain. Experiences of radio amateurs strongly support this conclusion. Thus, the gain of an aerial should not be overestimated; instead, a flat radiation angle should always be aimed for.

FLAT RADIATION FOR DX

The smallest radiation angles of 14° and 15° are featured by the aerials placed highest over normal ground (NG), almost irrespective of how large, short, long or thick they are. Even the $\lambda/4$ aerial of full length does not radiate flatter than 14°. The next better aerials are those mounted 4m over the more HF-defective urban ground (UG).

Aerials with a particularly bad radiation angle are all aerials standing directly on the ground – especially those mounted on defective urban ground, which radiate under the steep angles of 27° to 32° with inferior DX. According to our primitive observation, for ϕ = 32°, 42 reflections to the back of the earth would be required!

It is evident that the capacitively-loaded vertical aerials, of 2m length and standing 4m over ground (NG and UG), for the 10m band, have slightly higher gain values than the identically-mounted 'large' $\lambda/4$ aerials. This is because the vertical part with 2m length, which is used here, is not especially shortened for 10m wavelength ($\lambda/4$ = 2.63m) and that, through the capacitive hat, an even higher gain is achieved 'accidentally'.

THE GREATER THE BANDWIDTH ...

A few words on the bandwidth; remembering to compare the s=2 bandwidths given in Table 2 for aerials of the same type, we find that the 'bad' aerials have the higher bandwidths. This is understandable, if aerials are regarded as lossy 'open' resonant circuits. Variants, which are attenuated more, always have a higher bandwidth than those attenuated weakly. If, among those simulated aerials, a particular wide-band variant is wanted, high gain and flat radiation angle must generally be excluded.

If the table values are studied carefully, it can be seen that the non-shortened 'large' $\lambda/4$ aerials are quite wide-band, even for otherwise good aerial data. This is the principal advantage of the 'full-size' radiator compared with the shortened one.

The 'best' radiator with the most beneficial data in the 10m band is probably the aerial mounted 4m high (2m long and with capacitive hat); radiation angle 4° to 17°,

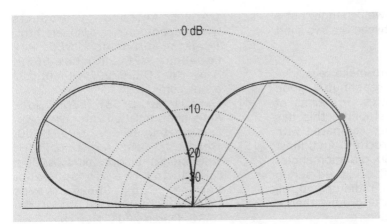

Fig 6: Radiation patterns of the 1m-long vertical aerial, subjected to a capacitive load, and of the Super-C aerial, both 0.05m above normal ground, 28.5MHz operating frequency. The gain of the vertical radiator with hat is -1.12dBi at an angle of 30°. The Super-C aerial is -1.38dBi at 30°.

adjust 75Ω to 50Ω, but more extensive and lossy to match the 9Ω effective resistance for the shorter radiator to the ripple resistance of the 50Ω coaxial cable.

SUMMARY

Is the Super-C aerial simulated in [1] now better or worse than the short 10m band aerial with capacitive hat? Let us compare the radiation patterns - they provide comprehensive information. **Fig 6** shows the diagrams of the Super-C aerial mounted directly over normal ground and the 1m (short) hat aerial: hardly any difference can be found.

gain over 1dBi, bandwidth 1.4MHz. Not much worse in gain and radiation angle is the only 1m-long radiator with, only half the bandwidth.

In practice, however, it must now be considered that the base resistance of the two aerials just compared has to be matched to 50Ω. It could be easier to

Thus, it would not have been worth making such a large material and mechanical effort for the 'cubical aerial'. If both aerials are mounted 4m high, the shape of the

TIPS FOR VERTICAL AERIALS WITH GOOD RADIATION

- For DX, the aerial with its 'counterpoise' should be mounted as high as possible over ground beneficial to HF.
- 'As high as possible' is a relative term. However, it always means that one has to go at least 1m over the ground. A vertical aerial erected at this height, as regards radiation angle and gain, already is much closer in quality to the good DX aerial mounted 4m high than the bad aerial only mounted 0.05m high. Each additional centimetre improves the radiation [7].
- A ground beneficial to HF - for all aerials - is damp horticultural ground or swamp; salt water is best. Concrete, road or rock under an aerial are bad.
- If a vertical aerial, including its radials, is at least a metre high over a ground which is not too HF-defective, the number of radials is no longer too important; only three to four radials are sufficient in most cases [7, p104].
- The effect of the actual vertical length on the radiation characteristics is not so significant. Even a geometrically-shortened aerial subjected, however, to capacitive loading at the upper end, is a good aerial.
- A high mounting position over ground is easier to achieve if the aerial is reduced in length and radial size and has a capacitive extension at the top (at the radiator end) and not an inductive extension at the bottom (at the feed-point). Only the capacitive extension introduces no additional ohmic losses to the aerial circuit.
- Radiation data worsened by radiator-shortening will be largely compensated by the higher aerial mounting now possible.
- One should not expect miracles of any (short) aerial, even if it is called 'Super'. Simpler geometries such as those shown here with capacitive hat can provide the same, if not better, radiation results.
- If a vertical radiator stands over the sea, even an expensive 'land aerial' can hardly compete with the piece of wire over salt water.

For reasons of space, the author's thoughts on the 20m band have been omitted. The full article can be found at www.cqdl.de/rubrik/technik

radiation pattern may well change, but a difference in quality between the two short aerials is hard to find.

A simple and very easy-to-make capacitive hat is sufficient for reasonably good radiation characteristics. In terms of mechanics and wind stability, this has considerable advantages compared with a three-dimensional structure. And, most importantly, for a flat DX radiation angle; it is much easier to lift a filigree aerial, with a low-mass upper radiator end, as high as possible over the ground than a (top-) heavy aerial structure.

LITERATURE AND SUPPLY SOURCES

[1]   Gerd Janzen, DF6SJ, ‚Super-C-Antenne Kritisch Betrachtet', *CQ DL*, 10/03, p702.

[2]   GAP Antenna Products www.gapantenna.com/superc.htm

[3]   Program author of *EZNEC*: Roy Lewallen, W7EL, PO Box 6658, Beaverton, OR, 97007, USA http://eznec.com

[4]   Gerd Janzen, DF6SJ, '*EZNEC 3.0* - Antennensimulation unter Windows', *Funkamateur* 10/00, 11/00, 12/00.

[5]   Gerd Janzen, DF6SJ, 'Antennensimulation mit *EZNEC*', a talk during the 4th Specialist Seminar on Short Waves (*Kurzwellen-Fachtagung*) of the DARC, March 2001, Munich.

[6]   Gerd Janzen, DF6SJ, *Kurze Antennen*, Franckh-Verlag, Stuttgart, 1986, reference: author.

[7]   Gerd Janzen, DF6SJ, *Monopolantennen und Vertikalantennen*, Kempten, 1999, reference: author.

THER GREAT TITLES AVAILABLE FROM THE RSGB & ARRL

The RSGB Amateur Radio Operating Manual

s 6th edition of the RSGB Amateur Radio erating Manual has been completely dated and redesigned this edition reflects e huge changes in hobby in recent years. cked with new material and updates this ok provides a completely new look at the ntent and approach to this classic title. This ok provides a comprehensive guide to erating across the amateur radio spectrum d is a valuable addition for every radio ateur's bookshelf. Size: 210mm x 297mm, 4 pages, ISBN 1-905086-00-8

£19.99 plus p&p

ARRL's RF Amplifier Classics

Includes two-dozen projects and articles from the pages of QST and QEX, published between 1980 and 2003. There are amps for HF, MF, VHF and microwave. These are high quality works from respected authors such as Gary Breed, K9AY; Jerry Pittenger, K8RA; Bill Sabin, W0IYH; Al Ward, W5LUA; Dave Meacham, W6EMD and others. Use this book and Shorten your discovery work. Find practical designs and construction details for classic tube and solid-state amplifiers at power levels from 5 W to 1.5 kW. Build safe and reliable amplifiers. Produce loud and clean signals 176 pages. ©2004. Published by American Radio Relay League (ARRL). ISBN: 0-87259-931-0 #9310

$19.95 plus p&p

Radio Propagation Principles & Practice

The book includes everything you need to know including radio waves and how they travel, the atmosphere, the Sun, ionospheric propagation (with the important modes and information), ionospheric storms and aurora, how to predict and assess ionospheric propagation, tropospheric propagation, meteor scatter, and space communications. 2004 edition , RSGB, paperback, Size: 174 x 240 mm, 112 pages, ISBN: 1-872309-97-6.

£14.99 plus p&p

imple and Fun Antennas for Hams

ts and lots of real world, practical antennas u can BUILD YOURSELF! Chapters include: ur first HF antenna, facts about transmission es, antenna masts and supports, HF rticals, more simple and fun antennas for IF, more HF dipoles, dual-band VHF/UHF tennas, an HF vertical that needs no radials: IF beam antennas, and getting the most out your antenna. © 2002. Published by the erican Radio Relay League, Inc. BN: 0-87259-862-4 #8624

$22.95 plus p&p

Command

Written for the experienced amateur, this book is aimed at the experimenter and home constructor who wants to get involved in the subject, and to understand how to take it further. 2003 Edn, RSGB, paperback, Size: 240 x 173 mm, 232 pages, ISBN: 1-872309-94-1

£16.99 plus p&p

Antenna Compendium Volume 7

This is the seventh in the very popular ARRL Antenna Compendium series. Inside, you'll find articles covering a very wide range of antenna-related topics such as: 30, 40, 80 and 160-Meter Antennas, Measurements and Computations, Mobile Antennas, Multiband Antennas, Practical Tips, Propagation and Ground Effects, Quad Antennas, Special Antennas, Stealth Antennas, Tuners and Transmission Lines, Vertical Antennas, VHF/UHF Antennas Wire Antennas, Yagi Antennas 208 pages. First edition, © 2002, The American Radio Relay League. #8608

$24.95 plus p&p

Books priced in $'s - order today from the ARRL
Books priced in £'s - order today from the RSGB

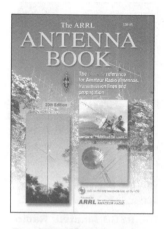

ARRL's HF Digital Handbook

All the information you need to get on air and enjoy the fascinating world of HF digital communication. All it takes is an HF SSB radio and your sound-card-equipped computer or an external multimode processor. ARRL's HF Digital Handbook includes a handy Resources section with Web addresses for downloadable software, as well as contact information for HF digital equipment manufacturers. You'll also find complete technical specifications of the various HF digital modes. Third edition, © 2003, The American Radio Relay League, Inc. ISBN: 0-87259-915-9 #9159

$19.95 plus p&p

LF Today

LF Today contains some theory and a little maths, but it is first and foremost a practical handbook. Written by the leading authority on LF, Mike Dennison, G3XDV this book is aimed at those who want to try out this fascinating amateur allocation, but it is also of great value to anyone already active on the band. It contains everything needed to succeed on 136kHz without unnecessary effort. Size: 175mm x 239mm, 128 pages, ISBN 187230999-2

£11.99 plus p&p

The ARRL Antenna Book
(book with CD-ROM)

The ARRL Antenna Book is THE SOURCE current antenna theory and a wealth of practi how-to construction projects. Extensively revis and featuring antenna designs enhanced by latest advances in computer modeling. In de coverage of antennas, feed lines, a propagation. Design, build and install a imaginable type of antenna. 944 pages, softco book with CD-ROM. 20th edition, © 2003, American Radio Relay League. ISBN: 0-87259-904-3 #9043

$39.95 plus p&p

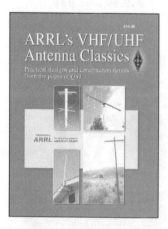

HF Amateur Radio

This book takes the reader through setting up an efficient amateur radio station, which equipment to choose, installation, and the best antenna for your location. It is packed full of information including which frequencies to use, how to operate on the bands, and the advantages of each type of transmission. 2002 Edn, RSGB, paperback, Size: 240 x 175mm, 128 pages, ISBN: 1-872309-75-5

£13.99 plus p&p

ARRL's VHF/UHF Antenna Classics

ARRL's VHF/UHF Antenna Classics includes antenna project articles gathered from the 1983 to 2003 issues of QST. Designs include ground planes, J-poles, mobile antennas, Yagis and more. Authors include well-known antenna designers such as L. B. Cebik, W4RNL, Dick Stroud, W9SR and Steve Powlishen, K1FO. Many of the projects included in this book require inexpensive parts which you can find at most hardware stores. First edition, © 2003, published by the American Radio Relay League (ARRL) ISBN: 0-87259-907-8 #9078

$14.95 plus p&p

Microwave Projects

Microwave Projects is packed full of ideas fr around the world this book covers the subject w a variety of projects. This title provides mu useful information as to what can be achiev effectively and economically. Aimed at both relative novice and the "old hand" the book a covers useful theory of designing microwa circuits and test equipment for the projects. Radio Society of Great Britain 2003, 200 page Size: 173 x 240mm. ISBN: 1-872309-90-9,

£14.99 plus p&p

Order today from the ARRL on their website
www.arrl.org or Tel: +1-860-594-0200

The Amateur Radio Mobile Handbook

e Amateur Radio Mobile Handbook vers all aspects of this popular part of the bby. It includes operating techniques, talling equipment in a vehicle and ennas, as well as maritime and even ycle mobile. This is essential reading if u want to get the most out of your mobile tion. 2002 Edition, RSGB, paperback, e: 240 x 175mm, 128 pages, 3N: 1-872309-77-1

£13.99 plus p&p

ARRL's Yagi Antenna Classics Yagis, Quads, Loops, and other Beam Antennas

Yagis, Quads, Loops, and other Beam Antennas. Enjoy this collection of some of the very best articles from QST, QEX, NCJ and other ARRL publications. The beam antennas covered in this book will provide the reader with a historical perspective, new and ambitious ideas, and computer-optimized designs for all-around best performance. Discover a wealth of ideas from some of the leaders in antenna design and experimentation of the last 70 years. 208 pages. © 2001, The American Radio Relay League, Inc ISBN: 0-87259-818-7 #8187

$17.95 plus p&p

The International Microwave Handbook

This book contains a wide selection of designs using the latest technology that can reasonably be used by radio amateurs and ranges from ones that can be reproduced by most radio amateurs to those that require a high degree of skill to make. With the explosion in consumer electronics using microwave frequencies the opportunity to experiment has never been greater and this book is simply the best guide to the area of microwave radio. 2002 Edition, RSGB, paperback, 480 pages, Size: 240 x 175mm ISBN 1-872309-83-6

£24.99 plus p&p

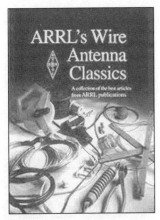

ARRL's Wire Antenna Classics

collection of the best articles from ARRL blications. So many wire antenna designs ve proven to be first class performers! re's an entire book devoted to wire tennas, from the simple to the complex. cludes articles on dipoles, loops, rhobics, re beams and receive antennas—and me time-proven classics! An ideal book for ld Day planners or the next wire antenna pject at your home station.Volume 1. First ition, third printing, 2002. © 1999-2002, e American Radio Relay League, Inc. 3N: 0-87259-707-5 #7075

$14.00 plus p&p

The RSGB Prefix Guide

The World's most comprehensive list of prefixes is newly revised and improved. Not just a listing of prefixes and their entities the guide provides a host of useful additional material. References include a prefix's continent, CQ Zone, ITU Zone, Latitude and Longitude and many other details.This book is an excellent tool for the beginner and the experienced hand alike. Designed with a "lay flat" wire binding for ease of use the new "Prefix Guide" is a must for every shack. 6th Edn, 2003, RSGB, paperback, Size: 210 x 297 mm, 48 pages.

£8.99 plus p&p

The ARRL Operating Manual for Radio Amateurs -- Everything for the active ham!

8th Edition - The most complete book about Amateur Radio operating. Includes: Rules and Regulations, VHF and HF digital, FM operating, DXing, Contesting and Award Hunting, Image Communications, .and many additional References. This book is designed to help you increase your enjoyment and skill. The ARRL Operating Manual belongs in every ham's shack! Eighth edition. 352 pages. © League, Inc. ISBN: 0-87259-913-2 #9132

$25.00 plus p&p

Order 24hrs a day from the RSGB on our website
www.rsgb.org/shop or Tel: 0870 904 7373

Hints & Kinks for the Radio Amateur

16th edition -- Hot Tips from the pages of QST. Hints & Kinks for the Radio Amateur is the first place hams turn for information about new modes, new projects, and the latest tips. You'll find something on every page to solve problems, improve your operating, and simply have more fun on the air: Equipment Tips and Mods, Batteries and Other Power Sources, Digital Modes, Troubleshooting, Restoration, Construction/Maintenance, Test Gear, Antenna Systems, Operating Station Accessories, Interference (RFI/EMI) 76 pages. © 2003, The American Radio Relay League, Inc. ISBN: 0-87259-892-6 #8926

$15.95 plus p&p

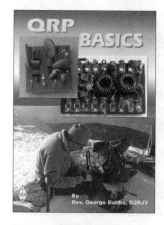

QRP Basics

Do you want a new challenge? Have you ever wanted to try QRP? Do you want to improve your QRP station? Do you want to build a working transmitter or receiver? QRP Basics will help you do all of these things. It will enrich your amateur radio. It will inspire you to start building. It may even get you out in the open air. Quite simply, QRP Basics shows just what fun can be had from amateur radio. © Radio Society of Great Britain 2003, ISBN: 1-872309-91-7, 208 pages, Size: 173 x 240mm

£14.99 plus p&p

Experimental Methods in RF Design

Immerse yourself in the communicati￼ experience by building equipment ￼ contributes to understanding basic conce￼ and circuits. Explore wide dynamic range, ￼ distortion radio equipment, the use of di￼ conversion and phasing methods, and di￼ signal processing. Use the models a￼ discussion to design, build and meas￼ equipment at both the circuit and the syst￼ level. Laced with new unpublished proje￼ and illustrated with CW and SSB gear. 5￼ pages. © 2003, published by American Ra￼ Relay League (ARRL). ISBN: 0-87259-879-9 #8799

$49.95 plus p&p

The VHF/UHF Handbook

This guide to the theory and practice of amateur radio reception and transmission on the VHF and UHF bands gives the reader the background to such essential topics as antennas, EMC, propagation, receivers and transmitters, together with constructional details of many items of equipment. Size: 272 x 199mm; 320 pages; ISBN: 1-872309-42-9

£19.99 plus p&p

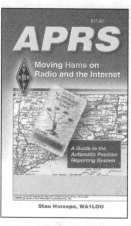

APRS
Moving Hams on Radio and the Internet

A Guide to the Automatic Position Reporting System. With a portable Global Positioning System (GPS) receiver, you have precise position information at your fingertips. Connect the GPS receiver to your APRS station, and you can transmit your location information even as you're moving! Track moving objects on maps . Display weather statistics and storm warnings, and find a hidden transmitter or jammer. Softcover. © 2004, The American Radio Relay League, Inc. ISBN: 0-87259-916-7 #9167

$17.95 plus p&p

Guide to VHF/UHF

Ian Poole explains just how to get the m￼ from your VHF/ UHF station: by studying ￼ weather to predict greatly enhanc￼ propagation; by using the correct part of ea￼ band; by choosing the right transmit￼ receiver and antenna, and by using ￼ correct procedure. A chapter explains how ￼ transmit and receive computer data on the ￼ bands. 1st Edn, 2000, RSGB, paperback, ￼ 112 pages, ISBN: 1-872309-58-5.

£8.99 plus p&p

RSGB, Lambda House, Cranborne Road, Potters Bar, Herts EN6 3JE, ENGLAND
ARRL, the national association for Amateur Radio, 225 Main Street, Newington, CT, 06111-1494 USA